en vlught na hollant en van daer na parys

De koninck in dienst onder turenne en don Jan de austreija.

De Coninck wort gekroont.

eert tot brest in Vranckryck.

Comt in vranckryck en wort verwellecomt van Lewis d xIIII

M. HEREDGE
JUNE 1976.

James II

SOLDIER AND SAILOR

James II, by Kneller

JOCK HASWELL

James II

SOLDIER AND SAILOR

HAMISH HAMILTON

LONDON

First published in Great Britain, 1972
by Hamish Hamilton Ltd
90 *Great Russell Street London WC*1
2nd Impression March 1973

Copyright © 1972 *by Jock Haswell*

SBN 241 02103 0

Printed in Great Britain by
Redwood Press Limited, Trowbridge, Wiltshire

For RICHARD

LIST OF ILLUSTRATIONS

vii

ANNE HYDE, DUCHESS OF YORK
Reproduced by gracious permission of Her Majesty the Queen
ARABELLA CHURCHILL
CATHERINE SEDLEY, COUNTESS OF DORCHESTER
*Studio of Lely. Reproduced by permission of the Trustees of the
National Portrait Gallery*

viii

Maps

ACKNOWLEDGEMENTS

SOME time ago, in a short history of the Regiment I once belonged to, I made one or two rather waspish remarks about James II: I had been brought up to believe that as a King he was quite unacceptable. It then occurred to me that I had made these remarks out of little more than prejudice and with no real knowledge of him at all; in fact I had done what so many others have done either deliberately or without thinking. So I read Hilaire Belloc's book but, as a Protestant, felt that perhaps the Catholic Belloc doth protest too much. With all respect, I thought he had rather overstated his case. I read other books and began to form various opinions which I have tried to set down.

A picture of James began to emerge: a forthright, courageous, honest, not very clever advocate of direct action, a soldier and a sailor; a man who thought he saw what had to be done and tried to do it, as quickly as possible and with the least amount of fuss. This is, of course, a personal point of view, but if one thinks of James's childhood, or indeed of the first twenty-seven years of his life, much of what happened later seems more easily understandable. In many history books he hardly features at all until he became King, and without any background it is difficult to come to any but the most obvious conclusions.

In piecing together the story of James II—I am not qualified to write the *history* of him—I owe great debts: in particular to Mr. King and his Staff of the Ministry of Defence Central Library, to Mr. Dineen and Miss Stephanie Glover of the Royal United Service Institution, Mrs. Sally Kington of the London Museum, Mr. Tompsett of the Folkestone Public Library, Mr. K. M. White of the Staff College Library, Mrs. Grace of the Sir John Moore Library at Shorncliffe and Miss Thomas of the Royal Albert Memorial Museum in Exeter. Many kind people in France—especially in the Department of Archives in the old city of Laon—were very helpful over Turenne's campaigns and James's exile, although the museum staff at Saint-Germain could not accept my suggestion that James's body might not be in the parish church across the square.

My daughter Frances did much work for me among archives in Exeter, and Annette, my wife, who feels that man's inability to learn from history is perhaps the factor which makes it so depressing, nevertheless spent many hours reading, extracting and noting on my behalf.

Without the help of Mr. F. J. Salfeld of the *Daily Telegraph* I would probably still be searching maps for the little village of Châtres.

Major Charles Cole gave me a great deal of his time and skill in reproducing illustrations, and we spent one happy day at Chiddingstone Castle in Kent, where Mr. D. E. Bower put his large and fascinating collection of Stuart portraits and documents at our disposal. When Charles Cole moved away into Wiltshire, Ken Jaggers of Bridge, near Canterbury, maintained the tradition of producing photographs of prints and pictures that improve on the originals.

I am so grateful to many people for contributing much to this story of James II.

Note: Except where the source is stated, or obvious, the quotations within inverted commas in the text come from either the Memoirs of James II or Clarke's *Life of James II*, which were both compiled from what was largely 'writ in his Own Hand'.

ONE

THERE was no sleep for anyone in the great rambling palace of Whitehall on the night of Saturday, May 8, 1641, for round it surged the mob which had marched from the City, howling for the blood of Black Tom Wentworth, the Earl of Strafford. Although the courtiers within the palace had given some thought to the problem of defence, trying to choose suitable stairways, landings and corridors where a swordsman could at least be sure of taking a few with him when he died, they all knew the place to be indefensible. If the mob broke in, there would be a massacre and that would be that.

The roar of the angry crowd enveloped everything in a blanket of fear, stifling coherent thought, and in an upstairs room where the death warrant, unsigned, lay upon a table, the King wrestled with the problem that was to haunt him for the rest of his life.

Barely half a mile away, beyond the deer-cropped grass and long ruled avenues of the Park, James, Duke of York, a little boy of seven, lay in his bed in St. James's Palace, listening to the ebb and flow of terrifying sound. This was not the first time he had heard it: twice in the past two weeks a rabble, several thousand strong and armed with clubs and staves, had thronged about Westminster and the Houses of Parliament, crying out for 'justice' against the Earl of Strafford, and James must have had some idea of what it was all about. His brother Charles—three years older—had been taken by their father to Strafford's trial in Westminster Hall, and Charles, who all his life was a great talker, would have described the spectacle and the excitement.

On that May night, while he and so many others lay uneasily in their beds listening to the voice of the people, James was in fact also listening —though he did not know it—to the distant rumblings of the storm which was to sweep away everything in his life that seemed to be established and secure.

It is most unlikely that at his age he understood why Strafford was in the Tower or knew that his father and Parliament, after eleven years of peaceful rule without a Parliament at all, were set on courses which must lead to civil war. If he did ask questions, like most children he was no doubt told by adults who could not be bothered to explain, that he would not understand. Children then were so vulnerable, so perishable, and parents seemed to regard them as expendable; treating them with an indifference which was perhaps a conscious effort to prevent themselves from loving what might soon be lost. James himself, in his Memoirs, says nothing of his infancy and little of his childhood, no doubt because he felt they were unimportant, yet events in his early years had a profound effect upon him and their influence can be traced throughout his life. But at the beginning, largely ignored by his mother who far preferred politics to the nursery, he led a sheltered existence with his brothers and sisters in St. James's Palace, where he had been born.

On that day, October 14, 1633, the room where it happened had been crowded, and no doubt his first wailing cry was scarcely heard in all the cheerful chatter of the cloud of witnesses, assembled according to custom, to make sure nothing odd or suspicious occurred at the royal birth. It was a pity he was too young to appreciate the interest taken in him by the distinguished gathering, for he certainly received more attention on that day than for the next fourteen or fifteen years.

'This Prince', wrote one of his contemporaries, Bishop Burnet, 'was much neglected in his youth', and therein lies the key to his character. All those 'persons of quality' as James would have called them, who had crowded into the tall-ceilinged room where Henrietta Maria, sister of Louis XIII of France, lay on the huge bed, dispersed as soon as they had seen and duly admired the third child and second son of Charles I, and then probably forgot about him. So few children survived the first year after birth that there was really no point in paying much attention even to those of royal blood until they showed signs of growing up.

His mother soon recovered from the ordeal of giving birth in public, and James was handed over to the care of nurses, a 'cofferess' who was presumably responsible for his clothes, and 'rockers' whose functions ceased when he grew out of a cradle.

Six weeks after his birth he was baptized by Laud, made Archbishop of Canterbury in that year, and his godparents were his aunt Elizabeth, Queen of Bohemia—the Winter Queen—his cousin Charles Louis, Prince Palatine, and Frederick Henry, Prince of Orange; all staunch Protestants.

Nearly all James's forebears on his father's side were Scots and from his mother he inherited French and Italian blood. His distant connection with England went back across five generations to Henry VII's daughter Margaret Tudor who had married the Scottish king James IV, killed at the battle of Flodden in 1513; but, born on English soil, he not only claimed English nationality but all his life retained a deep abiding love for, and pride in, England and her people. The real tragedy of his reign, and of the years when his brother was on the throne, was the failure of the English people to understand or appreciate James's unquenchable patriotism and his genuine concern for their well-being. Even in those last desperate hours, when his son-in-law the usurper was marching on London at the head of his Dutch troops, though all was not yet lost he refused to let that great and militant Royalist, Lord Dundee, 'gather ten thousand troops and carry his standard at their head' because it would involve his beloved country in the horrors of another civil war.

James and his brother Charles were brought up by the Countess of Dorset, their governess, who administered their own little 'court' with a generous allowance which today would amount to about £12,000 a year. Their toys, consisting of such things as drums, balls and hobby-horses, reflected the general adult lack of interest in children's amusements, but as they grew older their indoor activities were replaced by riding and archery and their toys were hoops and tops.

At the age of four and a half James was appointed Lord High Admiral of England, and this, as soon as he was old enough to know what it implied, was to be no empty title.

Then, three years later, the peaceful atmosphere of his childhood in the reassuringly solid surroundings of St. James's Palace was invaded by the growing tension between his father in Whitehall, and Parliament, led by the revolutionary John Pym, at Westminster.

Pym's initial target was Strafford, recalled from governing Ireland to sort out Charles I's differences with Scotland over revisions to the Canon Law and the introduction of a new Prayer Book. Strafford, the advocate of a king's divine right, preferably supported by an army, was impeached by the Parliament summoned, on his advice, to provide money for an army. His brilliant defence at his trial would have secured an acquittal had not Pym acted first by forcing an Act of Attainder through the Commons—using the mob which James had seen and heard at Westminster to prevent his opponents from voting against it.

Pym was a skilful exploiter of terrorism, well aware of the value of noise as a weapon of intimidation. He knew Charles had assured his faithful minister, in writing, that 'upon the word of a King, you shall not suffer in life, honour or fortune', so he sent the mob to Whitehall on that Saturday evening in May. Charles, faced with signing away the life of the man he had promised to save or, apparently, condemning everyone in the palace to death at the hands of the mob, gave in. But the rabble had to

3

work hard for Pym's victory; not until Sunday evening, after a weekend of agonizing indecision, did Charles sign, and, according to John Evelyn, the diarist, he was thereafter convinced that his own misfortunes stemmed from this act of betrayal and his own execution was an act of divine retribution.

Yet if Strafford's death had a lasting effect upon Charles, it was also a lesson which his son James never forgot. If there had been proper military guards about the King the mob which tried to intimidate him would have been dispersed—perhaps with the same force that Pym himself used later when he ordered dragoons to charge a crowd, mostly of women and children, who wanted to throw him in the Thames and stop the civil war. James saw clearly enough that a king unprotected is a king without authority. Years afterwards, in 1692, he wrote as advice to his son, 'Be never without a considerable body of troops, without which you cannot be safe.'

James says nothing in his Memoirs of the events just before the outbreak of the civil war; the horrors of the 1641 rebellion of the Catholic peasants in Ireland against the Protestant settlers and landlords; Pym's attacks on his mother as an instigator of this Papist rising, and his father's unfortunate visit to the Commons to arrest his principal enemies, Pym, Hampden, Hazlerigg, Holles and Strode. He begins his story with the family's flight from London, saying only it was 'because of the tumults'; but it was the end of the first chapter of his life.

Still only a little boy he was now caught up in a web of great events in which he was to be entangled for the next six years, and it was during these years, perhaps the most formative of a child's life, that the neglect Bishop Burnet wrote about was to have its effect on his character. Up to now he had seen little enough of his parents. Although Charles I was a devoted father he rarely had time to spare for his children, and there is no reason to believe that Henrietta Maria enjoyed motherhood at all. Neither showed much interest in James.

When his failure to arrest the five Members compelled Charles to leave London seven days later, on January 10, 1642, his family consisted of the Queen, Henrietta Maria; Charles, Prince of Wales, the eldest child who was eleven; Mary, the Princess Royal, now nearly ten, who had been married to the young Prince William of Orange nine months before; James, Duke of York; Elizabeth, aged five, and Henry, Duke of Gloucester, the youngest, who was only two. On the first stage of their exile from the capital they did not travel far, only a few miles westwards, to Hampton Court.

James, a high-spirited, attractive child, full of energy, must have

4

enjoyed this journey up the river, for except to go to Richmond he had seldom been away from the familiar surroundings of St. James's Palace gardens and the Park. But he hardly had time to explore Wolsey's great labyrinth of a house before his father decided to move on, further away from his enemies, to the great castle standing high above the river at Windsor. Here Charles realized that while his wife remained in England she would continue to be the target of Pym's campaign against the monarchy, and so he resolved to send her away to safety across the Channel, to her son-in-law, William. He therefore escorted her and his daughter Mary to Dover, making a wide detour to avoid London, and put them on a boat for Holland. At the same time he sent James and Elizabeth and their little brother Henry back to St. James's Palace, obviously feeling that any threat to his family would be removed by the departure of Henrietta Maria.

Having said goodbye to his mother at Windsor, James was not to see her again for more than two years—and then only briefly. He now found himself once again in the house he had known since birth, but everything had changed. Charles, the Prince of Wales, was no longer there; he had gone with his father to see his mother and sister off at Dover, and then accompanied the King to York. No one told James what was happening and no doubt this dissolution of the family made him feel isolated and uneasy. He was devoted to his elder brother and probably missed him a great deal. Then, suddenly, a few weeks later on Easter Monday, the Marquis of Hertford arrived at the palace after dark and told him he had come to take him to his father. It was all very secret and perhaps a little alarming. James probably knew the Marquis, for he was a trusted friend of his father, but when he climbed into the coach standing in the shadows of the palace courtyard, and it clattered out into James's Street at what was usually his bedtime, it is unlikely he was told there was danger of pursuit and capture.

Charles, after establishing himself at York, had in fact come to the conclusion that war with Parliament was now unavoidable, and he was afraid Pym and Hampden might try to kidnap James and use him as a hostage. He wrote to the Marquis of Hertford telling him to bring James up to York at once, but the spies of Parliament were everywhere and news of this message reached Westminster. Hertford, though expressly forbidden to take James out of London, was loyal to the King and obeyed his instructions; but he had to be careful. The danger would have been far less if he and James had been able to ride swiftly north with a small escort, but two hundred miles on horseback, most of them at night, was too much to expect of a child of eight. Although the York road was one

5

of the three great highways radiating out from London—the other two ran to Exeter and Chester—it was little more than a pot-holed, rutted track, and the unsprung coach, its body hung on straps, swayed and jerked continuously, and no doubt exhaustingly, as it lurched along.

James does not say when he reached his destination, only that he arrived safely, but travel on the York road was fairly quick and well-organized, with changes of horses at regular intervals. Clarendon writes of an astonishingly rapid mail service which was set up at this time, between the King and Parliament. It was 'undertaken by gentlemen', and if a letter was despatched from Westminster by midnight on Saturday the King's reply to it was always received from York by ten o'clock on Monday morning.

For the next four years, instead of living in the comfortable and settled atmosphere of St. James's Palace, James was surrounded by the bustle, excitement and tension of his father's army headquarters, which contributed much to his experience but little to his formal education. Soon after arriving in York, in a hollow little ceremony which emphasized by its informality the rift now widening between the King and those who could not share his views, James was made a Knight of the Garter—an honour which was to save his life at the siege of Mouzon when he was soldiering in France eleven years later.

A few days afterwards he became involved in the first incident of the civil war.

When reading James's own account of this, one forgets how young he was, and it is difficult to understand why his father used him as he did; but James at the age of eight cannot be compared with an eight-year-old of today. He had been brought up as a prince, enveloped in all the Stuart aura of majesty and divine right, and he had been taught to wear his royal authority like a cloak. But whereas his brother Charles could, when he wished, slip this cloak off and be all things to all men, James could not. All his life he commanded respect, for he had a presence which dis-couraged the taking of liberties—it is impossible to imagine his being involved in an exchange such as the well-known one between his brother and Lord Shaftesbury.* He had grown up amongst adults who treated him with the deference due to his rank and not as a little boy in need of the love he was denied by his parents. Having practically no outlet for his affections it is not surprising that he developed defences against a world in which no one, when he was small and vulnerable, told him he was either loved or wanted.

* 'Here comes', said Charles, 'the greatest whoremaster in England.' 'Of a subject, sire,' said Shaftesbury as he limped past in procession.

His 'home', such as it was, broke up when his mother fled to Holland, and if he was aloof, as many who knew him have implied, he had good reason to be reluctant to commit himself completely in any relationship since his advances in childhood had met with so little response. Starved of affection and with the background of a broken home, he learned to value his independence at an early age; he grew up rapidly, acquiring a protective authority which, despite a great deal of personal charm, gaiety, enthusiasm and an eagerness to make friends, stood always in the way of intimate friendship. Like many children of the time he was old for his age, and the transition from childhood through adolescence to manhood was accelerated not only by demands made on him as a prince but by the climate of war, rebellion and social upheaval in which he had to live. Thus, when his father sent him off to Hull with his godfather Charles Louis, the Earl of Newport and Lord Willoughby and 'some other persons of honour', he went as a prince with his attendants, not as a small boy going off on an outing with his cousin.

The town of Hull, some forty miles from York, contained an arsenal of weapons which the King needed for the Royal Army he proposed to raise. The Governor of the town, Sir John Hotham, was believed to be a Royalist but Charles must have had misgivings about being able to persuade him to hand over the town, for Hotham's son was known to be an active supporter of Parliament. Because the King felt the elder Hotham's position might be a delicate one, involving family loyalties, he determined on an indirect approach. On April 22 he sent James, with his attendants but without any sort of armed escort, into the town on what was ostensibly a sightseeing tour. Everyone was very friendly. The visitors, received with proper respect by the Governor and the Mayor, spent the whole day 'in viewing the beauty and the strength of the place and partaking of a banquet prepared by the Mayor and Aldermen of Hull'.

James and his party spent the night in the town, and next morning, St. George's Day, they were all invited to dine—at about midday—with the Governor, but just before dinner-time, when Sir John Hotham was chatting with James and Charles Louis, he was suddenly handed a message from His Majesty. This was to the effect that the King, with an escort of 300 Horse, was within four miles of Hull and also intended to dine with the Governor. Hotham 'turned very pale and struck himself on the breast', then he asked James politely to return to his lodgings and take all the other visitors with him.

When James had gone, Hotham went into consultation with a Mr. Pelham, Member of Parliament and an alderman of Hull, and several others 'pledged to the Parliament side', and they decided to send a messenger at once to beg the King to keep away, since the Governor felt he would be betraying his trust if he admitted Charles 'with so great a guard'. The message was delivered and the bearer galloped back with the information that the King was coming, regardless of the Governor's feelings. Whereupon Hotham 'drew up the bridge', closed the gates and ordered the garrison to man the walls.

A few minutes later Charles rode up to the Beverley gate, called for Sir John Hotham and ordered him to open it. Hotham, shouting from the gatehouse, pointed out that he had been 'intrusted by the Parliament with the securing of the Town for His Majesty's Honour and the kingdom's use', and that with God's help he intended to do this duty and his conduct must not be interpreted as disloyalty. If His Majesty would care to come in with the Prince of Wales and twelve more he would be very welcome.

Charles, furious, said it was all or none; but he had no means of taking the town by force, and Hotham's will to resist had been strengthened by a false report that he was to be tried for his life if the King managed to get in. Charles was now in the embarrassing position of being locked out of the town while his son and his attendants were locked in, but by one o'clock in the afternoon he had persuaded Hotham to let them out— presumably without any dinner. Then, having hung about the Beverley gate all afternoon, not knowing quite what to do, at five o'clock, angry and humiliated, Charles withdrew to Beverley, nine miles to the north, where he spent the night. Unable to arm even a hundred men, he had missed his opportunity to collect enough arms and ammunition, including artillery, for an army of 20,000 or more. In James's opinion, if his father had ridden straight into the town instead of giving warning of his intentions, there would have been no problem, 'for the inhabitants at that time were very affectionate to his service'. Whether or not James learned anything from this incident* cannot be confirmed, but subsequently, first as a soldier and then a sailor, he himself was always an advocate of swift, direct action to achieve surprise.

Ever since March 16, 1642, when the Commons voted for the adoption of the Militia Bill and the right to act independently of the King, war had been inevitable, but without money or arms Charles had great difficulty in raising an army. At first he was entirely dependent for funds on what 'the loyall Lords and Gentlemen about him did voluntarily furnish', and

* Ironically enough, both Hothams, father and son, were later beheaded on Tower Hill for disloyalty to Parliament. Charles, who had felt his repulse very keenly, went so far as to compose a long prayer begging the Almighty not to let him derive any secret pleasure from their execution; so he must have been satisfied, if nothing more, with their fate.

as Parliament had seized all warlike stores he was forced to try and obtain weapons from overseas.

His navy, on which he had spent so much time and money, had declared for Parliament, and now, under the Earl of Warwick, was patrolling the coasts energetically to prevent any gun-running; but a few of his ships had gone over to Holland with the Queen, and one of them, the *Providence* commanded by Captain Straughan, succeeded in breaking the blockade. Henrietta Maria had sold the crown jewels and most of her own, and bought weapons and 'pouder', some of which Captain Straughan brought to the Humber. Eluding two blockading warships by sailing over a sandbank where with their deeper draught they could not follow, he ran the *Providence* ashore not far from Hull. She was unloaded and her cargo taken to York. James, always an admirer of courage and resourcefulness, has described the adventure in detail, and one can easily imagine how excited he must have been when the carts loaded with munitions came safely into York, and so provided his father with the means to fight the Parliamentary rebels. James found it all such a wonderful change from what he now realized had been a very dull life in London. Things were happening all the time and there was always something new to see. The streets were full of men who had come to join the Royal Army; in the fields just outside the town walls foot soldiers were being trained to use muskets and pikes, and horsemen were learning how to be cavalrymen. They were using methods and acquiring skills which had hardly changed since the days of that great tilting champion Henry VIII; swinging and rotating dummies, and rings suspended from the branches of trees were the targets for their swords in the charge, and they were practising the picking up of a handkerchief on a swordpoint at full gallop. Yet even he could see that the number of men doing all these things was nothing like enough to make an army.

The whole trouble was that the gentry and farmers and freeholders of Yorkshire were far more eager for the King to settle all his differences with Parliament than to risk everything in his cause, and by the middle of June the Royalist force consisted only of one troop of cavalry and one infantry regiment formed from the local train-bands.

On July 2 a further consignment of munitions arrived from the Queen in Holland and included seven or eight pieces of artillery which were brought ashore at Bridlington. Finally, after an abortive attempt to besiege Hull, where the first shots of the war were fired, and the first blood spilt when two men of the Royal Army were killed in a sortie by the garrison, the King moved to Nottingham.

Here, according to Clarendon, 'upon the 22nd day of August, the standard was erected about six of the clock in the evening of a very stormy and tempestuous day, with little ceremony than the sound of drums and trumpets'. This 'raising of the standard' was Charles's formal declaration of war; he was prepared to defend the royal prerogative by force, and now there was no going back.

James, watching the great flag straining on its pike and listening to the roll of drums and thin trumpet notes before the wind swept the sounds away, must have felt that this was a great moment. What neither he nor anyone else at the little ceremony could have seen was the tragedy of it.

TWO

At Nottingham, Charles was joined by his two nephews, Prince Rupert and Prince Maurice, the sons of Elizabeth of Bohemia. Rupert was one of the greatest assets of the Royalist force, for although he was only twenty-two he had been a soldier since the age of sixteen—when he fought for the Prince of Orange in his invasion of Brabant. He was one of the few professionals in Charles's army; an expert swordsman, pistol shot and horseman, a student of gunnery and field engineering, and the first to introduce horse artillery into England. He also brought from the Continent new methods of siege warfare, which involved tunnelling into walls with a 'miner' and putting explosive charges, or mines, into the holes.

Charles made him General of the Horse, and his arrival in the head-quarters had an invigorating effect for he began to sort out the muddle and organize the Royalist resources. Rupert was not interested in politics and he took the uncomplicated view that anyone who opposed his uncle's authority was a rebel and a traitor. His influence was considerable, though it affected tactics more than strategy, and as a commander with an international reputation he must have been an impressive figure to James. When James grew up they had much in common. Rupert was abstemious, so was James. As a cavalry leader, and later as a hard-fighting naval commander, Rupert was highly competent and entirely fearless, so was James. Rupert was no statesman; nor, unfortunately, was James.

Despite occasional encouragement from his father, James had never shown any particular enthusiasm for his lessons, and at this age, when he should have been acquiring the education needed by a prince, he was far more interested and occupied in watching the soldiers, finding out how pistols and muskets worked and learning how to fight with a sword. Under the influence of his cousin Rupert he became fascinated by military matters, and it seems probable that his keenness for soldiering began in that wet and dismal summer of 1642.

Although the profession of arms offered permanent employment on the Continent, in England the approach to warfare was extremely amateurish;

the opinion of the nobility and gentry—who automatically became officers —being that their own personal courage and leadership were all that would be needed to win the day. Quite often they were right.

Apart from small skirmishes, raids and ambushes, military operations, broadly speaking, were of two types: the set-piece battle between two armies drawn up in formal order in an open space, and the siege. Both were governed by rules which, being generally observed, made it difficult for commanders on either side to achieve surprise.

The siege was largely a matter of sitting down round the walls of a town and first making a line of contravallation.* Then, if there was danger of attack by a relieving army, the besiegers built another ring of defences, a circumvallation, so that they would be secure inside two lines of defence works round the town—these lines also helped to prevent the usual shadowy spies and messengers from flitting to and fro. Batteries of artillery† were then set up, and the garrison was politely invited to surrender. Since at this stage very few shots had been fired, no man of honour could accept the invitation—nor did the besiegers imagine he would—and the siege then began in earnest. The artillery opened fire, concentrating their aim in a small area where the wall appeared weakest or, in the absence of overlooking towers, most difficult to defend. The heavy guns went on pounding away until the stones of the wall were so loosened and broken that the wall fell down, thus creating a breach. Meanwhile the besiegers dug trenches to provide a protected approach to the walls for the infantry, so they could be ready to storm the breach when the time came.

If, when the breach was made, the Governor of the town did not indicate his willingness to discuss terms, he was usually given another opportunity to surrender, and if he still refused, the attack went in, with a great deal of slaughter, rape and looting as reprisals for the garrison's unwillingness to accept defeat.

This system and its principles had not changed since Vespasian's son Titus sacked Jerusalem in A.D. 70, and the introduction of the 'miner' and his explosives was only a modification more economical in terms of time, powder and cannon-balls. It was of course customary to try and collect cannon-balls from the target area at night and use them again, though this was hazardous and had to be done secretly so as not to encourage the enemy by betraying a shortage of ammunition. James became somewhat of an expert at siege warfare.

* Defined as a chain of fortifications constructed by besiegers as a defence against sallies from the town.

† Siege cannon, too heavy to be dragged about by horses as field artillery, could be the 'cannon royal' of 8 in. calibre firing a 63 lb. shot, a 7 in. 'cannon' with a shot of 47 lb. or the 'demi-cannon' with a 6 in. bore and 27 lb. shot.

The set-piece battle was much the same, in essence, as it had been for five thousand years; since the armies of rival kings fought in the valley of the Euphrates. The object then, and in James's time,* was to break the opposing line, for when one side forced a way through it, the infantry of the other side, whose real strength lay in the mutual support afforded by a well-knit formation, were thrown off balance and, losing cohesion, also lost the confidence inspired by it. Those on the flanks of the breach in the line knew that their foes were now behind them as well as in front. Their natural reaction was to pull back, if not turn and run. In the close-range fighting of James's time every man who broke off the engagement ran to save himself, and the panic spread. So a line of battle which at one moment presented an orderly and formidable array could, if pierced, suddenly break up into small parties and individuals who, with their backs to the enemy, could be cut down without risk to their pursuers.

The cavalry arm had been developed to exploit this idea of bursting through the line. A body of yelling horsemen, the sunlight flashing on their naked swords as they thundered down in the charge, put the fear of God into men on their feet. The obvious counter-measure was cavalry, so that the horsemen could charge each other, but this was no solution to the problem of an enemy preponderant in cavalry who had enough left over to attack the infantry. The speed, mobility and sheer penetrative power of cavalry posed considerable tactical problems. It could, almost by weight alone, achieve the primary object of smashing through the infantry, unless the infantry possessed personal weapons which would prevent the man on a horse from riding down the man on foot.

There were three such weapons: the long-bow, a light, silent, quick-firing and deadly weapon with an effective range of 300 yards or more, depending on the wind; the musket, and the pike.

At the time when James was fighting for the King of France the bow had long since been replaced by the highly inefficient musket which could never, even in the hands of the most skilful musketeer, approach the performance of the long-bow. But the musket was almost a status symbol, a sign of progress. Unreliable, hopelessly inaccurate and having a ridiculously short range, it was nevertheless regarded as a step forward in the art of killing. It was nothing of the sort, for men exposed to musket fire suffered far fewer casualties than those faced by competent archers.

The matchlock with its cumbersome rest created a new problem, mentioned by William Barriffe in 1639 in his book on *Militarie Discipline* when he wrote of 'the danger of the musketeer and how he is unable to

* And today.

13

resist the Horse after he hath poured forth his piece without he be sheltered either by some natural or artificial defence'. The trouble was that the loading and firing of a matchlock musket involved twenty separate orders and drill movements, which resulted in a rate of fire of one round every two minutes—provided all went well. Another snag lay in the method of firing; each musketeer had to carry a 'match' with which to ignite the powder that propelled the shot from his matchlock, and this match was three yards of twisted cotton cord, soaked in saltpetre, which had to be kept smouldering and was thus a constant danger in view of the loose powder lying about in bandoliers and barrels. Furthermore, as James was to see often enough when he was on active service, the glow of matches gave away the position or movement of musketeers at night.

William Barriffe's point was that a musketeer was so busy coping with the mechanics of his weapon that for most of the time he was on the battle-field he was unable to defend himself. He certainly carried a sword but was hardly ever able to use it unless he threw away his musket and switched from the offensive to the defensive. Since he was so vulnerable someone had to protect him, and this became the responsibility of the pikemen.

They were burdened with a helmet, 'pistol-proof' back- and breast-plates, tassets, which were like a steel skirt protecting groins and thighs, a sword and a pike sixteen to eighteen feet long. A long march on a hot day in that outfit must have been completely exhausting, and the musketeer was little better off. He had to carry a matchlock four feet long weighing fifteen pounds, a forked metal rest for his weapon, several bandoliers of cartridges, twenty-five bullets, loose, a large powder flask and a small priming flask and a sword; all hung about his person and banging against him and each other as he walked. In addition he had his yards of smouldering match. His uniform consisted of a broad-brimmed hat with a plume, a full-skirted tunic, baggy knee breeches and boots. If it rained he got wet; the pikemen got rusty.

In action, the musketeers and pikemen were drawn up, usually in six ranks, sometimes with the pikemen in the centre and the musketeers on the flanks, in companies, and sometimes the other way round. There were anything from ten to seventeen companies in an infantry battalion, each of fifty men; usually thirty musketeers and twenty pikemen.

When attacking, the whole force advanced, the musketeers ready to fire, until they were within range. The musketeers then stuck the spikes of their rests into the ground, fitted their weapons into the crotches and fired a volley. For the next couple of minutes, while they prepared their matchlocks for what contemporary writers rather exaggeratedly call 'the fatal discharge', they were protected from enemy cavalry by a hedgehog display of steel-tipped pikes. The pikemen's drill was to form up with outstretched arms, each man just touching the hands of those on either side, to regulate the intervals. They then stuck the butts of their pikes into the ground and knelt on one knee, holding the pikes at the same angle, like the stakes the Romans used to plant in their defensive ditches. This system was all right in theory, but if determined cavalry put only two pikemen out of action a twelve-foot gap appeared in the hedge, and this could be exploited.

Many years before the civil war James's father had realized the short-comings of matchlocks and the attendant pikemen, for in 1625 he had tried to bring back the long-bow. Unfortunately the proud caste of muscular yeomen archers had long since vanished, taking with them their traditions and skills; he could not revive what had passed away for ever. Thus, when Charles I raised his standard at Nottingham and began to collect his army, he knew he would have to fight the war with sword, pike, matchlock and pistol—and cannon of various sorts—wielded and operated by amateurs whose enthusiasm could not make up for their lack of experience.

*

While the King was at Nottingham, the Earl of Essex, made Captain-General of the Parliamentary forces on July 12, 1642, was concentrating his army at Northampton—one of the reasons why Charles was having difficulty in collecting recruits—and when the Royalist Army, still virtually only a token force, moved westwards, Essex followed.

Robert Devereux, third Earl of Essex, was not entirely without military experience: in 1620, at the age of twenty-nine, he had commanded a company in Sir Horace Vere's regiment of English volunteers which had been formed to help in the defence of the Palatinate, but he had had to hurry back to his parliamentary duties before there was any real fighting. Five years later he had been appointed Vice-Admiral of the Cadiz expedition, and in 1639 he had been Charles I's second-in-command in what was known as the First Bishops' War—the confrontation with the Scots—when there had been no fighting at all. Though shy, and lethargic, he had a punctilious sense of duty, and he was in fact the complete opposite to his publicity-hunting father who had been sent to the scaffold by Elizabeth I. He knew very little about tactics or administration and had become the commander of the Parliamentary Army largely because at that time there seemed to be no one else in a comparable position of authority. In these first moves of the civil war his strategic plan was simple; his spy, a man called Blake, in the King's headquarters, had told him of Charles's intention to return to his capital, and he therefore decided to place himself between the King and London, and at the same time gain possession of the important city of Worcester.

From Nottingham the King moved to Shrewsbury, collecting weapons by disbanding the local train-bands as he went, and arrived there on September 20. He proposed to link up with his Welsh allies and then turn south-east to march on London. The strength of his army now began to rise rapidly. Leaving Shrewsbury on October 12 he managed more by luck than good intelligence to avoid Essex's army, and began the long march. Again, when he learned by chance that the King had out-flanked him, Essex followed, moving at very short notice and having to leave some of his infantry regiments behind. He told them to catch him up.

On the evening of October 22, Essex reached the village of Kineton, only some four miles behind the rear troops of Charles's army which had halted for the night in villages round the feature known as Edgehill, dominating that part of Warwickshire. Knowing how close his enemies were and that their army was incomplete, Charles held a Council of War. The decision was taken to turn and fight, and orders were given for the army to assemble on Edgehill by eight o'clock on the following morning.

In many ways it was a rash resolve. Charles's intelligence organization was not very satisfactory* and he knew very little about Essex's army except that it was far better equipped than his own and outnumbered him in infantry. In his own army, between three and four hundred men had no weapons except clubs or staves, none of the pikemen had any armour and very few musketeers had swords. But it was Rupert, conscious of the time factor and the superiority of the Royalist cavalry, who urged him to accept the risks. Rupert felt that if Essex could be checked, and if the King could return to London before a more effective opposition could be mustered, Parliament might be dealt a blow from which it could not recover.

James and his elder brother spent the night in Arlescote House and rode up to the rendezvous early in the morning of October 23, nine days after James's ninth birthday. As the two boys trotted through the lanes in the chill of that frosty dawn they could see around them the men of the Royalist Army, turning out of the barns and cottages and cowsheds where they had slept, and slowly assembling in their companies and

* He had nothing to compare with the efficient Blake, though Blake had bad luck after the battle. When Rupert pursued Essex withdrawing to Warwick, he captured all Essex's baggage in Kineton, and among the baggage was a despatch case containing receipts signed by Blake for payment for services rendered. Rupert galloped back to headquarters and hanged Blake.

regiments before climbing the hill. A few miles away to the west the men of the Parliamentary Army were making the same preparations, and no doubt many, on both sides, like most soldiers before and since, were feeling that peculiar combination of excitement and dread, and that odd sensation of concentrated awareness of life, that precede a battle in cold blood.

There is a story that William Harvey, 'Doctor of Physique and Chirurgery, Inventor of the Circulation of the Bloud', attended Charles I from the time he left London, and was at Edgehill with him where the young Prince of Wales and Duke of York were 'committed to his care'. Harvey told his biographer, John Aubrey, that he 'withdrew with them under a hedge, and tooke out of his pockett a booke and read; but he had not read very long before a Bullett of a great gun grazed the ground near him, which made him remove his station'.

This was probably what we would today call registration; Essex's gunners were in position and checking ranges during the long period of waiting before the battle began. Despite the orders issued the night before, troops did not begin to assemble on the hill until after ten o'clock in the morning, and James says it was not until three in the afternoon that 'His Majesty's Army was wholly drawn up in Battell'.

The two princes, both dressed in padded buff coats under breast- and back-plates of armour, had plenty of time to watch the slowly gathering armies; their own on the hill around them and that of Essex four hundred feet below on the open ground in front of Kineton village. According to Clarendon (then Mr. Edward Hyde) who was there, it was 'as fair a day as that season of the year could yield, the sun clear, no wind or cloud appearing', but it was far from warm; the autumn that year was unusually wet and cold.

In the afternoon, realizing that Essex was not going to climb the hill and attack him, Charles sacrificed the advantage of the high ground and moved his army down to the foot of the slope. He then rode down the line drawn up for the advance. He was accompanied by his sons, the Duke of Richmond, the Earl of Dorset and about fifty Gentlemen Pensioners. To make sure everyone knew who he was, a great scarlet cornet—a cavalry standard or flag—was borne before him and this, not surprisingly, drew considerable fire from the enemy artillery.

This was James's first experience of battle, and one cannot help wondering what he felt like, as a child of nine, walking his horse decorously behind his father while enemy artillery shot at him. The King's guns also opened fire and the exchange of cannon-balls went on for about an hour, without apparently doing very much damage. Even so, they brought down upon the battlefield that confusing hazard characteristic of combat then and for the next two hundred years: the thick, choking pall of smoke from the black powder used in every firearm.

The battle really began with Rupert's well-known charge, much criticized as 'wild'—but James, writing of it in his Memoirs years later, saw it as a well-controlled movement which by sheer disciplined weight routed all who stood in its way. Yet, as Rupert himself had foreseen, the fault lay in the inexperience and lack of training of his cavalrymen, and their inability to stop their horses running away once they were clear of the mêlée. Rupert knew well enough that it is one thing to charge and see the enemy fly, and quite another to check the pursuit, rally, and charge again in another direction.

After the charge Charles ordered his Foot to advance, which they did 'with a slow and steady pace and very daring resolution'. It was just before this move forward that Sir Jacob Astley, commanding the infantry, offered up his splendid soldier's prayer: 'Oh Lord! Thou knowest how busy I must be this day. If I forget Thee, do not Thou forget me.'

James and his brother rode with their father who, with his escort of Lords and Pensioners, was immediately behind the advancing infantry. The scarlet flag waved above them, and when they came within musket range of the enemy's front rank the musketeers on both sides opened fire; 'the King's still coming on and the Rebells continuing only to keep their ground, so that they came so near one another that some of the battalions were at push of pike': a descriptive measurement. It was in fact a slightly ridiculous situation, for the pikemen stood glaring at one another, trying to thrust and parry with their unwieldy weapons, while the musketeers wrestled with ramrods and powder flasks and matches to prepare their matchlocks for another shot to follow the first rather ineffective volley. But this pause was only momentary. Essex's artillery was still pounding away at the Royalists—he had ten more guns and far more ammunition than they—and when he saw his left wing disappear under Rupert's charge* he ordered his remaining cavalry to charge the King's Foot in the flank while they were 'engaged at push of pike with his men'. He himself showed no lack of courage, for when it had seemed that his whole line might disintegrate under the shock of the Royalist charge he had grabbed a pike from a soldier and stationed himself at the head of a regiment, perfectly prepared to die if the battle was lost.

His counter-charge did not break the Royalist troops but drove them back on their own cannon; the King's standard-bearer, Sir Edmund

* James refers scornfully to 'one Ramsay who commanded that wing of the enemy's was it seems so thorowly frighted that he never left running till he came to London'.

Verney, was killed and the standard captured during the confusion; and Charles resolved to go forward himself and personally rally his men.

The situation was now extremely critical. There was no sign of Rupert and the cavalry, there was no reserve for counter-attack, and if the ranks broke there would be a rout and total defeat. Charles would not expose his sons to the risks he was about to take and he therefore told the Duke of Richmond to take Charles and James up to the top of the hill where they would be safe.

Richmond begged to be excused and the King turned to the Earl of Dorset with the same command. Dorset, with an oath, said quite flatly that he was not going to be thought a coward for the sake of any king's sons in Christendom, and asked Charles to choose someone else. Determined to be obeyed, Charles then 'lay'd an absolute command' on Sir William Howard who, with a small escort of Pensioners, went off with the two boys. Edward Hyde appears to have been in this party, and they soon discovered that the top of the hill was almost as dangerous as the battlefield at the foot of it.

Hyde made for a little barn surrounded by a hedge on the high ground which was being used as a field dressing station, and as he and the princes approached it they saw a body of horsemen coming towards them. Assuming they were Royalists, one of the escort rode up to them and was immediately knocked off his horse and only escaped being killed by pretending to be dead. The enemy were now only about forty yards away and the small escort hurried the princes to the barn. Charles was most unwilling to be hustled out of danger.

'I fear them not!' he said, drawing one of his pistols from its holster and trying to turn his horse, but he was persuaded not to charge. No doubt someone kept a tight hold on James's bridle, for he would probably have followed unhesitatingly where his brother led.

Fortunately the enemy horsemen mistook the dressing station for a defended position and were just turning away when one of them, in full armour, spurred his horse from the party and charged straight down on Charles. He must have recognized the Prince of Wales. One of the escort, Sir John Hinton, took the charge, unhorsed the man with a pistol shot, and a Pensioner called Miles Mathews despatched him somewhat messily with a poleaxe. During this commotion the princes got away and by evening Hyde had brought them to Edgecote, some eight miles to the rear of the Royalist Army.

It had been a long, exciting and exhausting day. James had now seen war at close quarters. He had heard the drums beating in the chilly darkness just before dawn, summoning the army; he had heard the high clear call of the trumpets sounding the charge, the boom of artillery and the flat crackle of muskets. He had seen men and horses fall—no doubt he saw what Mathews did with his poleaxe—and had his father come back to Edgecote that night he would have pressed him for news and details of this momentous day.

But Charles did not come back. Towards dawn he spent a few hours resting in his coach above the battlefield where a thousand Englishmen lay motionless in the freezing darkness of the Vale of the Red Horse.

There was little enough to show for such loss.

THREE

THE night following the battle, which neither side won although the King's bravery in rallying his infantry undoubtedly saved the day for the Royalists, was made even more cold and miserable for the soldiers by hunger. Food was an administrative detail which both commanders had forgotten. Next day Essex withdrew to Warwick, and by leaving Charles in possession of the field and some of his artillery, conceded him the victory. The way to London lay open and Charles now had a chance to win the war if he could get there before Essex. Many Londoners had never supported or were disenchanted with Pym and would have welcomed a victorious King; but all was lost because of the pace at which the Royal Army moved.

The battle had been fought on October 23: on October 27 Charles took Banbury, ten miles from Edgehill, the garrison offering no opposition. Two days later, with his sons again riding beside him, he entered Oxford and on November 4 his army occupied Reading. But meanwhile Essex, marching eastwards while Charles moved south, had passed through Northampton and then swung south through Woburn and St. Albans. He reached London on November 7. Five days later the Royalists stormed Brentford, six miles to the west, and on November 13 took Kingston-on-Thames. Essex concentrated his army at Turnham Green, blocking the Royalist advance, and the King fell back through Reading to Oxford. He had won a battle but lost the campaign: now faced with a long war, his army spent the winter in the Thames valley round Oxford.

Up to now, James had thoroughly enjoyed the civil war, largely because everyone in his father's headquarters had been too busy with military problems to bother very much about what he was doing—provided he did not draw attention to himself. He and his brother spent much of their time on horseback, either hunting in the local countryside or, with their attendants, riding round with recruiting parties or watching the soldiers training for battle. Then there had been the battle, and afterwards the leisurely march to London where, unaccountably, that large dull man, the Earl of Essex, whom nobody liked, had halted the royal progress. Now, in the university city, things were very different. His father suddenly began to concern himself with his sons' education, as if he had just realized that neither of them had learnt anything for months.

No less than four tutors were appointed: the worthy churchman Brian Duppa, a Fellow of All Souls, ex-Dean of Christchurch and ex-Vice-Chancellor of the University, who had been consecrated to the see of Chichester by Archbishop Laud four years previously; two other Fellows of Oxford colleges, Broughton and Croucher, and a man called Massonett* who taught James writing and French. None of these tutors had very much influence on James who played one off against another and did the minimum amount of work for any of them. His real interests lay in the open air; all his life he was passionately addicted to hunting—he was one of the pioneers of foxhunting as a serious sport. As a child he 'delighted in quick and nimble recreations, as running, leaping, riding', and later he became an enthusiastic tennis player, golfer and skater. In fact he preferred the saddle to a chair and physical exercise to any sort of book. His Memoirs, particularly those parts written in the first person and known to be his own work, show a lack of literary grace which is a little surprising in an age when self-expression was considered an essential accomplishment of a gentleman.

He paid little attention to the arts but undoubtedly had a considerable interest in music, and took a lot of trouble to learn to play the guitar. Many years later he was the patron of Henry Purcell whom he commissioned, in 1688, to write an anthem to celebrate Queen Mary Beatrice's pregnancy.

James seems to have had little formal education, but one only has to consider the circumstances in which he grew up, to understand why. From the time when his father established the Court at Oxford, and thereafter regarded the city as his capital, James was given no incentives and hardly any encouragement to sit down and work. His father did, on one occasion, write to him telling him to 'ply his book more and his gun less', but this may well have been a routine, and therefore ineffective, admonition. Furthermore, he was not the heir to the throne, and all his training and upbringing—such as it was—inclined him not only to accept a secondary role but to regard his brother Charles as his future King and

---

* Massonett continued to teach James when he was in St. James's Palace in 1646, and he reappeared at The Hague when James was there in 1648; but he was an intriguer by nature who became a member of the spy organization operated by John Thurloe, Cromwell's Secretary to the Council of State. He must have been successful in leading this double life for after the Restoration he was employed by James as a physician in his household.

a figure to whom he owned total allegiance. This attitude to his brother, so encouraged by his parents and particularly his mother, coloured his whole life, and it is as well to remember that since Charles was only three years older and nearly always appeared to be indestructibly healthy, James never seriously expected to be king.

Charles was notoriously reluctant to apply himself to work of any kind, though he undoubtedly had a far more agile mind than James, so there was no mutual encouragement or competition between the brothers and both must have been a great disappointment to their learned tutors at Oxford. But James had a facility for languages; he learned to speak French fluently and colloquially, and later spoke Spanish with almost the same ease. This gave him an advantage over Charles in France during the long exile. Considerable differences in their characters appeared as they grew older, and perhaps the greatest was James's love of order and discipline, and his real industry in affairs of state and business. James always felt he must somehow do something to find the answer to a problem, whereas Charles was a great believer in the theory that problems left long enough will solve themselves.

At Oxford the difference between the heir to the throne and a royal duke became increasingly apparent as James was left more and more to his own devices. The Royal Family was widely separated. His mother was in France, his sister Mary was with her husband in Holland, his father was always either away on a campaign, taking the Prince of Wales with him, or immersed in the problems of the next one, and Elizabeth and Henry were in St. James's Palace, deep in 'enemy' country.

From now on he was to see less and less of his parents and there was little or no parental influence to affect him during the impressionable years between nine and twelve. He was allowed to go on one last military expedition with his father in the summer of 1643—he went first to Bristol, captured by Rupert, and then on to the unsuccessful siege of Gloucester —thereafter he remained in Oxford. Soon after returning from that expedition he heard that his mother had come over from Holland, bringing a large shipload of artillery and munitions. From Bridlington she went to York and reached Oxford in July. Nine months later, in April 1644, the pressure of a Parliamentary campaign compelled her to move westwards to Exeter where, in June, she gave birth to her last child. Henriette-Anne. A few days later the arrival of Essex's army—on his last disastrous venture into the West Country—made her realize she would have to seek safety in France, and Essex, who did not make war on women, gave her a safe-conduct to Falmouth. She left there on July 14 and arrived safely in Brest.

23

James never got on very well with his mother, perhaps because her interests were political rather than domestic, and there is no evidence to suggest she was a good mother to her children. The civil war had broken many of the links between her and James and it seems unlikely that he benefited much from her short visit.

He could have gained much from his father, for whom he had a deep affection and an admiration which led him to believe that all mistakes and misfortunes were the fault of his advisers. Charles I set a high standard in his private life, and his moral example, had he been able to spend more time with his son, might have helped him in later life to resist the temptations of which James himself, in his advice to his son, who should have been James III, wrote: 'Nothing has been more fatal to men, and to great men, than the letting themselves go to the forbidden love of Women. Of all the vices it is most bewitching, and harder to be mastered if it be not crushed in the very bud.'

As it was, James was to suffer agonies of remorse.

During the two and a half years that he lived in Oxford James was undoubtedly neglected and often lonely. He took no further part in his father's campaigns but he was able to keep up to date with what was happening. Like any other headquarters, Oxford was always buzzing with news and rumours, and he probably heard of Hampden's death from wounds after the cavalry skirmish at Chalgrove Field in June 1643, and that Pym had died of cancer in December of the same year. The main driving force behind the rebellion had gone, but even while he was dying, and both sides were thinking of compromise and peace, Pym had taken the steps which led to victory. On September 25, 1643, he persuaded Parliament to sign the Solemn League and Covenant with the Scots, whose army took the field and in so doing tipped the balance irredeemably on the side of Parliament.

Until that moment, things had been going well for the King. Much of England was under his control; his troops, man for man, were better material than the Roundheads and, most significant of all, a small but constant flow of deserters to his side had begun. There had been changes, too, in the French and Irish potential sources of reinforcements. In France, Cardinal Richelieu had died and power was now in the hands of Charles's brother-in-law, Louis XIII: in Ireland, James Butler, twelfth Earl of Ormonde, as Lord Lieutenant, had put an end to the rebellion by coming to terms with the Catholics who, despite the horrors of recent years, still accepted the King's authority. But the mere rumour of aid from French or Irish Papists did much harm to the Royalist cause.

In January 1644 the 'Counter-Assembly' of 83 peers and 175 Members, who had either fled or been expelled from what Charles declared was no longer a free Parliament, met in Oxford, and James received his writ to attend the House of Lords, but in the same month the Scottish army of 21,000 Horse and Foot crossed the border into England.

It was a memorable year. In June the dashing, dauntless Cavaliers under Rupert and the Marquis of Newcastle met the Ironsides for the first time and Cromwell wrote, 'God made them as stubble to our swords.' This battle at Marston Moor was the turning-point of the war, and James himself says that 'after this the affaires of His Majesty began visibly to decline'. But Charles's own campaign in the south was much more successful. When the two armies of Essex and Waller converged on Oxford in May, Charles eluded both of them and went to Worcester. In June he defeated Waller at Cropredy Bridge, then marched against Essex and penned him up in Cornwall. The Roundhead cavalry cut their way out and Essex escaped by sea, leaving his artillery and infantry with no alternative to surrender. The battle of Newbury, in October, was drawn, 'for though the King's Horse made the enemy's Horse often give ground,' says Clarendon, 'yet their Foot were so immovable that little was gotten by the other'. In November the King returned to Oxford.

During that winter the Parliamentary forces were completely re-organized. Essex was dismissed, Sir Thomas Fairfax was promoted to Commander-in-Chief and the New Model Army of 22,000 men was created. Cromwell was appointed General of the Horse.

At the beginning of March 1645, Charles sent the young Prince of Wales away into the Royalist stronghold of the West Country, but he was subsequently forced to seek refuge from Cromwell and Fairfax in Pendennis Castle. From there he escaped to the Scilly Isles and then to Jersey, accompanied by the faithful Edward Hyde and several other members of his father's Council. On May 3, leaving James and what was left of his Council in Oxford, the King marched away again, this time to Leicester, and at the end of the month Fairfax arrived with the New Model Army and sat down round Oxford.

After so much inactivity and having seen so little of the war James must have found this siege exciting, although there was nothing very alarming about it.

The Governor, Colonel William Legge, had an adequate garrison and plenty of supplies, and he was quite happy to let Fairfax waste his time in front of Oxford and so leave the King free to pursue his designs in the Midlands. But unfortunately Oxford was full of politicians who, on the whole, prefer brave words to brave deeds. Despite the assurances of the Governor they insisted on sending letters to the King, begging him to come back and relieve them. William Legge was a man of thirty-six, an experienced soldier who knew what he was talking about. When still a boy he had served in the Dutch and Swedish armies, Charles I had made him master of armoury and lieutenant of ordnance in 1639, and he had been in command of the second attempt to capture Hull in 1642. Taken prisoner at Southam in August 1642 he had been locked up in the Gate-house,* but escaped; at Chalgrove Field 'Sergeant-Major Legge's courage having engaged him too far amongst the rebels he so long became their prisoner till they themselves were routed', and at the battle of Newbury he so distinguished himself that Charles gave him a hanger† with an agate handle set in gold which he himself had worn during the fight. The King wanted to knight Legge with it first, but Legge refused the honour. He was a fanatical Royalist; Clarendon comments on his unswerving loyalty and fidelity to the King and Prince Rupert, so there could have been no question of an 'arrangement' between him and the Parliamentary Generals.

After the messages had been sent, to prove the worth of his assurances Colonel Legge sallied out on June 2 against the besiegers' positions on Hadington Hill and killed a number of the enemy. James implies that this sortie so alarmed the Parliamentary Generals that they raised the siege before they had news that Charles was returning, but in fact their intelligence system had brought news of the appeal to the King, which had reached Charles at Leicester, after he had taken and sacked the town. It was a pity that the politicians had not listened to Legge's professional advice for, as his enemies had foreseen, Charles turned back and was met by Fairfax, Cromwell and the New Model Army at Naseby.

This was the last set-piece battle of the civil war for Charles was never again able to put an army in the field. After this victory Fairfax and Cromwell swept on into the West Country—forcing the Prince of Wales to flee—and by the beginning of November the King 'had now remaining to him no place of tolerable security but only Oxford'. He spent the whole winter there, and for the last time he and his son James were together for a while. He was never to see his wife or his eldest son again.

At this time James's 'governor' was Sir George Radcliffe, a lawyer by profession who had been a personal friend of the Earl of Strafford—and Strafford was related to Radcliffe's wife Anne. Persecuted by Parliament because of his involvement in Strafford's trial, Radcliffe had become a

* The prison that used to stand in what is now the open space in front of the west end of Westminster Abbey.

† A short broadsword, curved towards the point, so called because it hung from a belt.

fervent Royalist, but it seems very likely that he found the task of looking after James somewhat of a trial. James, with all an active child's curiosity and vigour, felt hemmed in by the walls and tutors of Oxford; Radcliffe, a man of fifty-two, may have found difficulty in sharing the enthusiasms of his charge.

In December 1645 Charles thought seriously of sending James and Sir George Radcliffe off to Ireland while he himself went up to Scotland to join James Graham, the first Marquis of Montrose, who was fighting a brilliant campaign against the Covenanters; but he changed his mind and did nothing. Then, at the end of April 1646, the New Model Army arrived at Newbury, only a day's march away, and Charles had to decide whether to escape or be besieged and captured.

He chose escape, but he resolved to go alone, and what may well have been one of the bitterest moments in James's boyhood is recorded in one brief sentence in his Memoirs: 'the King had it once in his thoughts to have carried the Duke along with him, but did not'.

Once again James had to stay behind, and this time he was being left out of what might have been the greatest adventure of all. To have been able to ride away from Oxford beside his father might have made up for all the disappointments and restrictions of the last few years.

In the darkness, shortly after two o'clock on the morning of April 28, his father rode over Magdalen bridge, his beard shaved and wearing the clothes of a groom, to begin the long journey that was to end on the scaffold.

FOUR

JAMES, now a boy of thirteen, was well aware that he was now virtually on his own, and he also knew that when his father's enemies reached Oxford there could be no such escape for him. His cousin Rupert had also stayed behind, mainly because there was nowhere else to go and in any case he felt that a soldier ought to go on fighting the rebels, however hopeless it all might seem.

There was now no Royal Army to come to their relief and so the siege was merely a question of time. James describes it briefly, saying the enemy's fieldworks came no closer than one hundred paces from the town walls because Fairfax saw no point in wasting lives in a vigorous attack on a place which must fall. But Rupert was not the sort of man to sit quietly inside the defences and let the besiegers starve him out; there were continual skirmishes, mostly outside the north gate, and in one of them he was slightly wounded in the shoulder. James, too young to take part, had instead to be a witness of the final defeat knowing it was inevitable, and knowing too that he had been abandoned in the face of it.

The siege began on May 1, 1646. Negotiations for a treaty started on May 18, went on until June 20, and on June 24 the town was surrendered to Sir Thomas Fairfax. The terms were mild. Prince Rupert and his brother Prince Maurice were allowed to return to the Continent, and all the other Royalists, except James, could either go abroad or stay in England. If they chose to stay they were given six months to 'make their peace by compounding for their estates', in other words, buy their freedom.

So far as James was concerned, he was to 'be delivered into the hands of the Parliament, to be disposed of according to their pleasure'. He was left, temporarily, in Sir George Radcliffe's charge, and soon after the surrender he was visited by Fairfax and most of his officers.

It must have been a strange scene; the room full of officers, clumping about in their great thigh boots, jostling one another to get a look at the

28

boy whose mother they had driven overseas and whose father was now a fugitive. It was all over, and they had won. Parliament was now supreme and the Crown was in the dust, yet they all—except Fairfax—kissed James's hand and, of all people, Lieutenant-General Oliver Cromwell 'was so ceremonious as to kneel in the performance of that action'.

James had to remain in Oxford until the beginning of July; not locked up but not allowed to go outside the town unless guarded. During this time his mother sent a peremptory order to Radcliffe, telling him to escape with James at once and take him either to France or Holland. This put Radcliffe in a hopeless position; surrounded by enemies and closely watched by guards, spies and informers, escape would have been almost impossible, but even if there had been an opportunity, Radcliffe felt he could not undertake anything so dangerous to James without the King's permission. He therefore, very sensibly, ignored Henrietta Maria's instructions, but it seems likely that she had not heard of the surrender and thought there was still time to get away.

A few days later, Sir George Radcliffe was told by Fairfax to take James to London and hand him over to Algernon Percy, the tenth Earl of Northumberland, who, on March 18 of the previous year, had been appointed guardian of James's brother and sister, Henry, Duke of Gloucester, and Princess Elizabeth—with a salary of £3,000 a year. Elizabeth was now ten years old and Henry was seven; they were still in St. James's Palace.

Northumberland was in many ways a good choice for the role of James's gaoler for he was one of the most moderate of the King's opponents —one can hardly call him an enemy. A man of great authority and influence, he cultivated a positively regal manner. 'The proudest man alive . . .', wrote Clarendon. 'If he had thought the King as much above him as he thought himself above other considerable men, he would have been a very good subject. He was, in all his deportment, a very great man.'

Aware of his influence, Charles had anxiously sought his support; first conferring upon him the Order of the Garter in May 1635, and then trusting him with the most senior naval and military posts. In 1636 he was made an admiral of the fleet raised by Ship Money—the tax which caused so much trouble and brought Hampden to the fore as a 'revolutionary', yet, ironically enough, gave Cromwell his navy—and he tried hard to reform the navy as it then was, by bringing to the notice of the King and the Commissioners of the Navy numerous abuses and malpractices. No one paid any attention to him and he lost heart, saying as much in a letter to Strafford. In April 1637 he was again appointed to an admiral's command, then, on March 30, 1638, he was made Lord High

Admiral, but only on the understanding that he would relinquish the post as soon as James was of an age to take it over.

When Charles went off to confront the Scots in 1639, Northumberland was made general of all the forces south of the Trent and a member of the Council of Regency. He was, then, a trusted Royalist, a firm rock in the slowly rising waters of rebellion.

Then Strafford was impeached, and Northumberland infuriated the King by giving damaging evidence against him. Northumberland began to slide into opposition, and as Lord High Admiral he took the navy with him.

The rift came when Charles refused to appoint the Earl of Warwick to command of the fleet. Both Houses of Parliament ordered Northumberland to make him Vice-Admiral, and Northumberland did what he was told. Charles immediately dismissed him from the post of Lord High Admiral but it was too late to prevent the navy from acknowledging Warwick as their commander.

Charles was extremely upset by the defection of the man who, as he said, 'he had courted like a mistress'. He felt it was a poor return for all the trouble he had taken, and the rift was made wider still when, in July 1642, Northumberland accepted an invitation to become a member of the Parliamentary Committee of Safety. Yet the split between them was not so wide it could never be joined; in March 1643 Northumberland went to the King's headquarters at Oxford as head of the Parliamentary Commissioners, seeking terms for peace. Even though they came to nothing, the negotiations were friendly enough, and this was because Northumberland wanted nothing more than peace, and some sort of compromise solution to the problem of reconciling a parliamentary democracy with the Stuart concept of the divine right of kings. Subsequently, in the House of Lords he led the opposition to the trial and execution of the King.

When James with Sir George Radcliffe and his small household came from Oxford, Northumberland rode some three or four miles out from London to meet him, and James was distressed by the way in which Radcliffe 'was immediately discharged from his attendance'. So were all his servants, including a dwarf he particularly wanted to keep with him. He was thus suddenly cut off from all those who might be in a position to engineer his escape, but from the moment he arrived in London the plotting and scheming began. Outside the palace of St. James there were plenty of people who wanted, and tried, to spirit him away from his captors, but for a long time their efforts were unsuccessful.

For all his grandeur, the Earl of Northumberland treated the royal children very well. James himself says that he and his brother and sister might almost have been 'confided to his care by the King himself'. Soon after his arrival from Oxford James was given 'a very rich French embroidered coach and six excellent coach horses' in which to go driving in Hyde Park, but it is unlikely that he was ever able to persuade himself that the mounted escort trotting along behind was anything but a guard to prevent his escape. This gift of a coach may seem lavish but Northumberland was being given £7,500 a year for James's 'maintenance', in addition to the £3,000 he was already getting for the two other children.

James was, of course, a very useful card in the Parliamentary hand; before the fall of Oxford there had already been a suggestion that if the King refused to come to terms the little Duke of Gloucester would be set up in his place, with Northumberland as Lord Protector, but James was more of an age to be moulded into the sort of king to suit the Parliamentary leaders. In fact his father, away in the north, heard rumours of a proposal to compel him to abdicate and make way for his second son.

Having escaped from Oxford, Charles had gone to the Scottish Presbyterian army in camp at Southwell, not far from where he had first raised his standard at Nottingham. He had some rather optimistic idea about persuading the Scots to come over to his side, but he was never able to influence Scottish opinion. He became their prisoner until they handed him over to Parliament in February 1647, and then he was kept in Holmby House in Northamptonshire. He was taken from Holmby House early in June of the same year by Cornet Joyce and 500 Horse when Cromwell and Fairfax, then at Newmarket, brought off their military *coup d'état* which led to Cromwell's dictatorship and the rule of the Major Generals. For a time the army kept him on the move; from Newmarket to Hatfield, then to Windsor and finally to Hampton Court where he was at least near enough to his three children in St. James's Palace to see something of them.

Northumberland suggested moving the children to Syon House, his country mansion at Brentford, even closer to Windsor, but this was not permitted.

James was allowed to meet his father on the last stage of his journey to Hampton Court. He was taken under escort to Maidenhead, spent a little time with the King, and then was sent back to London. Thereafter there were several meetings at Hampton Court but Charles had apparently come to the conclusion he would never again be anything but a captive. Whenever his children visited him he did nothing but give them advice, almost as if he was dying, and telling them to be loyal and obedient to their elder brother Charles, now with his mother in France. But he had seen them so rarely during their lives that perhaps there was not very much else to talk about anyway.

In particular he encouraged James to escape and join his sister Mary in Holland, but James needed no urging.

The first of the escape plans had been made within a few weeks of being sent to St. James's Palace, at the King's instigation, by a Colonel Edward Villiers, but it had been discovered and reported to Parliament. Not very much could be done that winter because at the end of January 1646 James was ill for eight or nine weeks with 'a long ague'.

Another plot, involving the Bishop of Salisbury's sister, Mrs. Kilvert, one of Princess Elizabeth's attendants, and a barber called Hill, led to a great deal of trouble in the winter of 1647. A letter James had written in code was intercepted and he was interrogated by a committee consisting of two Lords and four Commoners. At first he denied all knowledge of the letter and the code but, threatened with far more uncomfortable imprisonment in the Tower, he told the truth, apologized and produced the key of the code. He also undertook not to do anything of the same sort again.

Yet, while all this was going on and he was being questioned by the committee, other plans were being made; this time by the Earl of Suffolk's brother, George Howard. It was George Howard who introduced Colonel Bampfield.

Joseph Bampfield—Clarendon says he was in fact an Irishman called Bamford but there is no other evidence of this—seems to have been a curious mixture of confidence man, soldier, spy, lover and mountebank; his main interests were plotting and intrigue. According to his own story he began to serve Charles I at the age of seventeen, and in 1644 was sent by him to London in disguise 'to penetrate the designs of the two parties in Parliament'—but he was a fluent and persuasive story-teller. It is not known whether it was directly through previous 'business' with the King that he became involved in the plans for James's escape, or whether he was simply employed by George Howard, but he appears to have handled the whole affair with considerable skill. He says that he received the sum of £20,000 to cover actual 'disbursements' of £19,559, but one cannot help wondering, if these figures are correct, how he managed to spend so enormous an amount of money on an operation which involved so few people. Furthermore, at the moment of crisis, when it looked as though he was going to need a large sum, he apparently had nothing left.

James had had a difficult time during the discovery of the Kilvert-Hill plot and he was determined to move cautiously, relying on Bampfield and having nothing to do with anybody else who might have plans and propositions. It was probably for this reason that he now refused to accept a letter from his mother. The bearer of the letter was surprised and disappointed, for he had waited a long time for a suitable opportunity to deliver it, finally slipping it into James's hand in the tennis court at the Palace and whispering that it was from the Queen. But James, who must have known that hitherto her excursions into important affairs had not always guaranteed their success, may well have felt it would be unwise, if not dangerous, to commit himself to plans she was trying to make on the other side of the Channel.

Henrietta Maria was furious, but there was nothing she could do about it. James had made up his mind not to listen to any proposal except Bampfield's, and after all the trouble he had had with the coded letter he was not going to commit anything to paper. George Howard acted as courier, carrying only verbal messages between James and Bampfield.

The first moves were made early in April 1648. Every evening after supper James played a game of hide-and-seek with his brother and sister and other children in the Palace. He became so adept at hiding himself in various cupboards and corners in the huge building that 'most commonly they were half an hour in searching for him: at the end of which time he usually came out to them of his own accord'.

This went on for a fortnight, and the household became accustomed to his disappearances. He thus knew that when the time came he could count on a period of at least half an hour before anyone raised the hue and cry.

On the evening of April 20 he had supper with Elizabeth and Henry at seven o'clock, as usual, and afterwards the game of hide-and-seek began; but this time it was different. James went off, ostensibly to hide, but he went instead to Elizabeth's room where he locked up a little dog which used to follow him about and could have given the new, and far more dangerous, game away.

He then slipped down two flights of back stairs to a door in the southeast corner of the building, clearly visible in the contemporary print of the Palace, being very close to the only gate in the wall of what was called the inner garden. This arched gateway led to the park; James had a key to it, provided by Bampfield, and having unlocked the gate he found Bampfield and a footman waiting for him outside. The footman was carrying a periwig wrapped up in a cloak. Bampfield put the cloak round James's shoulders and the periwig on his head as a very temporary disguise. It was fortunate that James, at fourteen, was tall for his age.

The three of them then started off on what was by far the most risky stage of the journey. James gives us no timings, except that supper was at seven, and even if he had taken an hour over the meal and the business of shutting up the dog and creeping down the back stairs, there is still enough light at eight o'clock on a late April evening for faces and figures to be recognized from a considerable distance, even from the palace windows. James and Bampfield and the footman had to walk, at a leisurely pace so as not to attract attention from other strollers in the park, all the way down the long line of the avenue, along the side of the Royal Garden, to Spring Garden,* a favourite haunt for those who came to listen to the nightingales, and where John Evelyn a few years later was wont to come on summer evenings for 'a collation'. They then had to cross Spring Garden to the road on the far side where a Mr. Tripp, one of Bampfield's associates, was waiting for them in a hackney coach.

It was probably getting dark by the time they reached the coach, and all four drove in it up to Charing Cross and then along the Strand as far as Salisbury House, near the Savoy. Here Bampfield and James got out, saying loudly for the benefit of the coachman that they were going to visit Salisbury House, and Tripp took the coach on into the City to lay a false trail. The coach, rumbling and creaking over the cobblestones, went on its way, and Bampfield hurried James down the dark and very narrow Ivy Bridge Lane which ran beside Salisbury House to the river. At the bottom of the lane was Ivy Bridge, a small jetty where ferry-boatmen waited for fares, and Bampfield hired a boat to take them to London Bridge, about two and a half miles downstream.

Landing on the north side of the river, just before the bridge, they went to the house of a Surgeon Low, where a girl called Anne Murray was awaiting them somewhat apprehensively. She was the daughter of Thomas Murray who had been tutor to Charles I and was later Provost of Eton. Her mother, Jane Drummond, had been under-governess to Prince Henry and Princess Elizabeth, and so Anne, though an ardent Royalist, not only had legitimate access to the royal children but knew James well.

In 1644 Anne had fallen in love with Thomas Howard, eldest son of Edward, Lord Howard, but her mother would not let her get married because neither of them had any money; but this link with the Howards involved in the escape plot seems to be a coincidence. Her mother died in August 1647 and soon afterwards, through her brother Will Murray, Anne met Joseph Bampfield. She seems to have been completely under Bampfield's spell, for she says herself that she was fascinated by his 'serious, handsome, pious discourse'—an approach he had no doubt selected specially, because she was a deeply religious girl and he must

* Perpetuated today in the little street on the north side of the Admiralty Arch over the Mall.

either have found this out from her brother or discovered it himself. But feeling as she did about the King and his family he would have had no difficulty in persuading her to play the vital 'inside' role in his plan.

She had reason to be apprehensive on that April evening of the escape because Bampfield had told her that if he and James had not arrived by ten o'clock something would have gone seriously wrong and she must look after herself. It was now just after ten, and the actual time taken by the boatman must have been longer than Bampfield had allowed for.

Some time previously Anne had taken James's measurements and arranged for her tailor to make 'a woman's habit'. The tailor remarked that he had never seen a woman of so low a stature to have so large a waist, but the clothes fitted admirably and in her account Anne says that when James had changed into the habit 'he looked very pretty in it'.

James ate some of the food she had prepared while she was waiting, then she gave him a Woodstreet cake which she had sent for, 'which I knew he loved', to take with him on the journey down-river. No time was wasted in Surgeon Low's house and as soon as he was ready James was led by Bampfield and the footman—back from laying the false trail in the coach—along Thames Street and down to Lyon Quay where 'a Barge of four oars' was ready to take them down to Tilbury on the ebbing tide.

Until now, everything had gone beautifully, but as soon as they were in the barge the bargemaster, a man called John Owen, became both suspicious and uneasy. When making all his arrangements some time before, Bampfield had told Owen only that he would be bringing 'a friend' with him, and now, finding that the friend was apparently a young woman without any other attendants or baggage, 'it made him jealous that there was something more to the business than he had first imagined'.

It is odd that the careful Bampfield should have made this slip. When he booked passages to Holland on the Dutch pink—a narrow-sterned sailing vessel like a ketch—ready to sail from Tilbury Hope as soon as he and James were on board, he had been prudent enough to say they were for Mr. Andrews and his sister. It was not surprising that, at a time when there were plenty of people, particularly Royalists, who had good reasons for wanting to leave the country secretly and in a hurry, Owen should have been reluctant to become involved in something which might lead to a lot of trouble. He was beginning to doubt whether the girl he had taken on his barge was in fact a girl at all. He refused to run the risk of being searched when he passed the guard ships at Gravesend, and he said that if Bampfield wanted to reach the ship at Tilbury he would have to land at Gravesend and hire a ferryman to take him and his companion across the river.

35

All his worst suspicions were suddenly confirmed when he peered through a crack in the door of the 'barge room' where James was, for by the light of a candle on the table he 'perceived his Royal Highness laying his leg upon the table and plucking up his stocking in so unwomanish a manner that he concluded his former surmises of him were undoubted truths'.

The bargemaster appears to have been shattered by what he had seen, and both James and Bampfield knew they were completely in his hands. For a moment the whole plan, now on the brink of success, was in jeopardy.

James seems to have risen to the occasion rather better than Bampfield. He was reasonably sure Owen was honest or he would not have been chosen to do what he was doing, so he took an even chance and told the boatman who he was. It seems likely that Owen was a Royalist, for neither James nor Bampfield had any large sum of money available to encourage him to change his mind and take grave risks if he were not; but James's offer to 'take care of his fortune and provide for him, and that if he thought it hazardous to return to London, he would carry him over with him to Holland' seems to have helped him to decide what he was going to do.

At any rate, when Owen knew who James was he changed his attitude completely. There was no more talk of setting anyone ashore at Gravesend. As they approached the guard boats lying off the great Block-house —which Evelyn had found 'stored with twenty pieces of cannon and other ammunition proportionable'—all lights were put out, the oars were shipped and in the pitch darkness the barge floated silently past on the tide. The seventy-ton pink, cleared for departure by the authorities in Gravesend, lay at the upper end of Tilbury Hope and the barge found her without any difficulty. On board the pink, which had a crew of a captain and only five hands, were Sir Nicholas Armourer, Colonel Mayard and Richard Johnson, each with a servant; and James says they were all in the plot and prepared, if necessary, to take the ship over by force and sail her to Holland.

James and Bampfield went aboard, and so did Owen. He probably had a shrewd idea that if the Duke of York's escape was ever traced to him he would certainly be ruined if not hanged, and the safest thing to do for the moment would be to accept James's offer. He may well have felt that his own disappearance might lend weight to any subsequently invented story of compulsion and kidnapping.

They sailed at first light, with a fair wind, and early on the following morning anchored off Flushing while the captain waited for the tide to

Charles I,
after Vandyck

Henrietta Maria,
after Vandyck

The Children of Charles I:
Mary, James, Charles, Elizabeth and Ann

Charles I with his son James in 1642

Algernon Percy,
10th Earl of Northumberland

Prince Rupert of the Rhine,
after G. Honthorst

The Beverley Gate, Hull, after Hollar

Musketeer and Pikeman

The Palace of Whitehall and the Holbein Gate in 1640

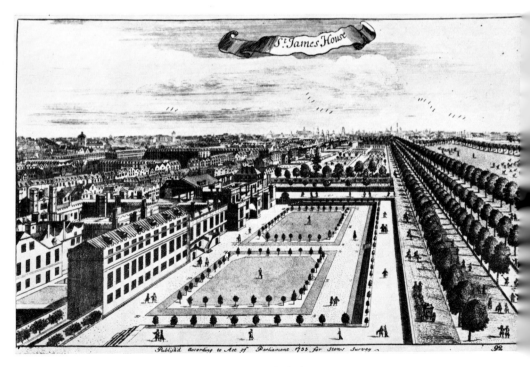

St. James's Palace

turn and carry him up to Middelburg. He went ashore with two of the crew, intending to be back at high water, and while he was away Owen suddenly rushed down to the little cabin to tell James and Bampfield and the other passengers that a Parliament frigate was coming up fast astern, obviously in pursuit of them.

This caused considerable alarm. The captain was away, the pink was unarmed and they lay helplessly at anchor. Owen, feeling a rope round his neck already, was in a most unseamanlike panic. The passengers found it difficult to believe that any pursuit could have been mounted so quickly and Owen was asked if he was absolutely sure the oncoming ship was a frigate. Owen said he was a seaman and knew an English frigate when he saw one. This silenced everyone in the cabin who, as James says, knew nothing of the affairs of the sea. Owen went on to say that their only hope was to haul up the anchor and make for Middelburg, so the three hands on board were ordered to get under way. They would not do anything without their captain. Owen said he could sail the ship safely to Middelburg, but they told him there was not enough water to let them get over the bar at the mouth of the estuary, and the ship would be lost.

All this time the frigate was coming closer, and perhaps Owen's fear was infectious, for the crew were finally persuaded to raise the anchor. The ship touched bottom twice but the tide had turned and on the flood they managed to cross the bar without doing any damage. As soon as the pink was clear of the shoal water on the bar the captain came on board— no doubt with a number of pungent comments on the matter of setting sail without him—and it then turned out that after all this excitement the 'frigate' was a harmless merchantman.

It was, of course, far too soon for any reaction in London to be felt off the coast of Holland. After James had let himself out of the palace to meet Bampfield, an hour elapsed before he was missed, and then more time was wasted in a room-to-room search. When it was clear he had escaped, Northumberland sent the news to Whitehall and to Sir Thomas Fairfax. Orders were issued at once to block all roads out of London, particularly the northern and western ones, for it was immediately assumed that James's rescuers would make for Scotland or Wales. Although Montrose had been defeated at Philiphaugh in September 1645 and had fled to France, there were Royalists in the Highlands who would have looked after James; and Wales was on the way to Ireland where the Royalist Earl of Ormonde was still in control.

Orders were also given to the ports but by the time they reached Gravesend James had long since passed the guard boats.

James's promise 'never to engage on such businesses' at the time of the

Kilvert-Hill plot was recalled, and though the general opinion was that he had not really broken his word because he was too young to have been put on oath, it gave Parliament a useful excuse for acquitting the Earl of Northumberland of all blame for the escape. Northumberland had in fact cleared himself several months before by formally asking, on February 19, to be relieved of his charge, saying he refused to be responsible if James escaped. A few months after all this he was allowed to hand over all 'the trouble and expense' of looking after Henry and Elizabeth to his sister the Countess of Leicester.

Bampfield's plot had been so well laid among such reliable people that none of James's pursuers had any idea where he had gone: the search went on until news came that he was in Holland.

Arriving at Middelburg, James went ashore, still in his woman's clothes, and spent the night at an inn. He caused some concern to the hostess, accustomed to the ways of young gentlewomen, by not allowing the maids to help him to bed.

It was the first night of an exile that was to last for twelve years.

FIVE

NEXT morning James went by boat to Dort, better known today as Dordrecht, then described by Evelyn as 'the first town of Holland, furnished with all German commodities, and especially Rhenish wines and timber'. From there James sent Colonel Bampfield to The Hague to tell his sister Mary he had arrived. He also asked urgently for clothes because he still had nothing but the disguise Anne Murray had given to him in London. Mary sent a yacht and came to meet him herself at Maassluis. She took him back with her to her husband's large house at Honslaerdyke.

Having safely delivered James to his sister and brother-in-law, Joseph Bampfield returned to England, saying that he had been 'summoned by His Majesty' although at that time Charles could not have known where he was. His real reason for going back was to see Anne Murray, to whom he proposed marriage despite the fact that his wife was alive and well. He told Anne his wife had died, she believed him, agreed to marry him, and became his mistress. While he was in England he had to stay in hiding, somewhere he describes as 'beyond the Tower'—presumably a village on the eastern edge of London—because his part in James's escape became known; and when he returned to Holland in the summer it was probably because Parliamentary agents were close behind him.

In June 1648, while Bampfield was still in England and James was at Honslaerdyke, a number of ships of the Parliamentary fleet lying off Deal suddenly 'declared for the King' and put on shore all the officers and men who would not join them. There had been a sudden upsurge of Royalist support in Kent and the fleet had been ordered to bombard Deal; the men refused to open fire, for the excellent reason that the town was full of their wives and children, and said they would no longer fight for men who gave such orders. The Earl of Warwick came down to win back their allegiance but made no impression, and the squadron of about twelve ships sailed to Holland. They arrived at Hellevoetsluis where James, exercising his rights as Lord High Admiral since Northumberland had been dismissed from that post, went aboard the flagship *Constant Reformation.*

The journey from Gravesend in the Dutch pink had been his initial experience of the sea, and this was his first brief taste of naval command. The sea fascinated him; he had a sailor's instinctive feeling for winds and tides; and it is to him, his industry and his understanding of all the implications of sea power, that Britain owes her naval tradition. James and that great civil servant Samuel Pepys laid the foundations of the British Navy, although their work for it did not of course begin until after the Restoration.

James sent at once to Saint-Germain-en-Laye where Charles was living with his mother—the brothers had not met for more than three years—telling him how Fate had so unexpectedly provided him with a fleet and that one of the ships had gone to Calais to meet him.

It was unfortunate that the appearance of this fleet in Holland coincided with Bampfield's return from England, for when Charles arrived in Hellevoetsluis he found everything in disorder, and at the root of all the trouble was Bampfield, whom James describes as a man of turbulent, intriguing head. Apparently he had been 'tampering with the Seamen and driving on a Presbyterian interest to the great disturbance of His Majesty's service'. What was worse, he had been using all the credit gained by his services to James to work up feeling against the young Prince of Wales, but for no particular reason. James was very angry and told Bampfield he had forfeited any favour or advantage he might have gained over the escape from London. Bampfield returned to England.*

James was loyal to his friends and never forgot those who served him well, and he might otherwise have found some place for Bampfield in his household, or at least remembered him after the Restoration. He did not forget Anne Murray,† who by that time had become Lady Halkett. But

* He at once renewed his relationship with Anne Murray, who in the autumn went to Scotland on business connected with a legacy from her mother. About to follow her, Bampfield was arrested and put in the Gatehouse. While there, the whole story of his wife being alive and his relations with Anne came out. On the night before his trial on charges of helping James to escape he got out through a window and fled again to Holland. On the boat he had the bad luck to meet a man called Sir Henry Newton, Anne's brother-in-law. The two men fought a duel as soon as they landed; Newton was severely wounded in the head. Having failed to ingratiate himself with Charles II, Bampfield went back to England where he joined Thurloe's spy ring. In 1666 he 'screwed himself into the Prince of Orange's favour', but apparently soon unscrewed himself. Then, in 1674, he 'conceived a fancy for hermit life in the country' and retired to write his story.

† Anne heard all about Bampfield's wife and at first tried to believe the story he had told her; but at length she broke off her liaison with him and married Sir John

40

Bampfield was a born trouble-maker and James could not afford to subsidize such a liability.

To restore discipline by giving the seamen something to do, Charles took his little fleet to sea, but he would not let James go with him, probably because he felt his brother was still too young for active service: he himself was eighteen. James was extremely disappointed, and said so, but no doubt by now he was getting used to being left behind. He watched Charles sail away and then went back to his sister at Honslaerdyke. He was still there when the expedition returned in the middle of September.

Soon afterwards, the Earl of Warwick with the Parliamentary fleet appeared off the Dutch coast, but the presence of Van Tromp, son of the great Van Tromp, and his ships, discouraged any attack. But the Parliamentary seamen were allowed ashore and as a result of their subversive activities several Royalist ships defected and others allowed themselves to be captured after a token resistance.

Charles became ill with smallpox in October, but he recovered sufficiently to try and cope with the problems of his fleet when Warwick went home in November; for the seeds of disaffection remained and the Royalist sailors, unpaid and having nothing to do, turned their minds to mutiny. The sale of a few prizes captured during the expedition provided money to pay off their arrears, and their mutinous spirit was broken by Prince Rupert, the obvious choice for command. The men wanted James as their commander but he was not old enough. Even the experienced Rupert had considerable difficulties, and Clarendon says that in one instance 'he had been compelled to throw two or three seamen overboard by the strength of his own arms'.

To make up for missing the first expedition James was told he could go to sea with his cousin Rupert, but when after much discussion and argument it was decided that the fleet would sail to Ireland, James refused to go. For some reason—it may have been only a prejudice inspired by the horrors of the Catholic rebellion in 1641—he had no wish to visit Ireland.

Rupert and his brother Maurice went off to Kinsale, on the south coast of Ireland not far from Cork, so as to be ready to support Charles's still tentative plans to regain the English throne through Ireland. James spent Christmas of 1648 with his sister Mary, and early in January 1649 set off for Paris to join his mother.

His father had made her guardian of all the children—though Henry and Elizabeth were still in England—and she instructed James to come

Halkett. After the Restoration she was given £500 from the exchequer and £50 from James himself. When James came to the throne he gave her a pension of £100 a year.

and live with her. Charles remained for the moment at the Hague. James travelled to Brussels and then on as far as Cambrai where he met a courier from his mother carrying a letter warning him that 'disorders' had broken out in Paris and for the time being he would have to stay where he was.

These disorders were in fact the start of the 'Fronde', a civil war very different from the one in England and more on the pattern of the Wars of the Roses. Now that Cardinal Richelieu was dead the French 'nobles and barons' were determined to assert their authority as individuals and to undo all he had tried to achieve. The war took its name from the word for a sling or catapult used by *les Frondeurs*, the street urchins of Paris, to throw stones at passers-by or the windows of the wealthy.

With the support of Marie de Medici, widowed mother of Louis XIII and Henrietta Maria, Richelieu had been the master of France for the last ten years of his life—until he died in 1642. His aim had been to create a strong, centralized government under a king who was an absolute monarch, in a France that was the greatest power in Europe. Against him were ranged the nobility and aristocracy, but Richelieu tore down their castles and in breaking their power, and at the same time involving France in the Thirty Years War—which wrested the leadership of Europe from the Holy Roman Empire—he became the most hated man in France. Even so, when the great Cardinal lay dying and the little Curé of Saint-Eustache exhorted him to forgive his enemies, Richelieu said, 'Enemies! I have never had any, save those of the State.' And there was a great deal of truth in this.

Louis XIII died a year later, leaving his five-year-old son, James's cousin and subsequently *le roi soleil*, in the regency of his widow, Anne of Austria. She came, and remained, completely under the influence of an Italian called Julius Mazarino, better known as Cardinal Mazarin.* While in the Pope's service, Mazarin was first noticed by Richelieu when the Italian showed great diplomatic skill in negotiating a treaty between France and Spain. He began to work for Richelieu in 1636 and became a naturalized Frenchman three years later. When Louis XIII died Mazarin's relationship with the Queen Mother made his position comparable with Richelieu's in the past. Opinions differ widely about Mazarin; on the one hand he is said to have been a brilliant politician and administrator, possessing great charm and a disarming kindliness, and that in an age of violence, when life was cheap, he never arranged for the death of political

---

* Though given a Cardinal's Hat—for political services—Mazarin never went to Rome to collect it, and it seems unlikely that he was ever a priest. There is little doubt that in due course he secretly married Anne of Austria.

opponents. On the other hand, Hume sums up the general opinion by describing him as 'artful, vigilant, supple, patient, false and intriguing', and adds that Cromwell dominated him. In fact, these opinions seem complementary, but he was certainly no military strategist; an attribute which would have been useful to him during the Fronde and the concurrent war with Spain.

James knew him well, but makes no comment about his character. There is perhaps a touch of irony in the fact that in fighting for the Royalist party in France James did much to thwart the revolutionary aims of the Party of the Princes, the Frondeurs, and thus help to establish his cousin's complete autocracy; the state which he himself, many years later, failed to achieve.

*

When James's mother, living in some poverty and little comfort in the Louvre, wrote of the troubles in Paris she may well have been reminded of her own family's flight from London six years earlier, for the Paris mob, on the side of the Princes, had compelled Mazarin, the Queen Mother and the young King, now ten years old, to leave the city and go to the palace of Saint-Germain-en-Laye. The Royalist army assembled and besieged the city, and so Henrietta Maria had to warn James to keep away, but he was now faced with the problem of finding somewhere to live until he could continue his journey. He had no money, and even if he had, the little frontier town of Cambrai had no accommodation for a royal traveller. Fortunately the Archduke Leopold, Governor of the Low Countries, heard what had happened and suggested James might like to stay in the Abbey of Saint-Armand, only a day's ride back from the frontier.

James accepted this invitation gratefully and 'was nobly entertained by the Monks of St. Bennet's Order'. He remained with them for several weeks and this was his first intimate contact with the routine of a Roman Catholic religious community. No one can say what effect it had on him— if any: it is not mentioned again in his Memoirs. He was a Protestant, and the father he loved and admired had often reminded him of his duties and responsibilities towards the established Church of England. Furthermore, he was in the middle of an adventure and at his age he had far more to think about than differences in religious belief and practices. Yet the memory of those calm days in the Abbey may have stayed with him.

On February 8 another letter arrived from his mother saying that although Paris was still under siege, arrangements had been made for him to pass through the opposing forces and rejoin her. James returned to

43

Cambrai and then went southwards through Peronne to Paris, where he arrived on February 13.

A day or two later, news came of his father's execution. It had taken a long time to reach Paris, for the King had been beheaded in the early afternoon of January 30, two weeks previously.

James had not seen his father for more than a year. Charles's escape from custody at Hampton Court on November 11, an operation planned and put into effect by the faithful Colonel William Legge, but which had resulted in further imprisonment in Carisbrooke Castle in the Isle of Wight, had put an end to the visits of his children from St. James's Palace. James himself had escaped five months later. His brother and sister, who had been moved to Syon House, had been brought from there by the Earl of Northumberland to say goodbye to their father in St. James's Palace on the night before he died. It was a tragic, tearful farewell.

Henry, Duke of Gloucester, was released by Cromwell early in 1653 and he went to his sister Mary at The Hague, but poor Elizabeth, so much of whose sad little life of only fifteen years was spent in captivity, died, lonely and forgotten, in Carisbrooke Castle in 1650.

There is no record of what James, at fifteen, felt about the judicial murder of his father, but there is little doubt about the long-term consequences. When his brother was on the throne, and when he himself came to rule, his determination and tenacity were the outward signs of his resolve not to repeat his father's mistakes, and it is again ironical that these qualities gave his enemies the means to bring about his own downfall.

Anne-Marie-Louise d'Orléans, daughter of Monsieur, uncle of the French King and therefore one of James's cousins, has left a description of him at this age: 'he is', she wrote, 'extremely good-looking and well made, and of fair complexion; he speaks French well and this gives him an advantage over the King his brother, for nothing in my opinion goes more against a man than lack of words. The Duke spoke to the point and I was much edified by the conversation I had with him.' She says nothing about his slight stammer, perhaps a consequence of the neglect and disruption and disappointments in his childhood.

Soon after James's arrival in Paris an uneasy peace was made between the Parisians and their King, and James was able to go and pay his respects to the French court at Saint-Germain. Somewhat to his surprise he was 'treated with all the magnificence due to his quality' and as if his father was still on the English throne.

His brother, now Charles II and titular King of England, Scotland and Ireland, remained at The Hague until the summer while he made up his mind to go to Ireland. Apart from isolated pockets of Parliamentary rebels in Dublin and Londonderry, Royalist forces under Ormonde held the country which could be the starting-point for the recovery of his throne. But before he left he felt he ought to go to Paris and explain to his mother that since he was now the King, nineteen, and quite capable of running his own affairs, she must no longer regard herself as his guardian. In other words, he neither needed nor wanted her advice, always so freely offered.

Poor Henrietta Maria was most annoyed. One small compensation for the loss of her husband had been the thought that she would at least be able to pursue her political interests in the career of her eldest son; and now, no matter in what way Charles put it to her, she was to all intents and purposes being told to mind her own business. Never having known her children particularly well, for she had seen so little of them, she was not now prepared to accept Charles's authority. She paid no attention to his refusal to talk about his affairs and continued to supply constant advice, until he gradually forced the point home by rising and leaving the room whenever she began to speak of subjects he would not discuss. She had always dominated her husband and it was a horrid surprise to find she could not dominate her sons—for in her opinion, James was every bit as difficult as Charles.

From that time onwards, until the Restoration, she and Henry, Lord Jermyn caused a great deal of unnecessary trouble by their machinations and squabbles in the exiled court.

In this rather tense atmosphere Charles made his plans for the journey to Ireland. He had written in March to congratulate Ormonde on his progress in strengthening the Royalist cause and said he would join him soon, but there was no money for such an enterprise, and the summer months were spent in trying to raise funds and make arrangements for departure. During this time Commissioners came from Scotland to make offers of help in recovering his crown, but Charles was not yet desperate enough to accept their conditions. Such plans as he had been able to make were then upset by news of Ormonde's defeat by General Michael Jones at the battle of Rathmines on August 2 and the locking up of Rupert's fleet in Kinsale Harbour by Parliament ships. Ormonde wrote to say that in these circumstances it would be most unwise to attempt a landing until the usual autumn storms forced the rebels to lift the blockade.*

* When Rupert and Maurice did at length manage to get their ships out of the harbour they were chased down to Portugal by the great Parliamentary admiral Blake. The King of Portugal allowed Rupert to take refuge in the river Tagus, refused to let Blake into the estuary and later helped Rupert to escape. Blake reacted sharply; he

Charles had to accept this advice but he was determined to get away from his mother. The Channel Islands were the only corner of his kingdom still remaining to him: he had been there before, after escaping from Cromwell and Fairfax in 1646, and he had found the islanders to be welcoming and loyal. In any event, Jersey could be a convenient base for an expedition to Ireland when the time was ripe.

On September 19, 1649, he left Saint-Germain, where he and his exiled court had been living, and this time he took James with him. Seven days later the two brothers arrived at Coutances, 200 miles away and almost due west of Caen. They were entertained by the local bishop with a magnificent display of Catholic hospitality, and next morning went on another twelve miles to the little seaside village of Coutainville, the nearest point from which they could embark for Jersey. While they were down on the shore, Charles was advised by several members of his entourage not to set out at once but to wait, preferably until next day, when it could be confirmed that the coast was clear of Parliament ships. It was known that some lay off Guernsey, to the north-west of Jersey, and might try to intercept the royal party.

James, with his natural flair for the sea, at once pointed out that 'the wind was but newly come up easterly, and therefore the Parliament ships which lay at Guernsey could not take advantage of getting up time enough to hinder him from landing; but in case he should defer it until next day they might have leisure enough to put themselves betwixt him and home'. This was sensible advice. Charles took it, embarked at noon and arrived safely at Elizabeth Castle, joined by a causeway to St. Helier at low tide, soon after three in the afternoon. The value of James's advice became apparent next morning when six or seven Parliament ships came up at dawn and chased the ships conveying baggage and horses, 'which had much ado to escape the Enemy'.

Jersey was at least a comparatively pleasant change from Saint-Germain and the brothers lived in far more state than had been possible in France.*

captured twenty Portuguese ships and threatened further reprisals, with the result that Portugal immediately renewed her alliance with Cromwell's England. Several ships of the Royalist fleet were lost in a storm off the Spanish coast and then Rupert made for the West Indies where his brother was drowned in a shipwreck, and his own flagship the *Constant Reformation* went down in a hurricane. The few ships left in his squadron resorted to piracy for there was no other source of income, and they preyed on English and Spanish ships in the Caribbean until in 1652 Rupert brought them back to France.

* There were about 300 people in Charles's court in Jersey, including such men as the Duke of Buckingham—who went with Charles to Scotland—Lord Byron and Sir John Berkeley of James's household, Sir Edward Nicholas and Sir Edward Herbert, Stephen Fox, James's secretary, and Dr. Richard Stuart, his chaplain.

Much of their time was spent in public ceremonies or shooting and sailing in Charles's pinnace, but, since the threat of invasion or blockade hung like a cloud over the island, they also checked and supervised the strengthening of the shore defences and the training of the militia. The ambitious but frustrated men who formed the court in exile quarrelled and duelled, and then, to add to a general feeling of ineffectiveness, came the news of Ormonde's defeat before Dublin and the raising of the siege of Londonderry. All hope of any adventure in Ireland was, as James says, 'absolutely laid aside', and Charles sent back to Holland the two Dutch men-of-war which his brother-in-law the Prince of Orange had provided to carry him to Kinsale.

Cromwell's conquest of Ireland; the dreadful massacres at Drogheda and Wexford followed by his policy of genocide, made it clear that any attempt to regain the throne must now be based on Scotland, and James writes of 'one Windram, a very Loyall gentleman' who brought various proposals from the Scottish Commissioners.

Despite the desperate situation in Ireland, Ormonde wrote at the end of September pressing Charles to go there and by his presence rally his supporters and encourage them to fight on, but by the time the letter arrived Charles was committed to the Scots. A meeting with the Commissioners had been arranged for the following March, in Breda, and on February 13, 1650—an unlucky day—he and James parted with tears as he left the island to return to France.

James was vehemently opposed to Charles's dealings with the Scots for he knew they would involve renouncing and condemning all their father's principles. He even dismissed Lord Byron and Sir John Berkeley because they voted for the Scottish project.* He had to be left behind when Charles went to Breda because he would undoubtedly have done his best to hinder if not wreck any negotiations. James felt that all the staunch Cavaliers—like Montrose†—who had fought so well for his

---

* In a latter to Edward Hyde, Berkeley wrote, 'My Lord Byron and myself as we were put into my master's bedchamber without our desires so are we put out at His Highness's instance without our consents; we could guess at no other reasons but that we were lately for that treaty which our master passionately opposed and voted against it when His Majesty voted for it.'

† A few weeks later, Montrose returned to Scotland to avenge the execution of Charles I but this time the Highlands would not rally to him. Betrayed into the hands of the Covenanters, he was taken to Edinburgh and tried as a traitor. On May 21, just before Charles II left for Scotland, he was hanged on a gallows made specially high so that all could see, taken down, drawn and quartered according to the abominable sentence of the time and, as Churchill says: 'his body, cut into an unusual number of pieces, was distributed for an example through the scenes of his triumphs'. He was a brilliant soldier and a master of guerrilla warfare.

47

father, would have sacrificed so much in vain if Charles agreed to the conditions likely to be imposed on him.

These were, in brief, that he must sign the Covenant* and dismiss those servants of his whose standard of 'godliness' fell below that of the Commissioners; declare void all treaties with the Catholic rebels in Ireland, suppress the Catholic religion in every part of his dominions, and acknowledge the authority of all parliaments which had met since the beginning of the civil war.

It was clear that by agreeing to all this Charles was likely to alienate most of the Cavalier support in England, but he had no illusions. Even as a young man he had an extraordinary insight into men's minds, and throughout his life he remained a cynical realist who never expected anyone to keep his word. For, as Macpherson says, 'adhering strictly to no principle himself, he was not much offended by the want of it in others'. He did not delude himself about the chances of effective Royalist support in England while Cromwell ruled, and the Scots with their Presbyterian army were offering a possible way back to the throne. He knew well enough that any arrangement with them must inevitably be a dangerous gamble, but the risks were worth taking. In France he was nothing but an impoverished exile with no future; for an end so great as the re-establishment of the monarchy, any means were justified.

On February 21 Charles met his mother at Beauvais; she had come from Paris especially to see him for she was well aware of the dangers ahead and that they might never meet again. They remained at Beauvais together until March 5 when Henrietta Maria returned to Paris and Charles went on to Breda. It is interesting to speculate on what would have happened if Edward Hyde, by far the most intelligent and wise counsellor in Charles's court, had been in Jersey at the time when the Scottish adventure was first discussed. Perhaps unfortunately, he was in Madrid, employed with the elderly Lord Cottington on a fruitless mission to win support from the unstable Spanish King, Philip IV; for it seems unlikely that so moral and uncompromising a minister would ever have recommended or condoned the plan Charles adopted.

James, now sixteen, was still in Jersey when Charles sailed for Scotland in June. To make amends for once again leaving him out of great affairs, Charles, before he left Jersey, had bought the governorship of the island on credit from Lord Jermyn and given it to James. This act of brotherly kindness was interpreted rather oddly by one of Thurloe's agents on the island.

In his report he stated that Charles did it in order to keep James in

* The undertaking to maintain the Presbyterian form of faith.

48

Jersey 'where indeed he is no better than a prisoner of his brother's jealousy, which is very great towards him'. The agent went on to say that Charles was worried about James because 'being very active and of a stirring nature and good parts, and withal being more plausible, may be like enough at one time or another to cause him trouble enough'. On several occasions before the Restoration Charles did indeed appear jealous of his brother, but it seems unlikely that the feeling was anything more than a passing irritation. Of the two, James was the more positive character who got things done, whereas Charles was always content to postpone things until tomorrow. Many years later James wrote, 'The King was far from being jealous, for besides that the Duke had never given the least occasion for such a mistrust, it was not in the King's temper to be so.' This is borne out by what is known of Charles from other sources.

All James's misgivings and opposition to the Scottish expedition were soon fully justified; Charles was made to sign the Covenant before he was allowed to land, and soon after there were rumours that the Scots would make Charles summon him to Scotland where he would become a hostage for his brother's behaviour. There was no truth in these rumours, but the young King was no more popular with the Scots than his father had been. One of the troubles was that he was attended by the young Duke of Buckingham whose disrespect for his elders allied with a gift for mimicry appealed to Charles's sense of humour. There was nothing amusing in their surroundings, and both disliked the way in which Charles was treated purely as a sort of symbol and expected to do exactly what he was told. Perhaps their only relief lay in the private jokes they were apt to make, and giggle over, about the sober Scottish divines who delivered interminable sermons they had to listen to, but they certainly caused deep resentment.

In August the unfortunate Charles, who could not now escape from the Scots even if he had wanted to, was made to issue a declaration which stated that he was 'deeply humbled before God because of his father's opposition to the Solemn League and Covenant, and because his mother had been guilty of idolatry, the toleration of which in the King's house could not but be a high provocation to a jealous God visiting the sins of the fathers upon the children'. It went on to announce that he detested prelacy and in future his only friends and enemies would be those of the Covenant.

Henrietta Maria was not amused, and Charles must have wondered how he was going to be able to explain things when, if ever, they met again. The English Parliament put out a rival document, which did not resort to euphemism: 'Who sees not the gross hypocrisy of this whole transaction, and the sandy and rotten foundation of all the resolutions flowing hereupon.' But the idea of accepting the humorous, pleasure-loving and irreverent Charles as a purse-lipped, sincere and devout Covenanter was just as ridiculous—and abhorrent—to the Kirk as the assumption of 'godliness' was to him. Such an alliance could not last.

Cromwell and his Ironsides invaded Scotland, and on September 3, 1650, the Lord Protector's 'Day of Destiny' and anniversary of the slaughter at Drogheda, he destroyed the Scottish army under David Leslie at Dunbar. The Scottish divines must be held largely responsible for the defeat, for in the early morning they announced that after spending the night 'wrestling with the Lord' they now knew how to win the battle. Having, at that time, more authority than professional soldiers like Leslie, they insisted on his abandoning his well-chosen and extremely advantageous position on high ground and descending to the plain below. Cromwell, with the sun rising out of the sea behind him, saw them coming. 'Now let God Arise,' he said, 'and let His enemies be scattered!'

3,000 Scotsmen were killed, 9,000 were taken prisoner, and Anne Murray was among the women who laboured and wept amidst the countless wounded. Yet, despite this disaster, in the following year a reconstituted army, purged of the godly influences and led by Charles, crowned King at Scone, invaded England.

There was, as he had foreseen, very little support from the quarter in which his followers' hopes lay, for the good reason that, as Hume says, 'the scaffold had so often streamed with the blood of the more active Royalists'. Cromwell, still in the north, allowed this new Scottish army to pass and then moved in behind it, severing its communications. At Worcester, on the next September 3, 1651, his 20,000 veterans of the New Mõdel Army, augmented by the English militia who hated what they regarded as the ranting, meddling invaders, utterly defeated Charles's army. Charles himself fought with conspicuous bravery but, unlike his father at Edgehill nine years before, he could not alone save the day.

His army was broken and his hopes shattered. He himself was forced to flee and disappear into the English countryside.

Apart from the reduction of the Isle of Man, the last stronghold where the gallant Lady Derby, after the execution of her husband, tried to keep the Royal Standard flying, this was the end of the Civil War. England was quiet under the dictator, Ireland was stilled by terror, and now Scotland had been conquered on the field of battle. Yet there were still men like Edward Hyde and the Earl of Ormonde who never gave up hope.

SIX

WHEN Charles went off, first to France and then to Scotland, there was little for James to do. He remained in Jersey until the beginning of September 1650 and then obeyed the instructions in a letter which Charles wrote to him from Scotland shortly before the battle of Dunbar, telling him to return to France. He reached Paris on September 17.

Several months previously, Charles had suggested to James that Sir George Radcliffe, who had been James's 'governor' at Oxford, might be a useful member of his household. Radcliffe had not, in fact, had a very happy time since the fall of Oxford and the handing over of James to the Earl of Northumberland. He had chosen to leave the country and in April 1647 was living in exile at Caen. A year later, hearing that Charles now had a small fleet as a result of the trouble at Deal, he had sailed from Dieppe in June to join him. The ship he was in was attacked by an Ostend pirate and he was robbed of £500 in money and jewels which probably represented his sole assets on which he had been hoping to live until the royal fortunes changed.

James, who almost always deferred to his brother's wishes, took Radcliffe into his household, and Radcliffe, now fifty-seven, became the leader of a small faction consisting of Sir Edward Herbert and the two chaplains, Dr. Killigrew and Dr. Stuart, which exercised considerable influence over James. They persuaded him that some 'ambiguous expressions', as he calls them, in Charles's letter meant he should go on into Holland; and they went further than that. They convinced him—and one must remember that they were all men of experience and he was still only a boy of sixteen—that the time had come for him to determine his own future. They urged him to throw in his lot with Charles, duc de Lorraine, whom they described as 'a pattern and example for all unfortunate Princes to follow', and who was now in Brussels. They also told him, quite untruthfully, that his brother Charles had arranged for money to be paid to him in Brussels.

James has been much criticized for being susceptible to the influence

51

of men like Sir George Radcliffe and Sir John Berkeley who were far more interested in their own advancement than his. Because he had faith in them he is generally regarded as having been a very poor judge of character whose downfall came about largely because he knew nothing of people and trusted the wrong ones.

These criticisms are of course based on hindsight, perhaps the most misleading possession of those who read history because it tends to make one praise or condemn or assess a man's character on the results of his actions, instead of on his reactions to a situation as it appeared to him at the time. One tends to forget, too, how young James was when events threw him out into the world to fend for himself and, further, that he had never had the continuous support and experience of wise, understanding parents to lean on, and whose example and advice could have been his criteria. He had, sadly enough, an affectionate and trusting nature which self-seeking advisers did not hesitate to exploit. It is hardly fair to condemn James as a gullible fool because he failed to see the long-term motives behind the charm and sympathy of a man three times his age who was determined to make use of him. We are told to put not our trust in Princes, but in whom may a Prince put his trust?

Henrietta Maria wanted James to stay in Paris, where she could exercise some control over him, but he had not forgotten the unpleasant atmosphere just before he and Charles had gone to Jersey, and preferred to listen to the men he regarded as his friends. He had never felt at ease with his mother and it seems probable that he resented her close association with Lord Jermyn whom he disliked. She widened the gap between them by continually making disparaging remarks about him to her friends, comparing him most unfavourably with Charles, and naturally enough, in a small community which spent much of its time intriguing, gossiping and back-biting, everything she said came back to him.

Brussels appeared far more attractive than Paris, and he had good reasons, and his brother's authority, for going there. Radcliffe had managed to raise funds for the journey from somewhere, and despite all his mother could do to restrain him, James left Paris on October 4 and arrived in Brussels on October 13; but he soon discovered that the advice given by Radcliffe, Killigrew and the rest, had been ill-judged. There was no money from Charles—who had none himself—and though the duc de Lorraine was courteous even to the extent of giving him a little money, there was no question of entering into any sort of association with him.

Lorraine was one of the great French landowners whose duchy had been taken from him by Richelieu, and now, as an exile and a soldier of fortune, he had sold his sword to the Spaniards in their war against France and was prepared, and eager, to support the Frondeurs against the Royalists. He was fickle and treacherous, and it is most improbable that there were ever any serious intentions behind his suggestions—made through a third party—of assistance in the reconquest of Ireland and of a possible marriage between James and his illegitimate daughter. Most of his energies at this time were devoted to obtaining the Pope's blessing on his bigamous marriage.

Despite his good looks, charm and delightful manners, James, at this moment, was not a particularly attractive proposition in any of the Continental courts. He was only the penniless younger brother of an exiled king whose chances of being crowned were generally regarded as negligible. Even if Charles did regain his throne, he was only twenty and was bound to have heirs, so there was really no likelihood of James ever being anything more than the Duke of York. In any case, by all accounts Cromwell's grip on the three kingdoms was secure; there was hardly any light on James's horizon.

It was while he was in Brussels that James heard first of the death of his forlorn little sister Elizabeth, and then of the defeat at Dunbar. After some weeks James realized that nothing had been and nothing would be achieved in Brussels, so he decided to go on and stay with Mary at The Hague. His mother, determined to make him return to Paris, had refused to send him any money or help him in any way and he was reduced to 'two dishes a meal in his chamber'. He wrote to Mary with some urgency and actually started out on the journey, but he and his party were stopped by a messenger from The Hague who told them that the visit would be 'inconvenient'. His mother had advanced another step towards getting her own way.

Mary was completely under her mother's influence, and when Henrietta Maria wrote to her soon after James left Paris in October, complaining bitterly that James would not do what he was told and therefore must not be allowed to go to The Hague, she obeyed. Replying to James's anxious letter Mary said she was sorry but he could not come until his differences with their mother 'could be composed'.

James had to stay in Brussels because there was nowhere else, except Paris, for him to go, and a few days after getting Mary's letter he was told that her husband had died suddenly of smallpox. James describes William's death as 'one of the greatest losses which could possibly befall the Royal Family', for with him died all hope of ever making any serious attempt to overthrow Cromwell. But soon after this blow and 'to allay this Sorrow in some measure' came the announcement of the birth of Mary's son, nine days after his father's death. This child, born when James was seventeen, was to become his son-in-law, usurper, and King William III of England.

In Brussels, James was now in considerable difficulties. He had no money left and had it not been for a sudden stroke of luck he and his small party would have starved. As it was, some Parliamentary ships were forced by bad weather to shelter at Dunkirk where they were captured by frigates from Jersey, and James, as Lord High Admiral, received a tenth of the prize money. Then, in the middle of December, his aunt and god-mother, Elizabeth of Bohemia, offered to lend him her house at Rhenen in the Dutch province of Utrecht. He was only too glad to borrow it, and while he was there Lord Jermyn, without Henrietta Maria's knowledge, paid him a brief surprise visit to try and persuade him to return to his mother.

Jermyn had no success, but Henrietta Maria now had a better idea. Feeling she could best influence James through his sister, of whom he was very fond, she wrote to Mary telling her she had changed her mind; she now had no objection to James's visit. So, when James wrote again to Mary soon after arriving at Rhenen, she was able to say she had 'the Queen's permission' for him to come. He reached The Hague on January 12, 1651, and stayed in Holland for the whole winter. His visit was marred by the arrival of English ambassadors, sent over by Cromwell, whom he had no wish to meet, and their representations and objections at length compelled him to move to Breda. To add to this embarrassment his retinue quarrelled continuously amongst themselves and caused a lot of complaints by their arrogant, intolerant behaviour to their hosts.

By the beginning of the summer James had had enough. His search for independence had failed. In May he wrote to his mother, asking her to recall him to Paris.

By now he had become disillusioned with the companions he had trusted; he may have seen himself, or someone may have told him, that the motive behind their advice had not been his own welfare but to ensure their own preference and promotion if anything happened to Charles in England. There were rumours that Charles was already dead, but these were proved false when, at the beginning of June, a messenger arrived, bringing a letter from him. This letter was the direct result of Henrietta Maria's complaints to Charles not only about James's behaviour to her but of the bad influence of men like Sir George Radcliffe. The letter instructed James to return to Paris at once and 'withal signifyd displeasure for his removal from thence'. He was also told to dismiss Dr. Killigrew and to disregard any advice given to him by Sir George Rad-cliffe. James was in Paris by the end of June.

The journey on horseback through the pleasant countryside in summer must have been spoilt by the thought of the approaching meeting with his mother. Charles had told him 'to submit himself and be entirely governed by her directions'. He had not forgotten how angry she had been when he left nine months before, and he was sure there would be trouble; but she surprised him by making no recriminations. Her plan was to treat him with a studied contempt and make his life as difficult as she possibly could. She even tried to prevent him from going to Protestant services and he had to appeal to Anne of Austria for permission to establish a private Protestant chapel in the Louvre.

He had no thoughts of becoming a Catholic, nor did his mother ever make any deliberate attempt to convert him to her faith. In fact she seems to have kept strictly to the promise made to her husband, and referred to in a letter written to her by her son Charles in December 1654, that she would not try to influence either him or James.

Henrietta Maria's treatment of James caused a great deal of concern to Sir Edward Nicholas, 'Secretary Nicholas', who in a letter to Ormonde wrote that everything James did which was 'not suitable to the Queen's mind' was regarded as part of some plot. He said he was afraid that James, who was no longer a child, being 'by the Queen and her sycophants rendered so contemptible in their table discourses' might be encouraged to 'give ear to counsels and persons that may put other things into his head than his natural good disposition inclines him to'.

James seems to have borne it all with extraordinary patience and restraint. He was perhaps one of the most confirmed and convinced monarchists who has ever lived and to him the word of the King was law. There were very few occasions when James failed to obey Charles's commands to the letter, and now, during this particularly difficult time, he was able to keep going because he was doing what the King had told him to do. It is characteristic of his loyalty, and his respect for his mother simply because she was the Queen, that no suggestion of her tiresomeness or the unpleasant atmosphere in which he had to live appears in his Memoirs.

In the autumn of 1651, shortly before he was eighteen, a suggestion was made to James which must have been extremely welcome for it offered escape from his mother. In his own words, 'being now of an age capable of enduring fatigue, the Queen his Mother out of the care she had for him, that he might improve his knowledge and form himself for action, resolved to send him along with the Court of France when they should leave Paris, of which there was then a probability'.

This was a polite way of saying that the Frondeurs were putting such pressure on the court that it would have to flee once again, and Mazarin's intention was to go westwards down the Loire towards Angers. Both he and Anne of Austria were perfectly prepared to take James with them and indeed had told his mother that he would be 'particularly in their care', but, quite suddenly, events across the Channel changed everything.

Charles wrote of what James calls 'the desperate resolution' to march into England, and the risks involved made Henrietta Maria unwilling to allow James, the heir to the throne, to become involved in the Fronde. Later came a brief report of the disaster at Worcester, and after that there was no news at all for six weeks. During this time the exiled court in Paris was in a fever of anxiety—James says it was 'a dreadful apprehension'—which lasted until Charles landed at Fécamp, a little port about thirty miles north-east of le Havre.

Henrietta Maria, James, the duc d'Orléans and several others set out at once to meet Charles. Mother and son met at Magny, the little hillside town of steep streets and cobbled squares almost midway between Paris and Rouen, and then everyone returned to Paris. James says that when they arrived there Charles was welcomed 'with all the demonstrations of joy which could possibly be expected', and it was almost as if he was returning from some great victory instead of a series of misfortunes which seemed, at that moment, to have placed the English throne beyond his reach for ever.

*

Of all the long dark winters of the exile, that of 1651–2 was perhaps the worst, for there was now practically no hope that things might perhaps improve. The ways back to the palace of Whitehall through Ireland or Scotland had been closed, the rebel fleet controlled the Channel, and no one, after so much blood had been spilt, seemed willing to try again.

In Paris the exiled court was preoccupied with the daily problem of keeping alive. There was no money, everyone was in debt and now, after Charles's gallant failure, credit was drying up. Everyone was cold and everyone was hungry, living to a large extent on the charity of the French court which had enough troubles of its own. Louis XIV was only a boy of thirteen, his mother and Cardinal Mazarin were both wrestling with problems which were the results of Richelieu's attempts to control the aristocracy, and neither had much time to spare for poor relations.

Edward Hyde's letters to Secretary Nicholas and Sir Richard Browne* stress the extreme poverty of the court: 'Five or six of us eat together one meal a day, for a pistole† a week, but all of us owe for God knows how many weeks to the poor woman that feeds us.' On another occasion he

_____
* Charles's Ambassador in Paris.   † A gold coin worth about 18 shillings.

wrote: 'I am so cold that I am scarce able to hold my pen, and have not three sous in the world to buy a faggot.'

Henrietta Maria had been granted a small pension by her sister-in-law, Anne of Austria, but it was not paid, and once when Cardinal de Retz—a minister of the French court—went to see her she told him that her daughter Henriette-Anne could not be present since, being unable to afford a fire, she had to stay in bed to keep warm. Oddly enough, according to Hume, the English Parliament angrily resented the way the Royal Family was being treated by a lot of foreigners.

During this winter two matrimonial schemes gave the English court something to discuss, for the success of either would have tapped sources of badly-needed income. The first concerned Charles and Anne-Marie-Louise, known as Mademoiselle, the eldest daughter of the duc d'Orléans. She was twenty-four, about a year older than Charles. James says that the idea was 'readily embraced' by Charles and his mother, and Mademoiselle herself offered considerable encouragement, but Charles suddenly found her becoming cooler and was 'forced to forbear his frequent visits'. He later discovered that someone had told her she might be able to marry Louis, the young King, who was far bigger game; but she was badly advised, and James's comment is, 'in reaching at what she could not get, she lost what was in her power to have had, and missed both of them'.

The other plan involved James, and was instigated by Sir John Berkeley, now reinstated on James's staff.

Berkeley was a brash, loud-mouthed, self-confident and conceited man who had fought well for the King in the civil war and was unwilling to let anyone forget it. After the fall of Exeter on April 13, 1646, he had joined his kinsman, Lord Jermyn, in Paris and became a favourite of Henrietta Maria. He was undoubtedly a man of some ability and he concealed a weak character behind a domineering, assertive manner. Like Sir George Radcliffe,* he managed to acquire considerable influence over James who appears to have regarded him as a bluff, rough, solid and dependable soldier—an opinion which no doubt Berkeley was careful to foster.

In all probability he was, in many ways, solid and dependable; he was twenty-seven years older than James who, growing up in a swirling tide of events and never knowing whether his feet were on firm ground, must have been grateful for the reassuring company of this competent man who seemed to know what he was doing and where he was going. Through his influence with Henrietta Maria, Berkeley acquired control of James's finances—such as they were—and styled himself, without authority, so Clarendon says, *'Intendant des Affaires de Son Altesse Royale'*.

* Now in disgrace for the failure of the Brussels adventure.

It was in this capacity, and with a somewhat predatory eye on James's potential income, and consequently his own, that he tried to arrange for James to marry Marie de Longueville, only daughter and heiress of the immensely wealthy duc de Longueville, described by James as 'at that time, next to Mademoiselle, the greatest match in France'. James, Charles, Henrietta Maria and Marie all seemed to be enthusiastic and matters went as far as the drawing up of a treaty which was sent to the court of France, then far away down the valley of the Loire at Angers, for formal approval. It went no further. The court took the view that James had no prospects and a girl with so much money coming to her ought to marry a Frenchman and keep her wealth in France.

Such alliances with Roman Catholics, even though the pecuniary advantages might be great, were opposed by Edward Hyde and the Earl of Ormonde, the two most sensible men among Charles's advisers, for they would not further the Protestant Royalist cause. Hyde in particular sought to avoid any risk of prejudicing a restoration, however distant and unlikely such an event might seem.

Meanwhile James, in common with the rest of the exiled court, was finding little pleasure in life. Nothing more had been said about an attachment to the French court, and in fact the affairs of the King of France had so deteriorated that Mazarin was unwilling to undertake the expense, however small, of James's entourage. James himself was becoming increasingly frustrated by a life of idleness and discomfort, surrounded by factions and cliques and enveloped in intrigue and malicious gossip. Something had to be done.

SEVEN

IN the spring of 1652 the Frondeurs and the Royal Party were still at war, for while Mazarin retained his influence there was little likelihood of any agreement being reached between the young King and the Princes. It was clear that there would be another summer campaign.

In the exiled Stuart court, affairs were becoming desperate, largely because, as James wrote, 'nothing was so rare as money'. It was impossible for James to maintain himself in any sort of state, and it was not in his nature to depend on the charity of his cousin Louis, sponge on his brother, and do nothing in the hope that something would turn up. In any case, at this stage of the exile it seemed unlikely that anything would turn up. Intelligence reports from England—some of the most valuable were in the form of letters written by John Evelyn to his father-in-law Sir Richard Browne—indicated that the Commonwealth had come to stay. Cromwell was only fifty-three and in excellent health. There was no reason why conditions in the English court should not grow even worse, and James, fit and active and with all the enthusiasms of a young man, had no mind to sit and starve.

He was living in a country disrupted by civil war, and while that war continued, his one saleable asset, his sword, could earn him a living. Furthermore, being certain in his own mind that Charles would never regain the English throne without fighting for it, he was 'very desirous of making himself fit one day to serve the King his brother in a useful capacity'. He therefore announced that he intended to join the army of the French King as a 'volonteer'.*

He had felt so sure any plan to relieve the financial pressures on the court would be welcomed that he was surprised by the immediate

---

* A term then used to describe gentlemen of officer status, entering military service of their own free will, who could be anything from highly professional mercenaries to youthful amateurs in search of excitement, and who were often of a nationality different from the bulk of the army they joined.

opposition to his idea from, according to him, everyone except Sir John Berkeley. In fact it was Edward Hyde who introduced and pleaded James's case in the King's Council, of which James was not a member. Hyde said that apart from the obvious advantages the real point was whether the King should make himself personally responsible for restraining James who was so eager 'to improve himself that he might one day be fit to command'.

Having got permission to go, James was immediately faced with another much greater problem: as he says himself, 'the want of money to furnish out an equipage and to maintain his expenses in the Army'.

The English court was in Paris, and Mazarin, Anne of Austria and Louis XIV were all still away at Angers, the town captured soon after their flight from Paris in the autumn of the previous year. Neither court could afford to spend money on fitting out for the wars this boy of eighteen whose value as a soldier was, to say the least, unknown. At length, from a Gascon called Gautier who had served in England, James borrowed 300 pistoles, later scrupulously returned, and made his preparations for leaving. His brother provided him with six Polish coach horses which had been a gift from Lord Crofts some time before, and although his *équipage* consisted only of Sir John Berkeley, Colonel Werden, two or three servants and as many grooms, he was still 'without so much as a led horse in case of necessity'. His camp-bed and all the baggage were carried on two mules which he had been able 'to hire only as far as the French Army where he hoped to be furnished with better conveniences for carriage'.

There was one advantage in the delay caused by all these preparations because, by the time he had fitted himself out with armour and the other necessities of civilized warfare, the French army which was escorting Mazarin and the Royal Family had moved up from Angers in the Touraine and thus made his journey much shorter. Mazarin was known to be at Melun, about twenty-two miles south-east of Paris, and James intended to go there and find out where the headquarters of the army was.

Mazarin at this time was almost as unpopular as Richelieu had been, because he was a foreigner in a position of supreme authority, and the French nobility, particularly the Princes of the Blood, felt very strongly that France ought to be ruled by a Frenchman. The split in the country was deep and wide, and it began in the Royal Family itself. On one side was Mazarin's Royal Party, and the other side, the Party of the Princes, was led by the young King's uncle, Monsieur, the duc d'Orléans, whose military commander in the field was Louis II de Bourbon, now aged thirty-one, a prince of royal blood and perhaps better known as the

Prince de Condé. Condé was a brilliant soldier who had won great victories over the allegedly invincible Spanish at Rocroi in May 1643, and at Lens in Catalonia in 1648, in the Thirty Years War. In 1645 he and the great Turenne had defeated the armies of Bavaria and the Holy Roman Empire at Nordlingen, and his reputation as a wise, humane commander stands high. He disliked Mazarin and resented his influence over the Queen Mother, and in 1650 his general attitude towards them both led to his arrest. He was released in the following year and immediately joined the Spaniards who, fortunately for France, refused to give him independent command, restricted him at every turn by their own ideas of conventional warfare and refused to forgo their siesta every afternoon, even when in contact with the enemy.

He seems to have been an extremely able, brave, charming and popular man whose distressing defection to the Spaniards—hereditary enemies of France—came about through provocation and losing his temper. Yet, with all his attributes, he was not in the same class as the soldier who commanded the Royal Army: Henri de la Tour d'Auvergne, Vicomte de Turenne.

Turenne was unquestionably one of the greatest soldiers in European history, as James was soon to discover. Without him there would have been no *roi soleil* and to him France owes her great military traditions. It was to this 'first soldier of his age' that James proposed to offer his services.

*

Things had not been going well for Mazarin; most of the great cities and towns of France—Paris, Orléans, Blois, Tours and Bordeaux for example—supported the Princes. The duc de Longueville who controlled the city and parliament of Rouen sat on the fence in a posture of uneasy neutrality inclining towards the Frondeurs, and at this stage in the war there were very few towns where the young King was welcome.

The whole civil war situation was aggravated by the presence on the north-eastern border of those ancient enemies, the Spaniards, in the Spanish Netherlands. They were always eager—though seldom alert—to exploit any opportunity for acquiring French territory, and at this moment they were exciting themselves with the most grandiose plans to conquer the Royal Army in battle and turn the whole of France into a province of the Spanish Empire. With men like Condé on their side they had reason to be hopeful, but the real snag was that their own commanders were disappointingly incompetent. James was being charitable when he wrote that they could at least 'have gone farther than they did, had they taken their measures more justly; but their too cautious maxims, both then and

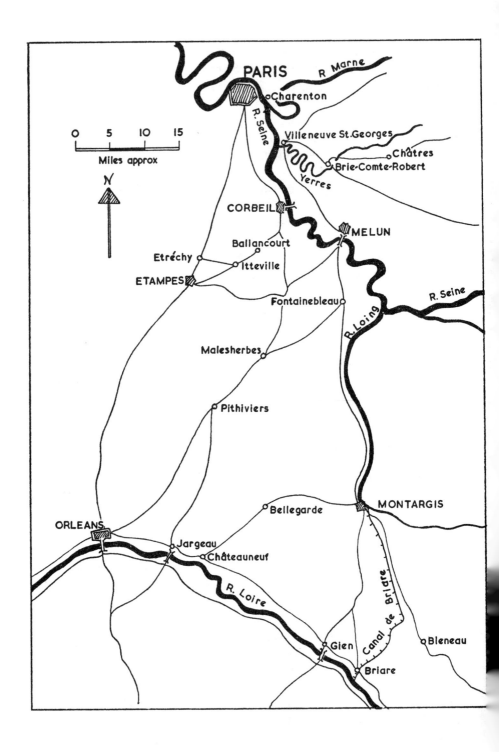

PARIS

R Marne

Charenton

R. Seine

Villeneuve St.Georges

Châtres

Brie-Comte-Robert

Yerres

CORBEIL

MELUN

Ballancourt

Etréchy

Itteville

ETAMPES

Fontainebleau

R. Loing

R. Seine

Malesherbes

Pithiviers

MONTARGIS

Bellegarde

ORLEANS

Jargeau

Châteauneuf

R. Loire

Canal de Briare

Gien

Bleneau

Briare

0   5   10   15

Miles approx

N

afterwards, rendered all their undertakings fruitless'. He wrote from personal experience.

During the early months of 1652 the Spaniards intensified the pressure of their psychological warfare, making large promises of support for the Princes and distributing sums of money to prominent malcontents and enemies of Mazarin. They then took more definite action by supplying the duc de Nemours, an envoy sent by the Princes to ask for help, with a Spanish contingent of 7,000 Horse and Foot which he led off to join the Army of the Princes at Montargis, which Condé was then commanding.

Meanwhile Turenne was bringing the Royal Army and the French court back from Angers towards Paris, along the line of the Loire but on the south bank of the river. Told of his approach, Condé hurried from Montargis south-west to Jargeau, to prevent Turenne from crossing by the bridge there. The forward troops of both armies met in the little town and there was a sharp action, but Turenne had no intention of crossing the river and fighting a formal battle with the army which lay between him and Paris.

Condé withdrew from the river while Turenne went on to Gien, twenty-five miles away, crossed there and occupied Bleneau and the neighbouring villages by the Canal de Briare.

Because of the eternal problem of food and forage, Turenne had to divide his army in two groups, and his second-in-command, Charles de Monchy, marquis d'Hocquincourt, took one of them off to Bleneau, so that the two halves of the army were separated by nine miles of woods and lakes and marshy ground.

Hocquincourt had been somewhat over-promoted; he had been made a Marshal of France in the previous year. In action he was impetuous and brave but his mind worked slowly and he was easily taken by surprise. His real interests were horses and women, in that order, and he had ridden and made love and fought all over Europe, but despite all his experience he was not a competent general and his subordinates were apt to make fun of his slow speech and ponderous manner.

Condé, who knew Hocquincourt's failings, attacked him during the night, routed his troops and then turned to deal with Turenne at dawn. But Turenne, with his genius for choosing ground, had taken up an unassailable defensive position protected by a wood and marshy ground. Both sides stood looking at each other without moving, and then Turenne set his trap. He began to withdraw, slowly and in good order. Condé was delighted; one cavalry charge, pushed right home, would settle the business. His squadrons began to move forward through a narrow defile which led to Turenne's position; beyond the defile was open ground where they could form up.

Turenne let them come on until the defile was choked with horsemen, then he turned his force about and went straight for them. The enemy cavalry tried to retreat, and what had been an advance to contact became at once a struggling mass of men and horses. Turenne reoccupied his former commanding position and opened fire with his artillery into the confusion below him. Later in the day he was joined by Hocquincourt who had rallied his disordered troops, and both of them drew away leaving Condé to salvage what he could of the Princes' army.

Not for the first time, nor the last, Turenne, by his professional skill and unruffled calm, had saved not just his small army but the crown of France.

Condé went off to Paris where he claimed a major victory, having left his army to be commanded by three lieutenant generals. All were reasonably competent as subordinates but none was capable of high command. Jealous of each other, they could neither co-operate nor co-ordinate; Turenne evaded them and thus created the opportunity for the French court to return to Paris. This was the main object of the move from Angers, but for several reasons, mainly lack of confidence and warnings of an unfriendly reception from the Frondeurs in the capital, the court halted at Melun.

James could not have known of Turenne's success at Bleneau before he left Paris, it was too recent, and if he had heard anything it was likely to have been some false report spread by Condé's supporters. He knew, of course, of Turenne's reputation, though that would have had nothing to do with his decision to join him rather than Condé. It would have been unthinkable for James to offer his services to any side but that of the hereditary monarch.

As it was, the whole business of joining the Royal Army had to be managed with secrecy because he was afraid that if his uncle the duc d'Orléans, 'against whose Party he was going to ingage', found out about it, he would be stopped. He was careful not to say goodbye to his uncle, and when the time came to depart he went first to Saint-Germain, with Charles, ostensibly on a hunting trip, and stayed with him in the palace for three or four days. Finally, on April 21, he and his small party set out for Melun.

James's decision to become a soldier was no new idea, born of necessity. His cousin Rupert had turned his mind in that direction years ago, and he had had enough personal experience in the civil war in England to know something of the excitements, the discomfort and the dangers. The whole prospect attracted him, and he knew perfectly well that there was no room in Turenne's army for those who merely wished to be associated with a battle and not part of it.

He was of the disposition that enjoys a fight, and danger stimulated him; all his life he was famous for being an extremely hard rider to hounds, in itself no mean test of personal courage. As a young man he was quick to anger; 'though hot and choleric by nature,' says Macpherson, 'he became sedate in his temper', and to his contemporaries he appeared to be entirely without fear.

As a royal duke, James had been brought up to believe sincerely that to lead is one of the inescapable duties of royalty, and it was failure to lead—as opposed to showing an example—that he felt was the greatest of faults in a king. He could not help criticizing his brother for his procrastination and his father, once or twice, for his hesitation, and he could not always see that there are times when it is wiser not to rush in.

He had the same high courage as his father, who, on the chilly morning of his execution, put on warm underclothing lest his subjects might misinterpret a shiver of cold. Fear might be felt, but could never be shown: James never showed it at any time; dismay and despair, yes, and concern for those he loved, but not fear—despite what his detractors have written. Even Bishop Burnet, who cannot be regarded as one of James's advocates, says 'he was very brave in his youth, and so much magnified by Monsieur Turenne that . . . he really clouded the King, and passed for the superior genius'. Charles was somewhat of a late developer.

James went off to join the Royal Army at a time when Turenne was far too busy fighting—usually against greatly superior forces and with subordinates who created their own problems—to spare time for any un-promising apprentice, even though that apprentice was a prince. James had to earn and hold Turenne's interest in him if he was to learn the soldier's skills. He won that interest, and Turenne's affection, for reasons which had very little to do with personal bravery. First, his attitude to soldiering was genuinely professional in that he looked after the men he led and never shirked an arduous or dangerous duty, nor held back when he should have charged. 'The Duke ventures himself and chargeth gal-lantly when anything is to be done', wrote Sir George Radcliffe in 1652. Secondly, he interpreted orders with a sensible regard for the intention in his commander's mind and not slavishly and to the letter. He was always prepared to act intelligently on his own initiative.

There is no doubt that he loved soldiering, and he really enjoyed com-manding men, particularly in the stress of battle. The account he gives in his Memoirs is entirely self-effacing and factual, to some it may even seem a little dull, but his rather prosaic style cannot conceal his enthusiasm, his fascination for tactical moves and counter-moves, the odd things that happen in war and how men behave under fire.

It was a pity James could not have spent all his life as a soldier, for the lessons he learned and the opinions and habits he formed in the years when he fought under Turenne were of no real help to him as a king. Soldiers, by experience, tend to adopt a comparatively simple approach to their problems, and their minds become trained by necessity to reduce the options to a straightforward choice of what is and what is not possible. The impossible can be rejected immediately, the possible must be translated into practical action.

As a soldier, James was frequently confronted with the clear-cut distinction between life and death, and between friend and enemy; and like many soldiers he prided himself on his willingness to accept responsibility and on the directness of his thoughts and actions. When he was fifteen Mademoiselle had commented on the fact that he spoke to the point.

Thus he was apt to see everyone and everything as either black or white and not, more realistically, in various shades of grey. On the battlefield he learned self-confidence and the need to trust in those who were on the same side. He supported them; they supported him. In friendship he was loyal and strong; when he gave his word there was no going back on it. He knew that at any time his life might depend on the mutual trust which soldiers develop. His friends knew exactly where they stood with him, and so did those whom he disliked. He never attempted to hide his feelings, for he was incapable of dissembling and guile was not in his nature.

Fundamentally honest, loyal and direct, he was, when the time came, quite unable to cope with his politicians because he was far too easily thrown off balance by treachery and deceit; he became their easy victim and their scapegoat, and they took care to see that their perfidy was concealed by the calumny they heaped upon his name. But all this still lay far ahead on that April morning when, with Sir John Berkeley and Colonel Werden beside him, he rode through the great archway of the palace of Saint-Germain and went off to the wars.

They did not get very far on the first day. Travelling due east from Saint-Germain they passed close to the walls of Paris on the northern side, turned south through the suburb of Saint-Antoine and spent the night at Charenton, where the river Marne flows into the Seine. On the next day they covered about twenty miles and reached Corbeil, due south of Paris and about ten miles from Melun.

On the outskirts of Corbeil (now Corbeil-Essonnes) James came across several companies of a regiment of the King's Guards, locked out of the town by the inhabitants who had declared they were neutral but preferred the Princes. When the company officers had told James what the situation was, he realized that a town so close to Paris, which was in the hands of the Frondeurs, was likely to be hostile to the Royalists, yet he went straight up to the gate, engaged the watchmen in conversation and persuaded them to open the wicket and let him in on foot. Once inside the town he induced the magistrates not only to let him bring in his own party with their horses and mules, but the companies of Guards as well.

He seems to have managed to introduce a large body of Royalist troops into an unfriendly town simply by representing to the local worthies 'the danger they ran in case they should refuse them entrance', and he gives no other details. Yet, no matter what methods he used, he had, on the second day of his career as a soldier, captured single-handed and without bloodshed a town of considerable importance to the Royal Party. If the inhabitants had refused to open the gate, Turenne, to whom the town was of immense value later in the campaign, could only have taken it by siege and storm, and this would have been a hazardous undertaking because of its strength and the nearness of a relieving force in Paris. One cannot help wondering whether James remembered his father's embarrassment when Sir John Hotham locked him out of Hull, and this prompted so swift and direct an approach.

The Guards sent a messenger to Melun at once, reporting what had happened, and Mazarin wasted no time in moving the court into the stronger town of Corbeil, where James was waiting. He says he was given 'a small recruit of money, another horse and two mules, all of which came very seasonably to him, for he and his poor retinue had not above twenty pistoles left amongst them at their arrival in that place'. At least he was now able to send back the two mules he had hired, but it seems a meagre reward for what he had done.

On the same evening, April 24, 1652, James and several other volunteers from the French court who had joined his party, went off to the little village of Châtres,* about twelve miles away to the north-east, where Turenne had just arrived with the headquarters of his army.

* Not to be confused with the cathedral city of Chartres.

EIGHT

IN the long war Turenne fought to defend his King against his political
enemies and his country against the Spaniards, James, his protégé,
campaigned over that wide, fertile region of northern France and Champagne where millions were to die in wars far greater, though not less
important for the security of France. A heavy silence seems to hang now
over those battlefields, where the wind sweeps across the open cornfields
and there are so few birds.

The horror and futility of those later wars have darkened all the
countryside where James once rode, his squadrons clattering along
behind him, and much has changed; but not the flowers. The poppies
and purple loosestrife, the clover and yellow vetch grew by the roadsides
and in the fields when he passed—and when the long crunching columns
of infantry passed, many years later—and they are still there today; a
constantly self-renewing link across the years. In the towns and villages
which James knew—Soissons, for example, and Saint-Quentin, Rethel,
Vervins, Fismes and Chauny—there are few traces he would recognize.
But the ancient town of Laon, where the long winter campaign of 1652–3
at last came to an end, must be very much the same as when he first saw it.
The pierced towers of its cathedral are still a landmark, as they were in his
time, visible for miles across the vast plain. The walls, almost intact, still
circle the steep-sided mound on which the town is built, and its gates,
narrow streets and squares have changed little since he rode up through the
Porte de Soissons. Twelve miles away to the west the massive walls of the
castle at Coucy are still there too, and the old *donjon*, much damaged by
Germans only thirty or so years ago, looks out over the woods and fields
southwards, across the valley of the Aisne.

James knew the rivers well, particularly the Aisne, though it was wider,
flowing more swiftly and was much more of an obstacle to infantry in his
day. He saw how Turenne made tactical use of them, much as Napoleon
did in the brilliant defensive campaign of 1814. Turenne was often on the

defensive because he was so frequently faced by forces far larger than his own, but he was a splendidly aggressive commander who never lost sight of his primary aim: to defeat the King's enemies in the field. This task was made difficult by the reluctance of his enemies to fight a set-piece battle, and the great difference between the civil wars in England and France was that in England the Cavaliers and Roundheads sought a military decision in the field, and fought such battles as Edgehill, Marston Moor and Naseby, whereas the Frondeurs preferred a more urban type of warfare; besieging and defending fortified towns.

This meant that the arm which could be the decisive factor in seventeenth-century wars, the cavalry, was seldom used in the role for which it was intended. There were few occasions—few by comparison with the cavalry actions in England—when James as a cavalry officer took part in a major action, though he fought often enough in local engagements in which only a few squadrons were involved.

The cavalry in France was organized on a regimental basis. A regiment had either two or three squadrons, each of three troops, and a troop consisted of three officers—a captain, a lieutenant and a cornet—and fifty men, mounted on heavy 'war horses'. So when James writes of a squadron he is referring to a unit of, on paper, nine officers and 150 men, who normally fought in three ranks.

Although one tends to imagine thundering hooves and a wild, heroic dash, the cavalry charge of those days was seldom more than a sedate trot. The big shire horses which cavalrymen rode were understandably reluctant gallopers for they had to carry a rider and his armour, his sword, carbine or fusil, pistols, ammunition, water, bedding, most of his worldly possessions as well as their own forage.

Dragoons, on the other hand, on the rare occasions when they charged, moved much more quickly, but they were basically infantrymen, mounted on far lighter, smaller horses, seldom above $14\frac{1}{2}$ hands. They were expected to fight on their feet, using their horses only for mobility, and in theory they possessed the range and flexibility of cavalry with the firepower of the infantry. They might have been far more effective if they had had a better firearm; as it was, they were neither one thing nor the other.

The matchlock musket—the principal infantry weapon in Turenne's army—threw a roughly spherical bullet weighing $1\frac{1}{2}$ to 2 ounces for a distance of about a hundred yards; the exact range depended, naturally, on the amount of powder used when loading. The 'effective' range might, at times, be as much as eighty yards but was rarely more than fifty, the maximum range of a pistol. The soft lead bullets made terrible wounds, so it was as well that they did not fly very far nor very straight. Since they did not fit the smooth, unrifled barrel of the musket or pistol, and tended to rattle about on the way out, the man who discharged them had almost no control over anything except the general direction at very short range. Furthermore, since the departure of the bullet was accompanied by a cloud of smoke the musketeer was unable, except when firing alone with a strong cross-wind, to see whether he had hit what he had aimed at.

In these circumstances the musketry battle was far more of a miss than hit affair, and we read of actions in which 'an extreme hot fire was exchanged' for several hours and then find that casualties in a forward unit amounted to three men killed and seven wounded.

James, like other writers of his time, is apt to give distances in terms of weapon ranges: 'the river was but half a pistol shot over'—about twenty-five yards wide; or 'when they were but a musket shot off' instead of about sixty yards away, and he makes much use of the 'cannon shot' as a measurement. He does not say which of the 'cannon' he is referring to, and they varied from the huge 8-inch calibre 'cannon royal' to the little $1\frac{1}{4}$-inch 'robinet' firing a $\frac{3}{4}$-pound ball. Nor does he say whether he is thinking in terms of a gun firing at 'point blank'—what we would describe as over open sights—or with the piece elevated; there was a great deal of difference. For example, the 5-inch culverin, firing a 15-pound shot, threw it more than a mile (2,650 yards) at ten degrees elevation, but only 460 yards point blank. But from other evidence in James's detailed descriptions of the actions in which he fought, it seems reasonable to assume that by 'cannon shot' he means a distance of between 1,000 and 1,500 yards.

Looking back on seventeenth-century warfare in the light of the weapons men have since devised, it may all seem amusingly archaic; but it was not funny to the men who had to stand up to the musketry volley, and avoid being slashed and trampled down in the great surge forward of the heavy cavalry. Fighting was a sweaty, bloody, hand-to-hand business, with men using as clubs the heavy matchlocks they had no time to reload, cutting and stabbing and fighting for their lives in personal combat with an enemy equally determined not to be killed. It called for high standards of courage, physical strength and endurance, and since there were no medical services worth the name, a wounded man knew he would probably die and that little or no effort would be made to look after him. There was no system of casualty evacuation, nor even of collection A man lay where he had fallen unless he had friends or a camp follower who came to look for him after the battle. Looting was a fact of life, and on the battlefield the wounded were often stripped naked with the dead and so perhaps died more quickly, of exposure.

Yet, despite the appalling wounds men received, particularly from bullets, James frequently mentions brother officers and men who were 'shot through the body', and even in the head, who recovered completely; but, riding along the dusty road from Corbeil in the calm of an April evening, he probably gave no thought to such things. He was simply going to join the army and earn his living.

*

The Army of the Princes, moving north under its three commanders after the action at Bleneau, reached Etampes at about the same time as Turenne came to Châtres, and the mixed force of French and Spanish were quartered in the walled town and its suburbs.

On his arrival in Chârtes, James paid his compliments to the commander-in-chief and was treated like any other volunteer in a headquarters on active service; allotted a billet by the Quartermaster, told to settle into it and obey such orders as the commander saw fit to give him. For the next few days nothing very much happened and so he had time to accustom himself to the routine of an army in the field.

Small fighting patrols of cavalry went out each day to the area round Etampes—a long ride of more than thirty miles—where they captured men and horses from the enemy's foraging parties, and from the prisoners Turenne found out what he wanted to know about enemy strengths, dispositions and morale.

The foragers were the most vulnerable part of an army, for if they could be captured or prevented from collecting the greenstuff needed in large quantities for the army's horses, the cavalry, which provided all the patrols and messengers and kept communications open, was put out of action. Julius Caesar's maxim that war must support war still applied, and armies lived off the country, thereby frequently causing starvation among the wretched local inhabitants whose crops they took. Whenever possible Turenne tried to establish 'magazines' of supplies in defended towns, so as to free himself from dependence on the local countryside and also from the need to move on, and perhaps have to abandon good dispositions, when it was 'eaten up'.

He was looking for an opportunity to start offensive operations against the Princes when, unexpectedly, he received a letter from Mademoiselle who was in Orléans, making sure the city remained loyal to her father's party. She wrote asking for a safe-conduct through the area held by the Royal Army on her way back to Paris. Knowing, through his intelligence organization, of her plans, he made his accordingly.

At eight o'clock in the evening of May 3, after only one hour's warning of a move and 'without beat of Drum or sound of Trumpett', the Royal Army set off towards Etampes, leaving only a baggage guard at Châtres. This was James's first experience of an approach march by night, always a difficult operation made more so then by the lack of roads, accurate maps and prismatic compasses. Circling round to the south the troops reached their destination, a narrow valley not far from Etampes, just before sunrise. Here they rested in the dead ground while reconnaissance parties went forward to see what the enemy was doing.

James makes it all sound quite easy, but to march thirty-five miles in the dark across broken country is difficult enough for a small patrol; Turenne was doing it with an army of several thousand men. The infantry could not keep together and, as James admits, a lot of them missed the battle.

The reconnaissance patrols came back almost at once, saying that the whole enemy force was drawn up in battle order on the plain outside Etampes, about three miles away. Turenne at once drew up his army and marched straight up over the hill which had concealed it, to attack. The enemy saw what was coming and tried to retreat into the town. Turenne swung his cavalry round to a flank to try and cut off some of the enemy infantry, while his own artillery and infantry went as fast as they could to get within the range of their weapons.

The Army of the Princes was being reviewed by Mademoiselle. Taken completely by surprise and lacking Condé's firm authority, the three lieutenant generals asked her anxiously what they ought to do. Mademoiselle, who always knew her own mind and had no patience with indecision, said she presumed they had standing orders from her father or the Prince de Condé which covered such situations. She then waved to them from the window of her carriage as she was driven rapidly away towards Paris.

The parade broke up in disorder, and when Turenne and Hocquincourt —and James—reached the high ground overlooking the whole area the enemy troops had all managed to withdraw behind the shelter of the low outer wall of the suburbs. Turenne did not hesitate. He had seen all the scurry and muddle and knew there was no unified command opposing him. The drums beat the 'charge', and James, riding in his wake, heard his sharp, clear orders, saw the guns come into action and watched their thick smoke roll away across the open plain.

It is a measure of James's enthusiasm as a soldier that although he himself fought hard that May morning, and though he must have been deafened by the constant explosions of cannon, muskets and 'grenadoes', blinded by smoke, and burdened by the weight of his armour in the hot sunshine, yet he was able to note and later record in his diary all the details of the fighting in the crowded streets. And he was always right up, as Clarke says, 'in that place where the hottest service was'.

The fight for the suburbs went on all day until 'finally', says James, 'the Royalists began to be more at their ease and finished happily their undertaking'. But the day brought little happiness to anyone. More than a thousand of the enemy were killed and many more taken prisoner. On James's side some 500 were killed or later died of their wounds.

Turenne's gamble, for it had been a gamble, had succeeded: largely because of the determination of his men inspired by his leadership. 'The Action as it was very daring,' wrote James, 'so it was also very fortunate.' Out of 5,000 infantry who had set off on the night march from Châtres, no less than 3,000 failed to appear until the battle was over, and the defenders of the suburbs had outnumbered the attackers by three to one.

The battle had been won, but a large force of the enemy still inside the walled town was a serious threat to Turenne's exhausted men. He ordered a general withdrawal, northwards up the main road to Paris as far as Etréchy.

Encumbered by the large number of prisoners they had taken, the soldiers 'were not a little glad when they got to their quarters'. Much had been asked of them since eight o'clock on the previous evening. Next day the Royal Army returned to Châtres.

From James's point of view this adventure had been a rewarding introduction to active service, for he had learned a number of valuable lessons. First, to attack and seize the initiative at once on any sign of disorganization among the enemy; secondly, that a leader must be seen to be leading; and thirdly, that withdrawal, from any position or situation, is nearly always difficult and can be disastrous. He seems to have applied these lessons with varying degrees of success throughout his life. Of them all, perhaps the most important was the need for a commander to command by force of his own example, knowledge and courage.

Warfare, at this time, was often conducted at a leisurely pace by commanders who were reluctant to get their feet wet. There was a tendency to send an aide-de-camp or a non-commissioned officer to find out what was happening rather than expose themselves unnecessarily to danger or discomfort. Neither James nor Turenne ever spared themselves in exercising the proper functions of command. James frequently makes such remarks as, 'M. de Turenne, having spent all night in the trenches', 'M. de Turenne went in person to view all the ground', and 'accordingly, M. de Turenne went before to observe it himself'. Turenne taught by example, and James was an apt pupil.

73

NINE

THE success at Etampes raised Royalist morale considerably. James says it 'revived the courage of the Cardinal', who ordered Turenne to take his army back to Etampes and 'blockade' it, because the enemy were beginning to run short of forage. On May 27, 'on the ridge of the hill and within musket shot of the enemy', Turenne's troops began work on a line of circumvallation.

The Royal Army had been able to camp within cannon shot of the town because they were on a hill and above the maximum elevation of the guns in the town below. A bridge was made across the river to prevent enemy foragers from going out on the far side, and James, patrolling the whole area with squadrons of cavalry, was constantly alert to attack anyone who came outside the walls. All was going well and it seemed probable that the enemy would either be starved into submission or forced to come out and fight a formal battle on ground unfavourable to them. Then the duc de Lorraine, whom James had met in Brussels, suddenly intruded and upset all Turenne's calculations.

Lorraine had raised an efficient private army in the duchy from which Richelieu had driven him, and earlier in the year had written to Mazarin saying he wished to take the Royalist side in the Fronde. Mazarin, unusually naïve, had believed him, and told Henri, duc de la Ferté,* then governing the province of Lorraine, to allow the duc to collect his scattered forces from their winter quarters. No sooner had Lorraine assembled his army but he marched into France declaring himself to be on the side of the Princes; with whom he had been corresponding secretly throughout his dealings with the Cardinal.

News that Lorraine and his army were marching rapidly towards Paris,

* La Ferté, a man of fifty-two, had been made a Marshal of France in 1651. He had considerable military experience and was one of Condé's subordinate commanders at Rocroi. Though loyal to the Royal Party he was not a good soldier, and his bad temper and inflated opinion of his value and importance created all sorts of difficulties for Turenne.

and of the building of a bridge of boats for him across the Seine just above Charenton, altered the whole situation at Etampes.

Well aware of the danger of being caught between the two enemy armies—one inside and the other approaching the town—Turenne realized he would have to raise the siege; but being the soldier he was, instead of simply abandoning the whole operation and pulling back to safety, he determined to make an all-out attack on the town while there was still time. Artillery batteries were set up to bombard the walls in two places, and an outwork built by the enemy near one of the gates was carried by storm in a night attack led by the gallant comte de Gadagne, a distinguished infantry commander. The outwork was on the south side of the town, near the Porte d'Orléans and only a pistol shot from the wall, and Turenne ordered the storming party to withdraw at first light because of the danger of being cut off. The party had difficulty in getting away—an attempt was made to get round behind them—and Gadagne himself, two or three sergeants and as many musketeers were surrounded, although they managed to cut their way out. Gadagne was not wounded but his good buff coat was ruined by more than twenty sword and pike thrusts through it.

When he saw that the enemy had regained this outwork, Turenne gave orders for it to be recaptured, and at three o'clock that afternoon the enemy launched a major counter-attack with twenty squadrons of Horse (3,000 men) and five battalions of Foot, to retake the outwork and destroy Turenne's lines and camp. In the desperate battle which followed, the Comte de Schomberg,* 'who was then only a Volunteer', was wounded in the right arm.

For a time it seemed that nothing would stop the enemy. 'Things,' says James, 'were now in a very sad state.'

The attack on the outwork that morning had drawn off most of

---

* He did not remain a volunteer for long; later in the year he obtained a company in the Gardes Ecossaises and in the following year was promoted Lieutenant General. His father had been Grand Marshal of the Palatinate, but after the loss of the family fortunes in the Thirty Years War he and his English wife went to Holland where their son, Armand Frédéric, grew up in exile.

Schomberg (son) fought for the French at Nordlingen and soon afterwards emigrated to France where he became one of Turenne's most trusted subordinates. In 1661 his command of the Portuguese army in the war against Spain did much to ensure Portugal's independence. Louis XIV made him a duke and a Marshal of France.

He was a Calvinist, and persecution of the French Protestants made him decide to leave France and return to Holland, where he formed the Huguenot regiments. In 1688 he went with William of Orange to London, became commander-in-chief of the English/Dutch army, and was killed in action at the age of eighty-two, at the Battle of the Boyne. Thus he was wounded in the first of James's serious land battles, fighting on the same side, and killed in his last, fighting against him.

Turenne's troops who were now on the other side of the town, by the Porte d'Orléans, and there were only two squadrons of cavalry and a few sentries left to hold Turenne's lines and camp. James, mounted on what he calls a pad or an ambling horse, felt there was no time to dismount and then mount the war horse which a groom had brought up, nor to put on armour before the enemy attacked. One of his staff, probably Sir John Berkeley who felt rather responsible for him, insisted that he wore armour, and this was strapped on to him while he sat his horse.

But the attack on Turenne's lines failed, and so did the attempt to retake the outwork. Hammered by repeated cavalry assaults—many of them led by James—the enemy finally withdrew inside the walls of the town, having lost more than sixty officers and a great many men, and while they were retiring one of Turenne's spies came in to report that the duc de Lorraine was rapidly approaching Charenton. Turenne himself was now forced to break contact with the enemy and go back up the road to Etréchy.

It was during this siege of Etampes that James first really distinguished himself as a fighting soldier—he was still eighteen and had about five weeks' service. 'The Duke of York hath gotten a great reputation and power in the French army', wrote Sir George Radcliffe. 'He is bold and active.' Writing of what happened at Etampes, Edward Hyde said 'in which action the Duke of York behaved himself with extraordinary courage and gallantry'. None of this is apparent in what James himself wrote but to be able to write as he did, he must have been in close contact with the enemy.

From Etréchy the Royal Army moved east, first to the village of Itteville, seven miles away, and then to Ballancourt, two miles off on the other side of the river Essonne. While at Ballancourt, Turenne heard that the duc de Lorraine's army was at Villeneuve-Saint-Georges, about fifteen miles to the north on the east bank of the Seine, and he decided to attack him at once, before he could link up with the army that had been besieged in Etampes. Since the enemy's bridge of boats at Charenton had not yet been finished, Lorraine had no means of crossing the Seine, whereas Turenne could use the bridge at Corbeil, only ten miles from Ballancourt, and come up on Lorraine's southern flank.

James mounted his pad and rode away from Ballancourt very early in the morning of June 14. He crossed the bridge at Corbeil—where he and the rest of the army left all their baggage—and then turned north, through the forest of Senart. It was typical of Turenne's planning and leadership that the march was so 'well order'd' and swift that Lorraine had no idea he was in danger until Turenne's army suddenly appeared at midday.

Unfortunately, as often happens when maps are bad and reconnaissance might warn the enemy, there was an unexpected snag: Lorraine's position could not be attacked from that side because it was protected by a stream called the Yerres, a tributary of the Seine. Turenne turned off up the line of this stream, looking for a crossing place. After marching all night through densely wooded country* he found a ford, and at first light his forward troops reached Gros Bois in the Bois Notre-Dame, due east of Villeneuve-Saint-Georges. Lorraine now found himself trapped by the Royal Army, the Seine, the Yerres and the forest.

Lorraine seems to have had some idea that this might happen, for he at once sent a messenger called Beaujeu to Turenne's headquarters to open negotiations for a treaty. Like all agreements with Lorraine, these were somewhat involved. Beaujeu turned out to be one of Mazarin's men, and it transpired that despite his invasion of France and his pledge to the Princes, Lorraine had been keeping in close touch with the Cardinal. There was also another complication. In the message carried by Beaujeu, asking Turenne not to come any closer, Lorraine said that the King of England was now with him, having arrived the previous night to help in the negotiations with the French court.

Turenne and James were extremely surprised to learn that Charles had become involved in the politics of the Fronde—already complex enough to confuse everyone—and Beaujeu handed Turenne a letter from Charles which said he would very much like to see his brother and that he had 'M. Lorraine's *parole* for his safe return'.

Turenne asked James to go and see Charles and find out what was going on. Meanwhile, having no illusions about Lorraine, 'his Army continued to advance and would not be hindered by artificial delays'.

Charles had gone to Villeneuve-Saint-Georges at Lorraine's direct request, for Lorraine wanted him to mediate on his behalf with the French court and also be the guarantor of a treaty which Lorraine said was on the point of being signed. Charles was in Paris when this request reached him, and it is interesting to note that although he was usually extremely reluctant to discuss anything with his mother, he at once went to see her. She was staying in the convent at Chaillot, on the north bank of the Seine near the present Place d'Jéna. He probably felt she knew a great deal more about local personalities than he did.

Henrietta Maria knew Lorraine and his reputation. She advised Charles

* Stragglers, stumbling along in the darkness, trying to match the pace of the main column, or more particularly sick or wounded men who could not keep up, faced other dangers than the enemy. Evelyn, who travelled a great deal in France, says that the forests 'abounded with stags, wolves and bears' and he writes of 'a lynx, or ounce' in the forest of Fontainebleau 'which had devoured some passengers'.

not to have anything to do with him, but at that time the stock of the English court was so low that Charles was prepared to do almost anything to raise his status in French eyes. Negotiating a treaty between the French court and so powerful and dangerous a man as Lorraine might do him a great deal of good. He ignored his mother's good advice and, 'not so much as staying to change his cloths', he set off for Villeneuve-Saint-Georges in a coach, taking Lords Jermyn, Rochester and Crofts with him.

At Charenton Charles heard that the gap between the two armies was closing—no doubt news had come down-river from Corbeil that Turenne was on the move—and he was handed another letter from Lorraine, asking him to hurry. Six miles further on, he found Lorraine's head-quarters—and met Beaujeu. He may well have begun to have misgivings when he found the Cardinal's man already doing what Lorraine had asked him to do.

Next morning James came in under flag of truce from Turenne's army and Charles spoke to him about Lorraine being 'perplexed and dis-quieted' by the approach of Turenne's army. Lorraine had good reason to be disturbed. He had been nicely caught by a notably aggressive commander, with a larger army, in a position from which he could not escape. Involved in dubious intrigues with both sides he was now being faced with reality. His troops had been up all night, building five large redoubts to cover his front. His army of 5,000 Horse, 3,000 Foot and a few guns, was deployed in defensive positions behind the redoubts, with the right flank protected by a thick wood and the left by a precipitous slope above the town, so that Turenne would have to make a frontal attack. James admits this was a good position; 'by which, to do him no more than common right, the Duke of Lorraine shew'd himself a great and experienced commander'.

Beginning to realize his mother had been right and that he had got himself into a very awkward situation, Charles asked James 'to use his best endeavours that the treaty might succeed', but James said there was not very much he could do. The propositions he had brought from Turenne gave little room for manœuvre: first, all work on the bridge over the Seine must stop at once, then Lorraine and his army must leave France within fifteen days, and lastly, Lorraine must 'oblige his word that he would never more assist the Princes'. Charles said he thought the demands were ridiculous, and Lorraine would never agree to any of them. James said bluntly that in that case the affair would have to be 'decided by the sword'. He knew how Turenne felt about Lorraine and he also knew that Turenne was not the sort of man to change his mind over something like this. He made little attempt to be conciliatory with his brother because he was irritated with Charles for entangling himself with Turenne's, and therefore his, enemy.

Lorraine came into the room while they were talking, and James handed him the draft of Turenne's proposals. This was the first time they had met since James's fruitless visit to Brussels nearly two years before, when Lorraine had treated him kindly and given him a little money. Lorraine took the paper and tried to make some joke about James's role as messenger but it was obvious he was very much on edge. He then said he was prepared to stop work on the bridge but could not possibly submit to the other shameful conditions.

James asked if this was the answer he was to take back to Turenne, but Lorraine, who was probably justified in feeling that James would far rather have an exciting battle than a dull treaty, asked Charles to let Lord Jermyn go back with James and ask Turenne to be more generous. Charles, now very worried about the way things were going, agreed at once. James and Lord Jermyn, never the best of friends, left the head-quarters together.

Meanwhile, Turenne had continued to move forward. His army was now only a couple of miles away from Lorraine's outposts and still advancing in battle order. Jermyn did his best, but with no success at all. Somewhat desperately, he tried to gain time by asking if James could return with him because he felt Turenne would not begin his attack until James had returned with a final answer. James refused. He knew very well that the real reason for Turenne's steady advance was his fear that the Army of the Princes, from Etampes, might at any moment appear on the far bank of the Seine. Should this happen, Lorraine would probably tear up the proposals and fight, whereas he would probably do everything he could to avoid a battle if he thought he was outnumbered and alone. The time factor was vital. Knowing that under pressure Lorraine might be stampeded into agreeing to the proposals before help could *reach* him, Turenne was giving him no time to think.

Jermyn galloped away, alone. Then, when the two sides were within cannon shot, Charles himself rode out to Turenne to make a last desperate attempt at persuasion, but Turenne 'begged his pardon for insisting still on the same conditions'. He then made the nice point that knowing how Charles felt about his cousin, the French King, he felt sure Charles would not continue to press him to alter proposals on which the safety of the crown depended.

Charles had no answer to this, yet, while the infantry were tramping doggedly towards the defensive positions, he asked Turenne to make one final approach to Lorraine. Turenne agreed and sent off the comte de

Gadagne—in, one hopes, a new buff coat—with the same terms in writing, telling him to give Lorraine the straight choice between signing or fighting.

Gadagne found Lorraine sitting in one of his gun positions by the town gallows on the top of the hill. Lorraine read the paper, heard the ultimatum, turned and ordered the gun crew to open fire. There was a rather embarrassing silence, for the gunners had different ideas about taking on Turenne. Gadagne broke it by saying it was a pity about the artillery's reluctance to start the battle and if the paper was not signed here and now, Lorraine must 'expect instantly to be attacked'.

Lorraine signed the treaty. Gadagne rode back with it to Turenne who halted his army and sent for hostages. Lorraine's Lieutenant General of Cavalry and a captain of his Guards came over and one of Turenne's officers went off with Lorraine to see him across the frontier.

It was most unfortunate for Charles that in Lorraine's camp was a young man called François de Vendôme, duc de Beaufort, who had brought a small force of 500 Horse from Paris to swell Lorraine's numbers. In his thirties and very good-looking, he was extremely popular with the Parisians—largely because he was a master of their argot—and had at one time exerted considerable influence over the Queen Mother, until Mazarin took his place and locked him up in the castle of Vincennes. He had escaped four years previously and joined the Spaniards, but had returned to France to join the Frondeurs.

Under the terms of the treaty just made with Turenne, Beaufort's troops were allowed to return to Paris, but nothing had been said about the future of their commander. He, 'not wishing to make a trial of M. de Turenne's generosity', rode back as fast as he could to Paris where he spread the story that the exiled English King had persuaded Lorraine to sign the humiliating treaty.

Charles was well aware that his mission had failed. He knew, too, that Lorraine had made him look a fool, and he was afraid the French court would regard the part he had played as completely ineffective and feel that he himself had been disloyal. But the result of Beaufort's malignity was far worse than anything he had foreseen. The story so inflamed the Parisian mob that neither he nor his mother, nor any member of his court, dared move outside the Louvre. At length, after several days, they all managed to slip secretly out of the city and hide themselves in the palace at Saint-Germain.

Charles had learned one of his first lessons in international diplomacy: that it seldom pays to intervene in the domestic problems of another country. But there was another lesson too: that he who tries to mediate in a bitter dispute will usually be blamed by both sides. This may perhaps be one of the reasons why thereafter he always tried to avoid committing himself and played for time in order to let tempers cool.

*

No sooner had Lorraine's army started off on the march to the frontier than the Army of the Princes appeared, as Turenne had feared it would, on the west bank of the Seine. It was just too late. Lorraine's troops were out of sight, there was no nearby bridge, and nothing Condé's force could do. It turned round and went back to Paris.

Next day Turenne moved to Lagny on the Marne and then marched round Paris to the north, finally going into camp at La Chevrette on the Seine, three miles from Saint-Denis where the French court had established itself after moving up from Melun and Corbeil. On his march, Turenne was joined by Marshal de la Ferté whose eleven years' seniority in age made him unwilling to obey orders or take advice from a man younger but senior in rank. Their relationship was always uneasy.

Condé, in camp at Saint-Cloud on the other side of the river, heard of these reinforcements, and anticipating an attack decided to move to a less vulnerable position behind the Seine and the Marne, near Charenton. To save time he proposed to march straight through Paris but the Parisians would not let him in and he had to go all the way round by the northern flank.

Turenne learned of this from a messenger who had come out of Paris in a basket, lowered down the wall because all the gates were shut. The Royal Army set off at once in pursuit, without waiting for la Ferté's infantry regiments which were building a bridge with the object of attacking Condé at Saint-Cloud, or for the slow-moving artillery. James, riding with the leading cavalry squadrons, made contact with Condé's rearguard in the suburbs of Saint-Denis and charged at once. He says that this part of the enemy's army was 'cut to pieces'. Condé himself, heading south for the river, was forced to turn and fight in the built-up area of the Faubourg Saint-Antoine.

The battle developed into a repetition of the storming of the suburbs of Etampes. James, who was in the thick of it, tells of assaults and repulses while the noise and smoke of the guns, and the crash of heavy shot going right through the flimsily-built houses added to the uproar of the street-fighting. During one attack on a barricade a young nobleman in Condé's army, the marquis de Flammarans, met a fate strange enough for James to record it in detail.*

* Soothsayers had foretold that Flammarans would die with a rope round his neck; a prophecy regarded as ridiculous because in France the nobility, when condemned to death, were beheaded. During the advance to the barricade he was hit by a musket

At length, when the Royal Army was clearly winning the battle, Turenne launched a final, all-out attack. Condé was in a desperate situation with his back to the river and the gate, the Porte Saint-Antoine, beyond the bridge, shut, and no hope of relief. 'All,' says James, 'was now disposed in good order.' La Ferté commanded the right and Turenne the left. Turenne, swinging out to the left towards the Bastille, to avoid the barricades, was just about to attack when, to his astonishment, the guns of the Bastille opened fire on him and, worse than that, the Porte Saint-Antoine was opened and Condé's troops withdrew thankfully into safety behind the walls of Paris.

There was now nothing for Turenne and his officers to do but curse the fickle citizens of Paris and return to La Chevrette.

Condé's rescue from his apparently hopeless position had been entirely the work of the warlike Mademoiselle. She had been annoyed by the refusal of the Parisians to open the gate to Condé's army early that morning, but when they gave as their reason the pride of good Frenchmen which, despite their hopes for the Cardinal's ruin, forbade them to allow an army partly composed of Spanish troops to march through their city, she accepted it. When fighting began in the Faubourg Saint-Antoine her father, the duc d'Orléans, abandoned hope and, convinced that Turenne would take the city, he shut himself up in his palace and told his coachmen to stand by to take him to Orléans. His daughter, knowing that Condé's defeat would be the defeat of all Frondeurs, roused the mob, obtained from the city fathers an order to the guard on the Porte Saint-Antoine to open the gate, and then went herself to the Bastille where she persuaded the gunners to open fire on the King's troops. For these exploits she was later exiled for five years to her château in the country and then returned to Paris to preside over the most brilliant literary salon of the day.

Forty-eight hours after the saving of Condé's army, a meeting was held in the Hôtel de Ville in Paris to declare the duc d'Orléans Lieutenant General of the Kingdom, to strengthen the party of the Fronde in indissoluble unity until Mazarin should be driven out of France, and to appoint the duc de Beaufort as Governor of Paris. During this meeting a mob surged into the Place de Grève demanding the death of all Mazarin's

ball and fell, apparently dead, close to a house defended by Royalist troops. They, 'judging from the richness of his clothes that his purse was proportionately well garnished', wanted to strip the body, but, being overlooked by the enemy, felt it was too risky to go out and bring him in.

They hit on the excellent idea of 'fishing' for him; 'fastening a rope to the end of a pike, and making a running knot, they passed it round his neck and so dragged him into the house, then just expiring'.

supporters, and when no one seemed interested in their proposal, the rioters tried to storm the Hôtel de Ville, set it on fire and began slaughtering with fine impartiality the members of both factions in and around the building.

Then, to add to the general turmoil of party strife and internal dissension, there came news of the approach of the Archduke Leopold—the viceroy of the Spanish Netherlands who had once arranged for James to stay in the Abbey of Saint-Armand—at the head of a Spanish army of 25,000 men.

Turenne was now faced with a threat far greater than the struggle between Royalist and Frondeur. This was an invasion—at the instigation of the Princes—flowing across a virtually undefended frontier, and he had practically nothing with which to halt it.

TEN

TURENNE, as imperturbable as usual, appeared to be quite unmoved by the Spanish invasion—merely working out how he would cope with it —whereas Mazarin, who had none of Richelieu's steely determination, was panic-stricken. The King's Council met at Saint-Denis on July 15 (1652) and, at Mazarin's instigation, resolved to flee.

The court, said Mazarin, could not stay where it was because it would be trapped between the invading Spaniards and the Army of the Princes, now in Paris. The young King would fall into the hands of his enemies and all would be lost. The only safe Royalist region left was at Lyon, 220 miles away to the south, and the court must take refuge there.

Turenne and James rode over to Saint-Denis from their camp at La Chevrette on the afternoon of the Council meeting and heard the news from Frédéric Maurice, duc de Bouillon, who was Turenne's brother. He said he agreed with Mazarin because, like the rest of the Council, he felt that after the actions at Bleneau, Etampes and the Faubourg Saint-Antoine, the Royal Army was not strong enough to offer effective resistance to Archduke Leopold.

Angered by these counsels of despair, Turenne told his brother the plan was nonsense. To run away, abandoning the whole of northern France to the Spaniards and the Princes, would mean the loss of all the frontier towns in Picardy, Champagne and Lorraine, now held for the King, and the garrisons, left to their fate, would inevitably go over to the enemy. The Princes, with most of France on their side and with plenty of time to make preparations unmolested, would attack and defeat the court in the south, and drive it from the country.

The King, said Turenne, must go to Pontoise, twelve miles away to the north-east, escorted by 'the Guard that usually accompanied him and which would suffice for that purpose'. The town was easy to defend, and once the court was there, he proposed to advance north-east to Compiègne, 'to observe the motion of the Spaniards, and by the favour of that Town, and the rivers which were near it, at least to delay their progress if not to stop them altogether'.

'Then,' says James, 'he added that he was sure the Spaniards, who were naturally suspicious and subject to taking exaggerated precautions, when they saw him advancing upon them would not fail with the ordinary refinements of their prudence to imagine there was some mystery in his move, and to believe that he would not dare risk it without good grounds; finally, that their opinion of the French temperament would make them fear that the Princes might be negotiating some secret treaty of which they would be the victims.'

This argument convinced Bouillon; and so he, Turenne and James all then went to Mazarin and convinced him too. On July 17 the court moved to Pontoise, and on July 20 Turenne's army arrived at Compiègne and camped close to the walls.

The Spanish army had by this time reached Chauny, twenty miles to the north-east of Compiègne, and when he heard of Turenne's advance, the Archduke did exactly what Turenne had said he would. He withdrew at once to Flanders, stationing the duc de Lorraine and his army on the frontier, and ordering the Duke of Würtemburg, with a detachment of the Spanish army, to remain nearby and 'help the Princes when it should be judged fitting'.

Mazarin himself had taken a great deal of the heat out of the political situation by leaving the country for a while, at the time when the court moved to Pontoise. But from the point of view of his own future, it was a calculated risk, for he depended on Anne of Austria's ability and willingness to recall him when Royalist affairs were less depressing. He was lucky in that while he was away the duc de Bouillon died suddenly; for James says that had he lived the duc would probably have taken Mazarin's place in the Royal Council and made sure he never came back.

*

Having countered the threat of invasion, Turenne brought his army back from Compiègne at the beginning of August and found quarters for it some five miles to the north-east of Saint-Denis. Here he was able to keep an eye on Condé's army and yet was in a position to cut off any reinforcements sent down from the enemy force on the frontier. Nothing happened for several weeks, and then, at the end of August, Turenne was warned that the duc de Lorraine—who at Villeneuve-Saint-Georges had undertaken 'never more to assist the Princes'—was on his way south with his own army and the Spanish detachment under Würtemburg. To avoid Turenne he had made a detour to the east, marching through

Champagne, and intended to join Condé outside Paris as soon as he could.

Acting on this information, Turenne took his army across the Marne at Lagny and moved on due east to a village five miles from the river. While he was there he received a message from the court, telling him to halt and do nothing because negotiations had begun with Lorraine; who had promised to stay where he was 'until terms were agreed upon or broken off'.

Knowing perfectly well that all Lorraine's talk of peace terms was a typical trick to avoid having to fight a battle with the Royal Army before he could link up with Condé, Turenne was sure that Lorraine was in fact heading back for the defensive position he had made above Villeneuve-Saint-Georges in June. The court, yet again, was being stupid enough to believe Lorraine, and, as Turenne told James privately, 'knowing it was for his Master's interests that he should march, he thought it better to venture his head by disobeying than to give M. de Lorraine the chance of reaching his goal and duping him'.

Next day, September 5, the Royal Army broke camp, sent the advance party of Quartermasters ahead to lay out a camp at Brie-Comte-Robert, and set off. Turenne's appreciation proved to be entirely accurate, for the Quartermasters of the opposing armies met each other on the camping ground both intended to use. Told of this, Turenne decided to move straight on to Villeneuve-Saint-Georges, and since he rightly anticipated that Lorraine would do the same, a race began for the excellent defensive position just outside the town.

Lorraine's forward troops were the first to reach, and take, the little town, and part of his army had crossed the Yerres before Turenne and James, coming up through the woods by another route, arrived with their vanguard on the high ground overlooking the town and the rivers. James charged at once, drove the enemy off and seized the bridge. Lorraine withdrew upstream to the Château d'Ablon where, a few days later, he was joined by Condé's force from Paris.

The combined enemy armies outnumbered Turenne by two to one, and both Condé and Lorraine felt they now had him in the trap he had once laid for Lorraine. 'They counted on certain victory', for Turenne, known to have enough bread for only five days in his supply waggons, unable to collect forage from a countryside already devastated, and prevented by the rivers from drawing on the stock of supplies he had put into Corbeil, was apparently unable to feed his troops. 'They hoped,' wrote James, 'to finish the war without striking a blow.' But nearly every great commander owes his success and his reputation not just to his own

86

skill but to the occasional stroke of pure luck. On the night of Turenne's arrival at Villeneuve-Saint-Georges, and just after the enemy had drawn back to the Château d'Ablon, about two dozen boats came down the Seine. Turenne managed to stop them and, with beams and planks taken from houses in the town, used them to build two bridges. 'The difficulties appeared insurmountable,' said James, 'yet they were overcome.'

These two bridges, protected by defence works on the far bank, gave access to large foraging areas on the other side of the river; then, when Condé left only a small garrison in the Château d'Ablon and marched east to cross the Yerres and get round behind him, Turenne saw his opportunity to capture the Château and thereby open communication by water with his well-stocked supply depot at Corbeil.

On the way to attack the Château d'Ablon a force of enemy appeared and James and Turenne 'at once put themselves among the skirmishers' —no one could ever accuse either of leading from behind—because Turenne wanted to see for himself what was happening. 'But he saw not clearly at a distance and would not trust his own eyesight', so he asked James to tell him what the enemy were doing. This is but one of many examples of the close professional relationship which developed between the commander and his youngest staff officer.

The capture of the Château d'Ablon solved many of Turenne's problems 'and rendered useless all the enemy's precautions'. His foraging parties were now ranging far and wide, even up to the walls of Paris, and Condé's inability to keep his promise to the Parisians that he would 'rid them of this trouble and force the King's Army to submit' was making them think very seriously that they might be backing the wrong side. The sparks of doubt were fanned industriously by Royalists in the city, negotiations were started with the court, which had come back to Saint-Germain-en-Laye from Pontoise, and Turenne was asked if he could leave Villeneuve-Saint-Georges 'without risking anything' and rejoin the King so as to 'promote the treaty which was being discussed with the Parisians'.

After crossing the Seine by night, he brought the army eastwards in a great arc, crossed the Marne at Meaux and camped at Senlis on the edge of the Forêt de Chantilly.

Just before dawn on October 5, the morning after Turenne had slipped across the Seine, Condé and Lorraine moved in to attack the Villeneuve-Saint-Georges positions in what they intended to be the final battle, only to find them abandoned.

Turenne's withdrawal took the Princes by surprise and 'completely ruined their credit with the Parisians who were tired of enduring the burden of a war that overwhelmed them'. Because of the approach of winter and the total lack of food in a countryside laid waste by foraging parties, Condé and Lorraine took their forces off to find winter quarters in the Champagne and Lorraine provinces, and arranged for the Spanish army to join them at Rethel on the river Aisne, 'to assist them in taking such places in those countries as would secure them in their quarters'. While they were away, the duc d'Orléans and Mademoiselle were to remain in Paris and do everything they could to 'hinder that Town from receiving the King'.

On October 14 the Princes' army, trudging northwards, passed close to the Royal Army at Courteuil, near Senlis, and as soon as the columns of men and horses had gone by, Turenne and James galloped off to the court at Saint-Germain, twenty-eight miles away.

At last, Turenne insisted, the moment had come for the King to return to his capital, and there was no time to lose. The Parisians must not be allowed to 'recover from the disgust they had conceived for the Princes'. Paris was a vital factor in the war; without it there would be no winter quarters for the troops and the army would be in no position to cope with the greatly increased enemy force in the next year's campaign. More important still, once the King was inside the capital, all the other great cities and towns now unwilling to admit him would be prepared to follow the example of the Parisians.

In the absence of Mazarin, still in voluntary exile, the King's Council accepted Turenne's argument. The court left Saint-Germain and crossed the Seine at Saint-Cloud, all the other bridges being broken; but as the convoy of coaches and escorting cavalry was passing through the Bois de Boulogne it was met by various 'persons' from the city, who may well have been employed by Mademoiselle. They said the time was not right and it was all far too dangerous. Gathering round the coach in which Louis and the Queen Mother were riding, they begged them to go back before anything dreadful happened. All the nervous gentlemen of the court—who knew nothing of the situation in Paris—agreed; their Majesties must return at once to Saint-Germain.

Turenne had probably foreseen that something like this might happen, for he and James were among the entourage, and he alone put forward an unanswerable argument. If, having come this far, His Majesty were now to turn round and scuttle back to safety it would not only dishearten his friends and encourage his enemies, but reveal the whole court as irresolute and easily frightened, and thus quite unfit to govern France.

The Queen Mother said at once that of course M. de Turenne was absolutely right. Great issues always involve great risks. If they went back now they would never live down the shame of so ignominious a retreat, and might never have another opportunity to return.

The whole of Louis XIV's future hung in the balance on that misty October morning in the Bois. There was a long silence, then the King stepped down from the coach. One of the cavalry escort came forward, leading a horse which he mounted, and at the head of his Guards he rode in through the Porte Saint-Honoré to receive a tremendous welcome from a great crowd chanting '*Vive le roi!*'

The pessimistic duc d'Orléans had always been afraid something like this might happen, and as the King came in at one end of the city he went out at the other. His daughter remained in her apartment in the Tuileries, though not for long. She was ordered to leave Paris, and obeyed.

Having safely delivered his King to his capital, Turenne rode back with James to the army, and at the end of October set off after the enemy who were now established along the line of the river Aisne. They had taken Rethel and Château-Porcien against little opposition and were now besieging Sainte-Ménéhould. Marshal de la Ferté had been worried by Condé's march to the east, and as Governor of Lorraine he hurried back to Nancy because he was afraid the enemy would 'take up their winter quarters in those parts'. His fears were justified.

The Royal Army, also marching due east, came on November 2 to the little town of Baslieux, about seventeen miles east of Château-Thierry. Here, a whole day was wasted because the troops found a large quantity of new wine 'after the Vintage in a Country plentifully stored with that liquour', and rapidly made themselves quite unfit for duty. One can hardly blame them. The enemy were now going into winter quarters while they were still marching through a barren countryside at a time of year when every man felt he ought to be sitting in front of a fire, telling stories of wars, not fighting them.

It was more a matter of common sense than custom that campaigning should cease in the autumn, for the rain, frosts and thaws of winter made movement on the roads, particularly of artillery and baggage trains, almost impossible. Furthermore, there was no forage and nothing for the men to eat except what had been harvested and stored by the local population for their own needs.

The Spaniards, who made war under a set of rules as formal as those which govern a bull-fight, invariably tucked themselves up comfortably for the winter as early as possible in October, and neither Condé nor the duc de Lorraine had any wish to tramp through the mud and freeze in the bitter winds of Picardy and Champagne when they might keep warm and dry within the walls of captured towns. They were the aggressors and, as always, the initiative had lain with them. They had been able to decide where, when and how they would attack, and during the campaigning season Turenne, as the defender, could only deal with each threat as it was made. Now, in the winter, when his enemies were no longer in a mood to make trouble and their Spanish allies were eager to return to Flanders, Turenne had an opportunity to reverse the roles. He began an offensive designed to drive them out of the twisting valley of the Aisne and push them back across the frontier of France.

For the next three months James remained continuously on operations, and Turenne maintained such pressure against the Princes that at one stage the Archduke Leopold sent one of his generals, Luis-Perez de Vivero, conde de Fuensaldaña,* and 'a considerable part of the Spanish army', to reinforce Condé.

At first, things did not go at all well for Turenne. Sainte-Ménéhould fell to the Princes; so too did Bar-le-Duc which was defended by one of la Ferté's generals whom James refers to as 'M. de Roussillon who had so little brains that he allowed the four best companies of his garrison to be taken in the lower town'. James felt strongly about this because the companies were of his own Duke of York's Regiment.†

The Royalist towns of Ligny, Void and Commercy were all taken, and then, on November 25, Turenne heard that Fuensaldaña had had quite enough cold weather soldiering and had led his army away to the north.

Condé and Lorraine were happily allocating quarters to their regiments in the captured towns, and looking forward to a quiet winter, when Turenne swept down on them. They turned and ran for the Luxembourg frontier, with James and his pursuing cavalry forcing a pace which 'kept their spurs busy' until they reached the border. Turenne halted outside Saint-Michel in the Vosges mountains and also in la Ferté's province of Lorraine. His men, exhausted by long marches and ravenously hungry, entered the town to take the provisions which the townspeople refused to supply; and la Ferté, hearing of this, rode thirty miles from Nancy with a body of cavalry and 'fell upon such of M. de Turenne's soldiers as straggled or were loitering behind, hacking and hewing them as if they had been enemies'. It was a long time before Turenne and la Ferté were reconciled after this incident.

* Fuensaldaña had been soldiering under Archduke Leopold for some years and was thoroughly imbued with Spanish ideas of warfare. His refusal ever to think or act originally, or to allow anyone to use their initiative, infuriated Condé, and it is not surprising that they disliked each other at first sight. As an ally, Fuensaldaña proved to be somewhat of a pompous and difficult liability.

† Consisting of English, Scottish and Irish Royalists and mercenaries.

Ligny was recaptured, and then Bar-le-Duc;* Mazarin returned from his brief exile at Bouillon (in Flanders, about fifteen miles north-east of Sedan) in time to see the town fall.

Condé then came back across the frontier, and Turenne, taking him once more completely by surprise, might have destroyed his army completely at Vaubecourt if la Ferté, out of sheer spite over what had happened at Saint-Michel, had not refused to attack without Mazarin's agreement. Condé escaped, and withdrew once more into Flanders.

This long campaign of 1652 had, from Turenne's point of view, been remarkably successful. He had overcome, one after another, difficulties which, as James said, appeared unsurmountable: the enemy forces had been driven out of France and the King was back in Paris. Now, in the depths of a bitter winter, it was time to shelter the troops in winter quarters, but Mazarin, refusing to listen to Turenne's plea that his men were worn out and literally dying of cold, ordered him to end the campaign in triumph by retaking the strongly fortified town of Sainte-Ménéhould.

The army left Contrisson on December 27 and marched to Sommieure.† James wrote a detailed description of what the conditions were like. 'The day they came to Sommieure the frost was so very sharp that all the horsemen were forced to march on foot to keep warm; thirty or forty soldiers perished the same day through the extremity of cold, for so soon as any of them who were not warmly clothed sat down for ease, the frost pierced them and they were never able to rise again.' James 'saw several frozen to death and a much greater number would have perished but for the care taken by the officers to put on horseback those whom they saw ready to succumb and to carry them to the first villages where they saved several of them by giving them brandy and other kinds of liquor. What made the frost keener and more penetrating was that they were then marching over the vast plains of Champagne, where there was no shelter against the piercing north east wind which was blowing directly in their faces.'

It was no weather for siege warfare, and Turenne said so: it was ridiculous to think of attacking Sainte-Ménéhould; the army would be ruined and nothing achieved. Mazarin agreed, reluctantly, and suggested

* James tells the sad little story of Charles-Henri du Tot, the oldest Lieutenant General in France, 'who had, as his custom was, drunk a little too much for a commander'. During the assault on the Gate Tower he went on too far ahead, not really realizing what was happening, and was killed by a musket ball.

James says 'this place was fatal to drunkards'—it was famous for its wines, though champagne, as it is drunk today, had not yet been discovered—but he adds that poor old du Tot 'was the only French officer he ever saw drunk in the armies'. But, as Turenne's biographer Longueville wrote, 'what else can one expect if people will fight in a champagne district?'   † The village of Sommeilles.

taking Rethel, but Turenne and James found it posed the same problems as Sainte-Ménéhould. The army turned westwards against Château-Porcien and took that instead, hoping Mazarin would be satisfied.

Everyone was now completely exhausted, the infantry being in a worse state than the men who at least had the advantage of horses to carry them. Turenne's Commissary of Victuals could find no food anywhere and the men were forced to eat horse flesh—then considered virtually uneatable—and anything else they could get hold of, especially cabbage stalks which they called Cardinal's bread.

On January 13, when on their way between Rheims and Fismes *en route* for winter quarters, Mazarin suddenly ordered the troops to turn about, go back across the Aisne and take Vervins, occupied by the Spaniards as a forward base for operations in the following spring.

'Never,' says James, 'did soldiers or even officers march on such an enterprise with more repugnance and murmuring.' The savage frost had given way to a thaw which had turned the clay soil of the roads into a quagmire, particularly between Pontavert and Laon—over the great ridge of the Chemin des Dames—'where the baggage nearly remained in the mud'. Most of the army's equipment was ruined on this march, a great deal of baggage was lost and many horses died, but at last, on January 25, they arrived at Voulpaix, three miles west of Vervins.

While the army was trying to shelter from the incessant rain, Turenne and James rode on ahead to plan the attack, and James as usual went as close to the enemy as he could 'the better to make his observations'. He had a very narrow escape. Mistaking a small party of horsemen for men of the Royal Army he did not realize they had come from the town until they were within pistol shot. Just as he was about to join them they opened fire. This warning gave him time to wheel his horse and gallop away.

The Spaniards being unprepared and unwilling to fight out of season, the siege lasted less than forty-eight hours. James noted that 'as the enemy, following his custom, proffered insults against the Cardinal from the walls of Vervins, the soldiers, instead of replying in his defence, only said *Amen* to all their curses'.

On the morning of January 28 he watched the enemy garrison march out, and then, with the rest of the Royal Army, took the road south. He crossed the river Serre at Crécy and could see in the distance the twin spires of Laon, high on their lone hill. He spent a few hours in Laon while the men were sent off to their winter quarters, and then he, Turenne, Mazarin, all the General Officers and 'persons of quality' 'went for Paris, where they arrived on February 3'. James's first campaign had lasted nearly ten months.

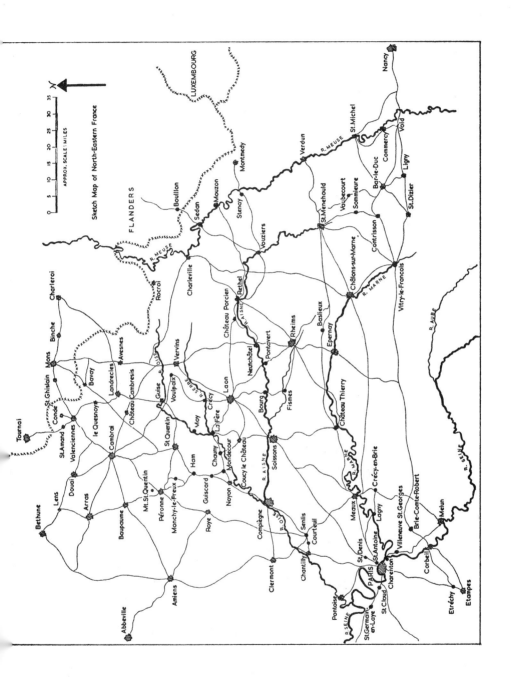

Sketch Map of North-Eastern France

APPROX. SCALE : MILES

0 5 10 15 20 25 30 35

FLANDERS

LUXEMBOURG

Tournai
Bethune
Lens
Douai
Arras
Bapaume
Valenciennes
St.Amand
Condé
St.Ghislain
Mons
Binche
Charleroi
Bavay
Le Quesnoy
Cambrai
Château Cambresis
Landrecies
Avesnes
Amiens
Abbeville
Mt.St.Quentin
Péronne
Monchy-le-Preux
St.Quentin
Guise
Vervins
Voulpaix
Crécy
Moy
La Fère
Ham
Chauny
Guiscard
Roye
Noyon
Mondecour
Coucy Château
Compiègne
R.OISE
R.SERRE
Laon
Rocroi
R.MEUSE
Charleville
Rethel
Château Porcien
R.AISNE
Neufchâtel
Pontavert
Bourg
Fismes
Soissons
R.AISNE
Bouillon
Sedan
Mouzon
Stenay
Montmedy
Vouziers
Rheims
Basilieux
Epernay
R.MARNE
Château Thierry
St.Menehould
Verdun
R.MEUSE
St.Michel
Vaubecourt
Sommieure
Bar-le-Duc
Contrisson
Châlons-sur-Marne
Vitry-le-Francois
Commercy
Vold
Ligny
St.Dizier
Nancy
R.AUBE
R.SEINE
Clermont
Chantilly
Senlis
Courteuil
Meaux
Lagny
Crécy-en-Brie
Villeneuve St.Georges
Brie-Comte-Robert
Melun
Corbeil
Etréchy
Etampes
R.SEINE
Pontoise
St.Germain-en-Laye
St.Cloud
St.Denis
St.Antoine
PARIS
Charenton
R.MARNE

FIRMLY established in the Royal Army as a fearless cavalry leader and admirable staff officer, James returned to Paris in far better condition physically, mentally, and financially, than when he had set out so secretly to earn his living, hiding his intentions from his uncle the duc d'Orléans.

Turenne was married soon after the end of the campaign, to a Protestant heiress,* Charlotte de Caumont, only daughter of the duc de la Force, a Marshal of France. James does not say whether he went to the wedding, but three months later, in June 1653, he and Turenne were back again with the army in Champagne.

Turenne's first success, at Rethel, in July 1653 was the result of a resolute attack made while the Spaniards, infinitely superior in numbers, were trying to decide which of their two armies should be sent to relieve the town. Condé, their ally and by far their best general, was powerless to make them hurry.

At a Council of War held soon after the capture of Rethel, when Mazarin and the King came to his headquarters, Turenne insisted that a policy of continuous offensive action by his whole army was the only way to check Condé and the Spaniards. Mazarin was all for splitting up the Royal Army into small garrisons for the defence of the frontier towns, but Turenne argued unanswerably for the principle of concentration of force.

At Mont Saint-Quentin, in August, where the two armies faced one another and la Ferté had made such errors in the dispositions of the army that, as James says, 'the enemy came on with great joy, knowing the advantage they had over us', Turenne did not do what most men in his position would have done: pull back and try to find a better position. Although la Ferté's men, convinced that defeat was inevitable, were beginning to break, Turenne marched directly at the enemy. He was, in fact, making straight for high ground which dominated the area and was

* Turenne himself was a Calvinist, and he did not become a Catholic until 1668, when he was fifty-seven.

vital, in tactical terms, for possession of it would be the deciding factor in the battle. He only just got there before Condé.

Turenne's men began to dig in at once, and Condé knew he had to attack before they could get established. But his ally, Fuensaldaña, said that three o'clock in the afternoon was no time of day to start a battle— one fought in the morning. His men were tired and thirsty after a long march, and one did not fight after a long march; one rested. After a good night's sleep, next morning, if it was a nice day, they would fight. In any case, what was the hurry? Turenne's little army could not escape.

The Spaniards slept. Turenne's men worked all night. In the morning Condé, to his anger, and Fuensaldaña to his mild irritation, found that Turenne's position was now unassailable, and after hanging about for a while, hoping something might happen, they went off to besiege Rocroi.

Missed opportunities of this sort usually caused annoyance but no one seems to have really minded very much—Condé's anger was directed at his dilatory ally, not Turenne. The two Frenchmen had, after all, fought on the same side before, and even now they remained friends and kept in comparatively close touch and exchanged 'post-mortems' on the battles they fought against each other.

Warfare in James's time was not the thoroughly unpleasant business it is today. While both armies were encamped near Saint-Quentin a certain cavalry officer, Lieutenant Bellechassaigne, whom James describes as 'a great goer out on partys',* took a mounted patrol of fifteen picked men to raid the enemy camp and kidnap one of Condé's 'Mareshalls de Camp' (Major Generals) called Ravenel. His idea was that the silent spiriting away of a senior officer in the darkness would be a nasty jolt to the enemy's morale. Unfortunately a servant gave the alarm just as Ravenel had been captured and Bellechassaigne had to let him go, and escape himself. 'He might have killed de Ravenel himself,' wrote James, 'but in those Countries they make not Warr so brutally, for I never knew any unhuman act committed either by French or Spaniards all the time I serv'd amongst them.'

Knowing he could not relieve Rocroi, Turenne laid siege to Mouzon, a garrison town on the Meuse almost midway between Sedan and Stenay, and it was in the trenches here, a week or so later, that James had personal experience of the strange rules of warfare. 'During the time of this whole Seige,' he wrote, 'wee were much troubled and hindered by perpetuall raines and stormes so violent, that they very often blew away our blinds,†

---

* This delightful description is a little misleading. James used the word 'party' for reconnaissance patrols, raids and other minor operations of war.

† Literally, screens put up to conceal movement up and down the trenches.

and wash'd down some part of our Trenches which for the most part were filled with water, the Sky being seldom clear for above three hours to-gather: and that which makes me remember this the more particularly, was, that one morning very early, going down with some others to the approches, when wee came into the ditch of the Envelope, which went straight upon the great Tower, and was our only way to the lodgement,* wee kept closs to the pallisado, where the blind should have been, and thō nothing but the very beginning of it was left standing, all the rest being blown down, yet all of us were so busily imployed in piking out our way (the ditch being full of dirt and water) that not one single man tooke notice that the blind was ruined, and consequently wee were in open view, till we were gotten half our way, and then, one of the company who observ'd it first, propos'd that wee shou'd return; to which I well remember I would not consent, urging, That since wee were now so far onward, the danger was equall in going forward or in returning: so wee continu'd going on to the head of the attacke as wee first intended; but in all the way while wee were thus exposed, there was not one shott made at us, at which we wonder'd; but afterwards when the Town was sur-render'd, the Governour inform'd us of the reason, That he himself happening to be upon the Wall at that very time, and knowing me by my Starr,† had forbid his men to fire upon the Company, which is a respect very usuall beyond Sea.'‡

James goes on to say that the Governor did not have the same con-sideration for the soldiers subsequently ordered to repair and replace the screens; several were killed and others wounded.

James describes the siege of Mouzon carefully, giving a great deal of information on the various means of getting close to a wall and 'lodging the Miner' in it. Anyone who walks round this little town today will have little difficulty in following events from his description. There have been changes; the 'very good dry ditch' faced with stone on the river side of the town is now a canal, but the large tower 'towards the Hill' is still there and so is the ditch James was in when the Governor refused to let his men shoot at him.

He had other escapes during this siege: one morning he was in a forward gun position when 'a great shott came from the Town, which pass'd through three barrells of powder, without firing them, which had it done, all who were in the battery had inevitably been blown up: But the danger

* A hastily constructed entrenchment, usually to defend a captured work.
† His father had made him a Knight of the Garter at York in 1642 (see page 6).
‡ There is good reason to believe that this passage is as James originally wrote it. Even in an age when nobody seems to have bothered very much about spelling, his, in general, shows interesting vagaries.

came so suddainly and was so soon over, that none of us had time to be concern'd for it'. A little while later, while he was in one of the trenches, a 'small shott', presumably a musket ball, came in through the lodgement, glanced off the head of a brother officer, M. de Humières, went through the leg of one of the pioneers and 'lastly strook the toe of my boot, without doing me any harm'.

Both Bishop Burnet and, later, Macaulay, would have us believe that there was a strong streak of cruelty in James and that he rather enjoyed the sufferings or misfortunes of others. This was all part of their efforts at denigration and to justify their championing of his son-in-law; it is not easy to substantiate. Turenne was an extraordinarily humane and compassionate man, outstanding for these qualities in an age when the horrible activities of executioners on the scaffold provided a popular entertainment; and as in many other things James followed his example. James certainly found no pleasure in the incident he relates of a captain, who had just arrived to join the army, reporting to Turenne in the trenches at Mouzon. As he was bowing politely he was hit in the head by a musket ball and fell dead at the commander's feet. 'At which unhappy chance,' says James, 'some who were present made this unseasonable raillery, that if the Captain had been better bred he had escap'd the bullett, which only hitt him there for not bowing low enough to his General.'

Mouzon surrendered on September 27, and on his way to see if anything could be done to relieve Rocroi, Turenne heard that it had fallen. It seemed to be a fair exchange. Much had been achieved with very little fighting. Although his army was less than half the size of the forces of his enemies, Turenne had prevented any advance on Paris and driven the enemy further back towards the frontier. He had taken Rethel on the Aisne, and Mouzon compensated for the loss of Rocroi. Furthermore, the enemy alliance was in some disorder. Condé was doing all he could to arrange for Fuensaldaña to be removed from the theatre of war, and the duc de Lorraine had made such a nuisance of himself, demanding that the Spaniards help him recover his lost duchy, that they finally arrested him and sent him off as a prisoner of war to Spain where he remained until the Treaty of the Pyrenees in 1659.

The campaign ended and James returned to Paris at the beginning of October. He found that affairs in the exiled court had changed little in the four months he had been away. In his brother, enforced idleness and ill health had bred a disinclination to do anything. There was much talk of leaving Paris, but no money, no transport and nowhere to go. Then, in the spring, Charles's usual good health returned; money arrived from

England, sent by Royalists who were alarmed by the apparent friendliness growing between Cromwell and Mazarin, and it became clear that the King of England ought not to stay in France. Charles wanted to go, and the French court wanted him to go—so that Mazarin could pursue a plan for enlisting English help against Spain—but there could be no departure until his debts were paid. At length, with Mazarin's assistance over the sale of guns from some of Rupert's warships, and 'various assignments' as Clarendon calls them, Charles's creditors were either paid off or temporarily satisfied and Charles was able to leave Paris early in July 1654.

The timing of his journey coincided with James's return to the army—then at Peronne—and the brothers rode together as far as Chantilly, 'where they took leave of each other in hopes of a more happy meeting thereafter'. It was another sad parting, reminiscent of the one in Jersey before Charles went off to Scotland. Of the two brothers, James was the happier for he was at least leading a useful, active and enjoyable life in the army, whereas for Charles things could not have been much worse. Now that his firm base in France had dissolved, he was an aimless wanderer and an embarrassment to the local authorities wherever he went.

He travelled first to Spa where he met his sister Mary, but left after a few weeks because of an epidemic of smallpox. He went on to Aix-la-Chapelle (Aachen) and then, in the autumn, to Cologne. Here, as he told Evelyn some years later, he found 'the best people in the world, the most kind and worthy to him that he ever met with', and decided to stay.

James went to Peronne. He reported back from leave in the second week of July, and when he rejoined the army this time he was no longer a mere 'volunteer' but a Lieutenant General, properly promoted as such. With a hint of justifiable pride he says that he was the youngest officer of that rank in the French army. He was not yet twenty-one.

It would be wrong to imagine he was promoted entirely on merit—his royal blood must have been a great help—but Turenne was fighting a war and he could not afford to have incompetent or ineffective subordinate commanders in his army on active service; least of all, ones he had promoted himself. James, in two years, had shown he was fit for command. He deserved his promotion as a soldier; Turenne would never have given it to him just because he was a prince.

When James came back to Paris at the end of the 1653 campaign one of Thurloe's spies, who had no axe to grind, reported that he was 'much esteemed in the French Army', and Clarendon (then Edward Hyde), writing to Sir Richard Browne on December 6, said 'the Duke of York is returned hither full of reputac'on and Honour'.

*

The campaign of 1654 started late in the year because the war had had to wait for the coronation of Louis XIV, now aged sixteen, at Rheims. But the attendant pageantry and military displays served a useful purpose in bringing together all the Royalist officers and soldiers in a place conveniently close to the area of operations.

Turenne made the first military moves that year by besieging the town of Stenay, which belonged to the Prince de Condé, and assuming that the Princes and the Spaniards would try to relieve it, he made suitable arrangements for the arrival of the allied army. But the enemy did not come. For once Condé outwitted Turenne by ignoring the fate of Stenay and moving instead, by a series of forced marches, to invest Arras, in which James says 'the Garrison was not so strong as it ought to have been, thō not so weak as to oblige the Governour to quit any of his outworkes which were very great'.

Turenne left Hocquincourt to deal with Stenay and moved to Peronne. He could not march straight for Arras because the combined forces of Condé and Archduke Leopold amounted to 25,000 men whereas he had only about 14,000. He felt unable to undertake any relief operation until he was joined by the troops he had left with Hocquincourt, after Stenay had fallen. All he could do was move closer to Arras—Peronne is thirty miles away to the south-east—and take up a position from which he could intercept enemy convoys bringing up ammunition and supplies from Douai and Cambrai, and harass their foragers.

James says he rejoined the army just before it moved and then marched out of Peronne towards Arras on July 16. Two days later he arrived at the village of Monchy-le-Preux, on high ground some three to four miles east of the besieged town and an excellent base for sending out raiding parties.

By August 14 the enemy had completed their lines of contravallation and circumvallation which defended them against Turenne's army and prevented the garrison of Arras from coming out, and since the besiegers were now able to concentrate their efforts on breaching the walls, the Governor, M. de Mondejeu, sent messengers to Turenne telling him that matters were approaching a crisis. It may seem odd that messengers were still able to pass to and fro through double lines of defence works, and James makes the point that only 'some came safely to our Camp'.

He goes on to say that 'one of these Messengers having swallowed the Note he brought, wrapt up in lead (that in case he had been taken and searched it might not have been found about him) and coming at a time when the Generalls were very impatient to hear from the Town, the Messenger was not able to voyd the paper in above 24 houres, though severall purges were given to him to bring it out of his body: This gave them great anxiety, and particularly Monsr. de la Ferté cryd out with a great passion, *Il faut éventrer le coquin!* "the rascall must have his belly ripped up", since he will not voyd it: This put the fellow into such a Fright, he being just then at the door of the Tente, the peice of lead came immediatly from him; and by the account it brought, made us defer attacking the Lines of the Enemy before the Stenay troopes were come up to us'.

Having taken Stenay, Hocquincourt and his troops rejoined the army on August 17, and it was decided to attack the enemy line of circumvallation in force and relieve the town on the night of August 24.

The attack was made, as planned, on the Eve of St. Louis, and James comments on the fact that there were 'publick prayers at the head of each Battalion and Squadron for severall days before, and as many as could, confessed and received the blessed Sacrament: So that I am confident no Army ever show'd more markes of true devotion than ours at that time'.

He recorded the whole operation, for example, 'Wee had in our march thether a vary still faire night, besides the benefit of the moon, which sett as favorably for us as wee could desire, that is, just as wee came to the place appointed. As the moon went down, it began to blow very fresh and grew exceeding dark, in so much that the Enemy could neither see nor hear us, as otherwise they might; and they were the more surprised when the first news they had of us, was to find us within half cañon shott of them. I remember not to have seen a finer sight of the nature, than was that of our Foot when they were once in Battell,* and began to march towards their Lines; for then discovering at once their lighted metches, they made a glorious shew, which appear'd the more by reason of the wind, which kindled them and made them blaze throw the darkness of the night; for the breeze keeping the coal of their metches very clear, whensoever any of the Musketeers happened to shog against each other, the metches struck fire, so that the sparkles were carry'd about by the wind to increase the light. We were no sooner discover'd by the Enemy than they fir'd three cannon at us, and either made fires or sett up lights along the line: Our Foot then lost no time in falling on.'†

Arras was relieved, and James added greatly to his reputation as a soldier. Condé retired in reasonably good order to Cambrai, while the Archduke and Fuensaldaña galloped off to Douai leaving the remnants of their scattered forces to seek their own salvation.

The French court came up to Arras and stayed for several days, returning to Peronne on August 31, the day on which Turenne marched to le Quesnoy, fifty miles to the east near the Flemish border. He captured

* Formed up for the advance.   † Getting to grips with the enemy.

Turenne

Condé

Photos: K. Jaggers

Photo : A. C. Cooper

James, Duke of York
—in Flanders, at the age of nineteen

Photo : Charles Cole

Mary, James's eldest sister, by her cousin
Louisa, daughter of Elizabeth of Bohemia

Photos : K. Jaggers

Louis XIV and Mademoiselle

James, Duke of York

Anne Hyde,
Duchess of York

Photo: A. C. Cooper

Arabella Churchill

Catherine Sedley,
Countess of Dorchester

the fortress in two days and went on to Binche in the enemy's country east of Mons, arriving, and taking the town on September 16. The army remained here until September 22—'only to eat up the Enemies' Country' —and then withdrew to le Quesnoy before the autumn rain made the roads impassable for artillery. From le Quesnoy Turenne moved south to Cateau-Cambresis (le Cateau)—where James spent his twenty-first birthday—and then, after taking and demolishing two frontier castles not far from Rocroi, the troops were sent into winter quarters.

James arrived back in Paris in the middle of December.

TWELVE

JAMES, back in Paris at the end of the 1654 campaign, found himself in the middle of a first-class family row. His mother, encouraged by the French court, had been making strenuous efforts to persuade his younger brother Henry, Duke of Gloucester, now fifteen, to become a Catholic. She had been working through the Abbé Montague, her almoner, who at one stage had taken Henry off to his own quiet abbey at Pontoise where he could be isolated from dissuaders.

Charles, in Cologne, hearing what was happening, was extremely angry with his mother, and feeling that his brother might need a really good reason for refusing to obey her, he wrote to Henry saying: 'if you do hearken to her or to anybody else in that matter, you must never think to see me or England again, and whatsoever mischief shall fall on me or my affairs from this time I must lay all upon you as being the only cause of it'.

Henry had no intention of obeying his mother, but living with her and his sister Henriette, and subjected to continuous pressure, he was finding resistance difficult. Charles had written to James, on active service at Arras, and James had despatched a firm letter to Henrietta Maria which greatly annoyed her. When he came back from the war she forbade him to speak to Henry at all unless in her presence, but in the end Henry informed the Abbé he would not change his religion. Montague then told him that since he had adopted this attitude the Queen had commanded 'he should see her face no more'.

In fact Henrietta Maria went much further than that. She gave strict orders to her household forbidding everyone to help him in any way. That night his horses were turned loose out of her stables and next day, when he got up, the sheets were taken off his bed. Forced out of the palace, he could find nowhere to go until Lord Hatton gave him shelter and the Earl of Ormonde, sent by Charles to bring him to Cologne, by pawning such things as his insignia of the Garter, at last managed to raise enough money for the journey.

From this it is clear that whatever James's private thoughts about religion may have been—and we have no means of knowing what they were—he was at this time totally opposed to any plan to convert his younger brother to Catholicism. The unfortunate Henrietta Maria had now succeeded in alienating all her sons, for she could not tolerate disobedience and seems to have found difficulty in accepting the fact that they were all growing up and had minds of their own. During that winter she moved in an aura of tension and ill-feeling, and James must have been happy to get away when the soldiering season began again.

The campaign of 1655, which lasted from June until November, consisted mainly of sieges. Turenne began by capturing Landrecies, and after considerable manœuvring against the combined armies of the Princes and the Spaniards, attacked the town of Condé, in Flanders, north of Valenciennes. It was here that in unfortunate circumstances Turenne lost two valuable officers.* One of them, a 'Captain LLloyd', is described by James as 'a Welshman and an Engeneer who had been bred up under the Prince of Orange and was a stout colerick man'. Perhaps it was because he was so very Welsh that James gives him no less than three 'l's' to his name.

The town of Condé was taken on August 19 and next day the Royal Army moved to Saint-Ghislain, nine miles to the east, which was surrendered by its Spanish Governor five days later. For the next month Turenne remained in enemy territory and then moved south again at the end of September. By November 4 the army had reached Moy on the Oise, between Saint-Quentin and Laon, where Turenne received an urgent message from the Cardinal instructing him to leave the army where it was and to come at once to the court, now at Compiègne. Hocquincourt was making serious trouble† and Mazarin wanted Turenne's advice.

* Coming back from the trenches where he had been laying traces and giving orders for engineer work to begin, Captain LLloyd met Captain Vautourneux of the Guards who said he was sure LLloyd could not have done all he was supposed to do in so short a time; 'after which he let fall some words as if he doubted of his courage. At which the Engeneer was so incensed that it made his Welsh blood boyle within him'. He told Vautourneux to come with him and see for himself. But 'the shott from the Enemy flew so fast' that both were killed in the open, before they could reach the trenches.

James, full of it himself, was always sensitive to national pride.

† Hocquincourt, older and in his own opinion more experienced than Turenne, had expected to be made Commander-in-Chief in 1655, and was furious when Mazarin appointed Turenne. As compensation, Mazarin made him Governor of Ham and Peronne. Establishing himself in Peronne he came under the influence of a great Frondeuse Madame de Châtillon, a friend of Condé. She told Condé that if Hocquincourt were offered the post of Lieutenant General of Flanders and a large sum of money, it was more than likely that to spite Mazarin he would hand over Peronne and Ham to the Spaniards. Condé made the offer, Mazarin heard of it and asked

'Accordingly,' says James, 'he went thether leaving the Army under my command, who was then the only Lieut Generall remaining with it, all the others having had leave given them before to go away, when they askt it, there being no probability of Action. By this accident I came to have the command of the Army committed to me, at the very time when the Peace betwixt France and Cromwell was concluded and actually publish'd, and by which Treaty, I was by name to be banish'd France. The Army stayed at Mouy during some days, and there I received orders to march with it to Mondêcour on the 10th of November.'

For some time Cromwell had been watching the struggle between France and Spain and trying to make up his mind which side to support: he had at last decided that France was going to win. He therefore made a treaty with Mazarin which was a shattering blow to James, for in addition to clauses covering the end of the state of hostility at sea and the resumption of peaceful trading, there was a secret one. This stipulated that Charles, the Dukes of York and Gloucester, Ormonde, Edward Hyde, Nicholas and fourteen others of the court in exile were to be 'excluded' from French territory.

James's comparatively secure life as a general in the French army was suddenly to cease. As a soldier, serving the King of France, he was successful, admired, popular and happy, and it was more than likely that he would soon have been promoted Marshal of France.

Naturally enough, immediately Turenne returned from Compiègne, James asked for leave. It was granted—the campaign was over, anyway— and he went straight to the court. Both Mazarin and Anne of Austria were extremely apologetic, explaining that much against their personal feelings for him they had yielded to political necessity. Mazarin in particular was worried about losing his services, not only because he was a loyal and excellent officer but because his presence in the French army had attracted a large number of Irish troops—who had previously fought for Spain—as well as all the English Royalist 'volunteers'. With some justification, he was afraid that when James left France he would take these valuable soldiers with him, and if he joined forces with Spain they would all fight against France.

Turenne what should be done. Turenne advised making a counter-offer. Mazarin said the King could not possibly negotiate with a rebellious subject. Turenne pointed out that the loss of these two towns would probably cause a general uprising in France. (largely because Mazarin was now vastly unpopular) and no matter how much money Hocquincourt wanted, it would be less than the cost of dealing with another rebellion. Hocquincourt settled for 20,000 crowns and handed over the governorship of Peronne to his politically more reliable son.

Condé, who had been hovering about, ready to take immediate advantage of Hocquincourt's acceptance of his offer, returned to Flanders.

Therefore, despite the secret clause in the treaty with Cromwell, and with Cromwell's concurrence, he was in no hurry to send James out of France and he even suggested that James should continue his military career, with promotion, as Captain-General and Generalissimo of the Army of Italy which consisted of the combined forces of France, Savoy and Modena under Charles Emmanuel II, the Duke of Savoy who was his cousin.* James himself says that he had 'a strong inclination to get more and more experience in arms, and the tender love which his aunt, the Duchess of Savoy, had shown him on every occasion, caused him to embrace this decision with the more pleasure because he felt much gratitude for her kindness'. But his brother Charles had very different plans.

Then, at the beginning of February 1656, there occurred a comparatively minor event which was to have far-reaching effects not only on James's life but on the history of England. His sister Mary, widowed now for nearly six years, came from Holland to visit her mother, and James rode out to meet her between Peronne and Cambrai. In her entourage was her Maid of Honour, a girl of nineteen called Anne, the only daughter of Edward Hyde, and James saw her for the first time.

In his Memoirs it is simply recorded that they met and afterwards married.

Anne's father, whose duties for the past ten years had kept him away from his family—for whom he found lodgings first in Antwerp and then in Breda—had not wanted her to join a royal household. When the previous Maid of Honour died of smallpox and a friend suggested he might apply for the vacancy on his daughter's behalf, he said 'he had but one daughter, who was all the company and comfort her mother had, in her melancholie retirement, and therefore he was resolved not to separate them, nor to dispose his daughter to a court life'.

Princess Mary herself wanted Anne—if only to show she was independent of Henrietta Maria who even tried to choose her daughter's household —and Hyde finally left the decision to his wife. She was not prepared to stand in Anne's way.

Mistress Anne Hyde was no beauty though perhaps she was more attractive as a girl than after her marriage. Elizabeth of Bohemia, James's aunt, writing to Secretary Nicholas in January 1655 and describing a fancy dress party at Teiling, said that Anne 'was a shepherdess, and I assure was very handsome in it: none but her mistress [Princess Mary] looked better than she did'. Evelyn said on several occasions that she was

* Charles Emmanuel's mother Christina, Duchess of Savoy, was Henrietta Maria's sister.

'a great favorit of mine', and Burnet wrote that she was 'a very extra-ordinary woman. She had great knowledge and a lively sense of things.' He adds that she was 'generous and friendly but was too severe an enemy'. James himself said that 'besides her person, she possessed all the qualities proper to inflame a heart less susceptible than his, with the fire of love'—but he married her. She was certainly extremely intelligent, literate, witty and gay: qualities which James, the soldier, did not possess to any remark-able degree and which may therefore have been doubly attractive to him.

Nothing of any interest appears to have happened at their first meeting, in any case James was preoccupied with the problem of his future. Soon after Mary's arrival in Paris he heard that Charles had left Cologne and was travelling incognito to Brussels. It was obvious that Charles was planning something with the Spaniards, and James, the friend of France, had no wish to join him.

Cromwell, extremely well-informed as usual by Thurloe's spy organiza-tion, knew that Charles was hoping to persuade the Spaniards to help him win back his throne, and it was because he was only too glad of an opportunity to create dissension between the brothers that he had no objection to James's remaining in France—or serving with the French army, provided he was not in the operational area of Flanders. Cromwell shared Mazarin's fears of an exodus of trained soldiers from France who would follow James if he joined the Spaniards.

Charles, who had arrived in Brussels in March, had, by April 2, managed to negotiate a treaty with Spain under which it was agreed that whenever Charles could 'cause a good port Town to declare for him in England, his Catholic Majesty would assist him with a body of 6,000 Foot'—and their equipment and transport. There were other clauses, open and secret, covering such things as naval assistance to Spain in her war against Portugal and great concessions to English and Irish Catholics (provided there was a restoration); and Charles, a little rashly, also undertook to withdraw from France all the Irish and English troops whose real loyalty lay with James. Therefore, as soon as the treaty was signed and ratified, and Charles had established himself at Bruges, he sent urgently for James, though he was only repeating instructions which he had sent at regular intervals ever since Mazarin and Cromwell had signed their treaty on October 24, 1655.

James played for time. He was thoroughly enjoying himself in Paris, frequently dancing until four o'clock in the morning, and he had no wish to leave so delightful a place where he was well known as a handsome, brave young Lieutenant General, the right-hand man of the greatest military commander in Europe. Nor was he particularly interested in Charles's political manœuvres; they may in fact have caused him some amusement because he knew that Mazarin was also trying to arrange a treaty with Spain and a marriage between Louis XIV and the Infanta. Not surprisingly, Philip IV would not hear of such a proposal, and he was determined to prosecute the war against France with even greater vigour. Much to Condé's relief, Fuensaldaña was recalled and Archduke Leopold was removed from command. This may have been a mistake,* for these two experienced if unexciting generals were replaced by Marshal Caracena, even more addicted to 'Spanish methods of proceeding' than his predecessors, and Don Juan of Austria, who was the result of Philip's interest in an actress in Madrid called Maria Calderón. Don Juan was at least young, and reasonably energetic when he felt inclined, but without either education or experience.

Mazarin's negotiations with Spain delayed the start of the campaign in 1656—in which James took no part—and it was not until June that Turenne went off to besiege Valenciennes on the river Scheldt. Before he went, James, 'who was used to speaking in confidence of his affairs with Monsieur de Turenne', asked him for advice.

Turenne suggested he should write to Charles and tell him how reluctant he was to leave France, where he had so many friends and where all his interests lay, particularly since the Spaniards had apparently shown no enthusiasm for Charles's proposal that James should fight for them. No mention of James, by name, had been made in the treaty with Spain and the presence of Charles himself, and the Duke of Gloucester, in Flanders was surely enough to satisfy the Spaniards. Turenne then went on to propose an elaborate deception: that if the Spaniards should ask for James's services, Charles, secretly consenting to his remaining in France, could express public vexation for James's disobedience, and this, again, would probably satisfy the Spaniards.

James thought this was an excellent plan. He discussed it with his mother and she agreed. The actual explanation of the whole idea was entrusted to young Charles Berkeley, son of Sir John Berkeley, James's comrade in arms, but at the last minute Berkeley broke his leg and could not go. Another messenger was despatched, who did all that was asked of him, but Charles replied by simply sending his brother 'an absolute order to come and join him in Flanders with all possible diligence'. He

* In Clarendon's opinion, Fuensaldaña was 'of a much better temper, more industry and more insinuation than the Spaniards use to have: his greatest talent was to civil business; yet he was the best general of that time, to all other offices and purposes than what were necessary in the hour of battle, when he was not so present and composed as at all other seasons'.

was not prepared to connive at any scheme which would give everyone the impression he could not even control his own brother.

Sadly, at the beginning of September 1656, James made his farewells to the French court, then at Compiègne, and to all his friends in Paris who had made life so enjoyable. Mazarin, who seemed grateful for all he had done for the royal cause, undertook to continue paying him a pension so long as he did not take up arms against France. Having sent all his servants and baggage on in advance to wait for him at Abbeville, James left Paris on September 10, travelling in his coach to Clermont from where he intended to ride post for the rest of the way.

At the gates of Clermont the servant he had sent on to arrange about post horses met him and said that Sir William Lockhart,* Cromwell's new ambassador to the court of France, had taken rooms at the best inn, *l'hôtellerie de la poste*, and things might be awkward if they met. Lockhart had heard he was coming and was afraid there was going to be a most unpleasant scene, largely because James was well-liked and the English, allies of the hated Mazarin, were not.

James's servant brought the post horses to the door of the inn, and as the coach rumbled into the yard in front of it Lockhart and his party stood in an upper room with drawn swords and pistols at the ready, in case James encouraged the crowd which flocked up to greet him to 'fall on' the ambassador. But James was not a rabble rouser, nor was he likely to embarrass his friends in the French court with a 'diplomatic incident'. He got out of his coach, mounted a post horse and rode away up the Abbeville road. Passing through Montreuil, Boulogne and Calais, and 'received with much civility in every town', he at length arrived at Gravelines, the first town across the border in Spanish territory, where the Earl of Ormonde was waiting to meet him. Next day they travelled on towards Bruges, and Charles, considerably relieved now that James had at last obeyed his orders, came to meet him at Veurne.

*

Throughout the long, dreary years that the Stuart court spent in exile runs one constant theme of discord, jealousy and intrigue, usually surrounding James and apparently the main occupation of the courtiers. The political manœuvring had sickened him and had been one of the reasons why he joined the army, and his absences on active service increased rather than lessened the tension. For a long time a faction in the exiled court

* Lockhart had fought for, and been knighted by, Charles I in the civil war. Subsequently, after Charles II had ignored his offer of service on the Scottish adventure, he joined Cromwell's administration. He commanded Cromwell's expeditionary force in Flanders, and in 1674, recalled from retirement in Scotland, Charles II sent him back to Paris as ambassador.

which was hostile to him had been trying to get rid of his trusted friends, the unpopular Sir John Berkeley, Harry Berkeley, his Master of the Horse, and Henry Jermyn, son of Henrietta Maria's favourite. The principal instigator of the plot seems to have been Henry Bennet (after-wards Lord Arlington) who in 1653 had joined James's household as his secretary, but at Charles's request; in fact he had always served Charles's interests more than those of James because he knew very well which brother would be the source of preferment if there were ever a restoration.

Now, when he rejoined Charles's court at Bruges after a long absence and found the situation had deteriorated James began to realize he had made a great mistake in ever leaving France. Every sort of pressure was applied to make him dismiss men who had been his close companions in peace and war for some five years. Then he discovered that if he did join the Spanish army the Spaniards made everyone swear allegiance to his Catholic Majesty, so that his own subordinate officers would be made to pledge their loyalty to Philip IV and not to him.

The last straw was Charles's insistence that Sir John Berkeley must go, and for the first, and last, time in his life, James deliberately disobeyed his brother. He pretended to obey, openly dismissing Sir John but privately telling him to go to Flushing and wait for him. Two days later, James arranged a shooting trip with his brother Henry and the two young men, Charles Berkeley and Henry Jermyn. Near Sluys he told his brother he had business in the town and if he was not back by a certain time, to return without him to Bruges. He crossed to Flushing with his two friends and rejoined Sir John Berkeley.

His behaviour caused amazement and dismay in Charles's court, for everyone found it hard to believe that his fervent loyalty to his brother the King had found its breaking-point. Charles was extremely distressed. Cromwell was delighted and James was firm in his determination to return to France and abandon all ideas of fighting for the Spaniards against his friends.

He wrote an excellent and dignified letter to Charles, saying this was the first time he had ever apologized about anything—or had need to— and he would not have had to if 'violent persons had not induced your Majesty to press that upon me which was never proposed to anyone else'. He stressed his zeal and affection and said that no one would ever hinder him 'from sacrificing all interest but that of my Honour to your Majesty, and I hope you will excuse me if I am somewhat tender therein, since I have little else left, and that without it I shall never be able to be of use and service to your Majesty . . .'

Reading the details of all the squalid squabbling that went on among the courtiers one becomes increasingly aware of James's intense dislike of political intrigue. His values were clear-cut; honour, loyalty and friendship meant far more to him than influence. His tall, lean figure overshadows the opportunists: the men who spent their time flattering those who might be of use and denigrating those apparently in their way.

Charles could not afford a permanent break. James had an international reputation as a leader whereas he was an exiled, uncrowned king. The Irish and English soldiers would follow where James led: to many of them Charles, whom they had never seen, was only the figurehead of the Royalist cause. Without James he could not keep his side of the bargain with the Spaniards. He sent an intermediary to ask James to return, bringing all his servants except Sir John Berkeley. James replied with what was in fact a long complaint against Henry Bennet's intrigues, and he made a number of proposals, including the retention of Sir John Berkeley in his service.

Charles gave in. He agreed to all James's requests about his personal staff and Henry Bennet was sent off as an envoy to Madrid.

James returned to Bruges, and when he had had time to consider everything he was full of remorse for having defied his brother: as Burnet says, 'he was bred with high notions of kingly authority, and laid it down for a maxim that all who opposed the king were rebels in their hearts'.

Yet this reconciliation did not lessen the deep reluctance with which James regarded the prospect of joining the forces of Spain. There was some slight palliative in the thought that they were now taking the field against Cromwell's troops, and Cromwell had murdered his father, but he had no wish to fight against his former brother officers, least of all against Turenne who had treated him like a son and taught him all the soldiering he knew. But professional soldiers in the seventeenth century—and James was a professional soldier—were not unlike lawyers who fight (in court) for the side which asks, and pays, for their services. No one thought any the less of James because a sudden and radical change in the political situation forced him—much against his will—to change sides. He was a man of honour who felt he was doing something dishonourable but, as events proved, this opinion was not shared by his friends nor did his change of allegiance affect his relationship with them.

As Mazarin, Cromwell and Charles had all foreseen, a great many Irish, Scots and English soldiers went across to Flanders at the same time as James, and from them a British force of six regiments,* 2,000 men, was

* Commanded by Lords Ormonde, Taaffe, Bristol, Wilmot, Newburgh and Colonel Maccarty.

raised. James says the number would have been far larger if the Spaniards had been less jealous and more co-operative, but he did at least get his promotion to Captain-General and was appointed force commander. Lords Ormonde, Bristol and Middlesex were his Lieutenant Generals. The Spaniards provided him with a mounted escort and gave him a generous ration allowance of £200 a month while actually in the field.

In May 1657 Cromwell's expeditionary force of 6,000 infantry—the finest in Europe—was brought over by Sir John Reynolds and joined the French army under Turenne's command. In return for sending troops Cromwell stipulated that the combined French and English force was to capture Dunkirk and hand it over to him. If either Gravelines or Mardyck were taken first, the town was to be held by Reynolds's troops as a surety until Dunkirk was taken.

The campaign began in the latter part of May with an attempt by Turenne to take the border town of Cambrai but, prevented by Condé from establishing himself, he then moved to Saint-Venant, which fell largely because neither Don Juan nor Caracena was prepared to devote any energy to relieving it. James spent most of the year in command of the infantry which, on the orders of Don Juan, marched and counter-marched about the countryside almost continuously, achieving nothing. On one occasion, to support an attack on Calais, James and his weary soldiers plodded 120 miles over muddy roads in seven days, only to be told that the project had been abandoned. A Spanish attempt to besiege Ardres was also given up when Turenne approached, after his success at Saint-Venant, and Don Juan withdrew his army behind the defences of Dunkirk. This left Turenne free to attack and capture Mardyck, which he handed over to Cromwell, and he and his English allies then made an attempt to take Gravelines. But their efforts were frustrated when the garrison opened the dykes and drowned the surrounding country: a defensive manœuvre which brought the fighting season to an end.

On several occasions when the two armies had been in reasonably close contact James had had very friendly conversations with his old comrades in arms. At one time, when he took a cavalry escort and went to see what was happening at Mardyck, several officers who rode out to drive his party off recognized his dog, a big greyhound—James was an inveterate dog-lover—and calling out 'sur parole !' asked to speak to him. In a matter of moments James was surrounded by some two or three hundred old friends. They all dismounted, chatted for about an hour and then James rode back to Dunkirk. He was later warned, privately, that 'the Spanish character is suspicious and circumspect, and though they gave no sign of it, they might not be at all satisfied'.

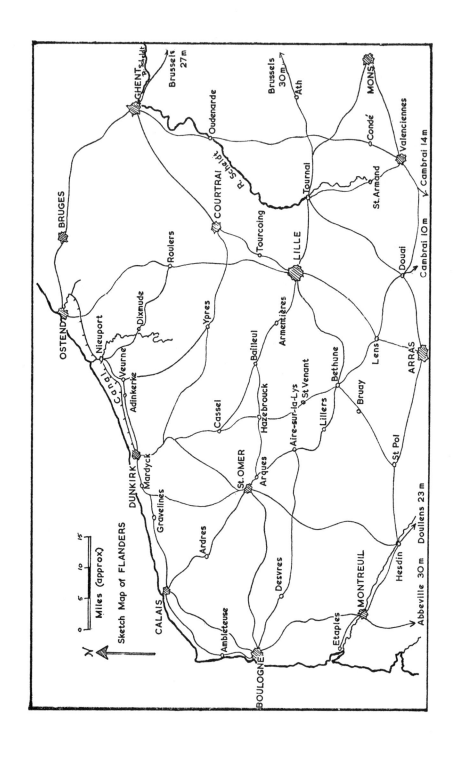

Sketch Map of FLANDERS

Miles (approx)

0   5   10   15

James said he really was not very worried whether they were satisfied or not. He had been talking to old friends but the fact that they were his friends would not prevent him from 'attacking as even the most zealous Spaniard might do'. Yet he took the hint and was a little more careful when he talked to French officers. The fact that they were eager to see him again is a clear indication not only of his popularity in the French army but of the lack of any animosity over changing sides.

Although Turenne had no intention of continuing the campaign, Don Juan decided that he would recapture Mardyck, but his army was greatly reduced by an epidemic of what James calls 'fevers'. Henry, Duke of Gloucester, who had been with James throughout the campaign, had to be medically evacuated, and James says that 'the Prince de Condé was holden with such a fever that the doctors feared for his life'.*

James now remained in Dunkirk in command of the army. There was a great deal of talk of retaking Mardyck but no firm plans were made although a great store of equipment for a siege was collected. On January 1, 1658, James was ordered to send the troops off to winter quarters, and he himself followed Don Juan and Caracena to Brussels. He says, 'I made no long stay in that city, for so soon as I had despatched my small affaires I went to my sister who was at Breda where my brother, the Duke of Gloucester had been already for some time to recover from his ague, which at my arrival had just left him.'

James stayed at Breda until the middle of February and then he and his brother and sister all went to Antwerp to stay with Charles. While they were at Antwerp, George Digby, Earl of Bristol, who was no friend to James and almost as bad as Colonel Bampfield in his passion for intrigue, involved himself in an elaborate plot to combine the British force with Condé's troops and overawe the Spaniards into making a descent on England. The 'good Port Town' mentioned in the treaty with Spain could thus be seized and the invasion—and the restoration—set in motion. Convinced that the Spaniards 'would never be induced to suffer it', James kept aloof from the plotting. Bristol approached Condé, now recovering from his fever, who told Don Juan of the plan and his dislike of the whole idea; and this 'made an end of the affaire and of the Small remaining credit of My Lord Bristoll with Don John and the Spanish Ministers'. James did not care for Lord Bristol very much either.

* When Anne of Austria heard that her 'enemy' Condé was seriously ill she sent from Paris a doctor in whom Condé had particular confidence, to treat him in Brussels.

THIRTEEN

THE campaign of 1657 had involved a great deal of marching, several wasted opportunities and no decisive engagements. It was only the prelude to the far more important events of 1658. This year began badly for Turenne because his subordinate, Marshal d'Hocquincourt, who had already proved himself to be a security risk, announced that he was now joining the Prince de Condé. Furthermore, Turenne was given no freedom of action because Cromwell had been pestering Mazarin with reminders about the taking of Dunkirk.

Although Cromwell's importunity was no secret and it was perfectly obvious to almost everyone that Dunkirk was going to be the main objective of the 1658 campaign; and despite the fact that Charles produced abundant evidence of this in the form of intercepted letters and letters from friends in England, Don Juan and Caracena were quite convinced it was all an elaborate deception plan. They were sure Turenne would make another attempt to take Cambrai, one of their main supply depots, and Charles, whom they seem to have regarded as rather an ignorant civilian, could not persuade them to reinforce Dunkirk.

James stresses how surprised he was that two men 'of much good sense and wit and bravery could be attached to formalities which they well knew to be prejudicial to their Master's service and their own reputation'. Caracena had risen, by merit, from the lowest commissioned rank. Don Juan had admittedly the misfortune of being brought up as a 'Son of Spain' but he had 'qualities which could have made him a great man'. Yet, so far as was possible, both avoided contact with their troops. On the march they rode at the head of the army, followed by their guards, directly to the quarters marked out for them. Arriving in camp, Don Juan went straight to bed where he remained for the rest of the day and until the following morning. Except when the army was on the move he seldom left his tent. He took no interest in the camp or his soldiers, he never went out on reconnaissance and he prided himself on being inaccessible.

When there was any alarm or emergency he had no idea of the dispositions of his men, the defences of the camp, nor where his subordinate officers were. Success, understandably, eluded him.

Both generals having, as James says, 'flattered themselves into a belief' that Dunkirk was in no danger, Don Juan began to disperse his forces, sending infantry to strengthen the garrisons of towns such as Artois, Aire-sur-la-Lys and Saint-Omer, and a considerable reinforcement of Horse and Foot to Cambrai. Meanwhile Turenne made his preparations and set out for Dunkirk. News of his arrival reached Brussels at the end of May, causing some concern to the Spaniards because, almost at the same time, they heard that 'Generall Montague' (afterwards Lord Sandwich) and the English navy were blockading the port. It was now too late to send in reinforcements and any relief would have to be by land.

Don Juan ordered all his available troops to rendezvous at Ypres on June 7, and he then moved the army into camp between Veurne and Adinkerke, near the coast and about ten miles east of Dunkirk, where he was joined by Marshal d'Hocquincourt, described by James as 'just revolted from the obedience of the King his Master'.*

On June 11 Don Juan summoned a Council of War, attended by Condé, Caracena, Hocquincourt and the Prince de Ligne; James, bringing up the rearguard of the army, was not present. At this Council Don Juan proposed that the army should march towards Dunkirk, camp as near as possible to the enemy lines 'and watch their opportunity of attacking them'.

After a long silence, perhaps because his subordinate commanders were stunned by his suggestion, Don Juan said: 'Since I see you all approve of what I have proposed, let us now consider what manner, and what time, we shall march thither.'

The army marched on the following day. It had no artillery because continuous rain had made the roads impassable and the guns could not be dragged through the mud; all the baggage, which included the entrenching tools, was left at Veurne, and there was not enough powder for the musketeers. 'Without all which necessarys,' wrote James, who was appalled by Don Juan's plan, 'wee came and camp'd within less than twice cannon shot of the Enemies Line.'

Turenne saw the allied force moving into this camp at eleven o'clock on the morning of June 13, and could hardly believe his eyes; but while he was watching, a captured Spaniard was brought to him whose information confirmed that Don Juan was more unwise than Turenne had ever

---

* This transfer of allegiance did him no good, for two days later he was killed by a bullet in the stomach while reconnoitring the French lines.

imagined. He decided there and then to give battle next day and at once sent for the English contingent which was at Mardyck.

At five o'clock next morning the whole of Turenne's army moved out of their lines to attack. Told by James that the enemy were 'drawing out to give us Battell', Don Juan said there was nothing to be concerned about: their intention was only to 'drive in our horse guards'.* James, without bothering to hide his exasperation, said 'that it was not the custom of the French to march out with such a body of Foot, as I had seen, compos'd of the French and Suisse Guards, the Regiments of Picardy and Turenne, all of which I knew by their Colours, as well as the English by their redcoats, and with so great a body of Horse as those I had observed with their cannon before them, with a bare intention of forcing in our horse guards'.

Condé then came up and asked the Duke of Gloucester, sitting on his horse beside James, whether he had ever seen a battle. Henry said he had not, and Condé said 'that within half an hour he should behold one'.†

On the Spanish side, all was confusion. The Spanish officers were unprepared for Turenne's attack and from their point of view five o'clock in the morning was no hour to start fighting. Yet, with Turenne bearing down upon them with Horse, Foot and Guns, they had to move fast, and being unable to arrange their forces with the stately precision required by Spanish tradition there was, inevitably, a good deal of muddle. However, they succeeded in drawing themselves up in line of battle between the sea and the Veurne (then known as Furnes) Canal, just in time to be attacked.

James, describing the dispositions of the army, says that the infantry, posted on a dominant sand ridge, 'had a great Advantage of the Enemy'— but only in ground. In total strengths the armies were almost equal, both having about 14,000 men on the battlefield, but Turenne had 8,000 Foot to Don Juan's 6,000, whereas Don Juan had 8,000 Horse opposing 6,000 French cavalry. Anyone who has ever walked through dunes knows that the steep, wind-blown slopes of soft sand are difficult enough for a man to climb on foot; they are an exhausting—though not unsurmountable— problem to horses laden with armed and armour-clad riders, and therefore the Spanish preponderance in cavalry was no advantage.

* Known as 'vedettes', they formed a light cavalry screen and were responsible for observing and reporting enemy movements.

† Ramsay, Turenne's biographer, improved considerably on this, out of his own imagination. He says that Condé asked Henry if he had ever seen a battle won. Henry said no, and Condé said, 'Then in half an hour you will see one lost.' This version of the conversation is repeated by Longueville in his *Marshal Turenne*.

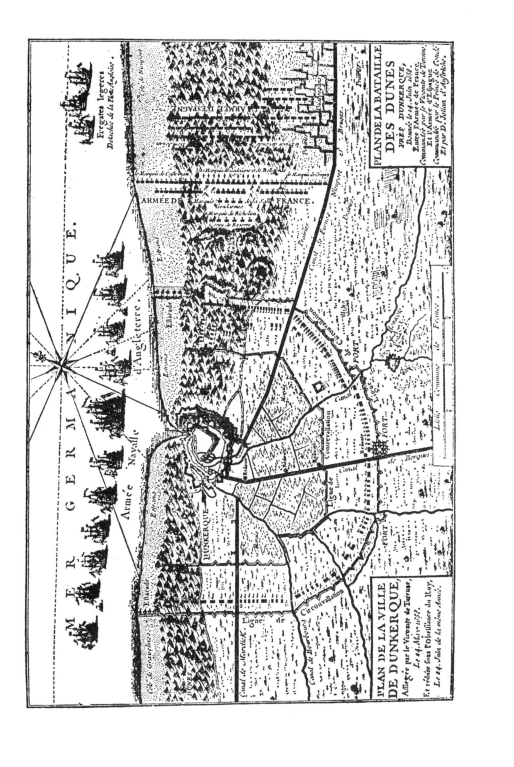

MER GERMANIQUE.

Armée Navalle d'Angleterre

Frigates legeres
Detaché de la Flote Angloise.

ARMÉE D'ESPAGNE

ARMÉE DE FRANCE

DUNKERQUE

PLAN DE LA VILLE
DE DUNKERQUE,
Afſiegée par le Vicomte de Turenne,
Le 24. May 1658.
Et reduite ſous l'obeïſſance du Roy,
Le 24. Juin de la même Année.

PLAN DE LA BATAILLE
DES DUNES
PRÈS DUNKERQUE,
Donnée le 14. Juin 1658.
Entre l'Armée de France,
Commandée par le Vicomte de Turenne.
Et l'Armée d'Eſpagne
Commandée par le Prince de Condé.
Et par D. Jouan d'Auſtriche.

Despite their march through the mud from Mardyck, the English infantry, led by a Major General Morgan, were 'the first who engaged', and James, with pride in his countrymen, says that their 'great eagerness and courage' and their 'heat' were such that they outmarched the French and so exposed their flanks to cavalry assault. But no one took advantage of this. Pausing to get their breath and straighten their line at the foot of the main Spanish defensive position, they then charged up the hill, sweeping all before them. When they came down the hill, on the Spanish side, James led a cavalry charge against them but he says, again with some pride, 'I was beaten off and all who were at the head of my own Troop were either killed or wounded, of which number I had been one, had not the goodness of my armes* preserv'd me'. Young Charles Berkeley was wounded.

Don Juan's lack of artillery was a major factor in his defeat, and Turenne's advantage in this arm was greatly increased by the guns of the blockading warships in Dunkirk roads which caused much distress to the right flank of the Spanish army. Once battle was joined neither Don Juan nor Caracena showed any lack of personal bravery, and they remained in the thick of things, trying to rally their men who were falling back as Lockhart's infantry pressed forward. At one time James sent a hundred men of the King's Regiment† to stiffen up a Spanish regiment which came under heavy attack, and later, when the Spaniards began to break, James saw a Lieutenant Elvige (this is James's spelling of the name) and some of his men from the King's Regiment standing firm. When he asked where the Captains and the rest of the Englishmen were, Elvige said they were all dead and he was the only officer who had escaped unhurt. 'Upon which,' wrote James, 'I commanded him to stay with me, and call his men together, which he did, and crying out aloud to them, That the Duke was there, those who heard him faced about immediately, and came up to us. At the same time seeing the Major of that Spanish Regiment, I call'd to him, That he should make his men follow the example of those few English, it not being the custom of Spaniards to run when any others stood; and upon the Major's reproaching them with that, they stopt, and drew up in good order.' At that moment Caracena rode up and asked James why he did not charge the enemy with his cavalry. James said he had 'already done it, and been worsted for my paines'; he then pointed out that while the enemy were in their present position, protected by a sand-hill, it was not possible to charge them. James, who never hesitated to attack whenever possible, must have been very irritated by this implied

* His actual armour rather more than his sword and pistols.
† Later the 1st Guards, and much better known as the Grenadier Guards.

criticism from a man he regarded as an indolent and inefficient commander who preferred his siesta to his soldiers.

Caracena rode away over to the left flank and James saw the English battalion which had previously beaten off his cavalry charge advancing through the dunes. He told Lieutenant Elvige and the Spanish major to 'charge them in the front, whilst I with my Horse fall into their flanque'.

The infantry stayed where they were but James, at the head of his forty mounted guards, rode straight at the enemy and 'charged so home that I broke into them' . . . driving them back towards the beach.

'Tis very observable,' he wrote, 'that when wee had broken into this Battalion, and were gott amongst them, not so much as one single man of them ask'd quarter, or threw down his armes; but everyone defended himself to the last: so that wee ran as great danger by the butt end of their muskets, as by the volley which they had given us. And one of them had infallibly knock'd me off from my horse, if I had not prevented him when he was just ready to have discharg'd his blow, by a stroke I gave him with my sword over the face, which lay'd him along upon the ground.'

Henry, Duke of Gloucester, fought throughout the action as James's 'second', that is, protecting him from any attack from the rear, and 'behaved himself as bravely as any of his Ancestors had ever done'.

Despite all James's personal efforts on the right flank, the battle was lost. Away on the left there was no way of coping with four of Turenne's well-sited field guns which did terrible damage to the Spanish infantry and cavalry in front of them; and when the cannonading was followed by an infantry attack, Don Juan's men 'making a very fainte resistance, ran away'—and who can blame them? Condé led a savage cavalry counter-attack—in which his horse was killed and, unhurt, he mounted another —but it merely delayed the inevitable retreat.

'I know not,' says James, 'of any Spanish Horse that behaved themselves well in the battle, or if they did, it never arrived to my knowledge.'

James, forced at length to leave the battlefield, narrowly escaped capture, in the village of Zudcote which was jammed with fleeing men and their pursuers; but he, his brother Henry, Don Juan, Condé and Caracena all managed to get away. The Spanish army and its allies had been thoroughly defeated: a thousand men were killed or wounded and between three and four thousand taken prisoner, but the remainder of the force, consisting mainly of the British infantry units which had withdrawn in reasonably good order, assembled at Veurne, where the baggage had been left and the artillery had now arrived. It was at Veurne that James heard of an incident which probably cheered him considerably after what must have been a very depressing day. That gallant soldier Charles-Félix de

Galléan, comte de Gadagne, the man whose buff coat had been ruined at Etampes and who had taken Turenne's terms to the duc de Lorraine on the gallows hill at Villeneuve-Saint-Georges, had been promoted Lieutenant General and was commanding the French infantry during the battle. When it was all over and 'none left standing on the field', he heard that James had been taken prisoner by one of Lockhart's regiments. Collecting three squadrons of French cavalry, 'whose Commanders were his particular friends', he led them across the battlefield 'to the place where the English then were', quite determined to rescue James by force, if necessary.

Finding there was no truth in the report he rejoined his own command, but the fact that he was perfectly prepared to risk his life for James, in such circumstances and nearly three years after James had been made to leave the French army, is an interesting indication of the feelings his brother officers had for him.

Turenne had won a great victory, and in his tent that evening he sat down and wrote about it to his wife. He seldom wasted words: 'The enemy came to us and God be praised they have been defeated: I was pretty busy all day, which has fatigued me: I wish you good night: I am going to bed.'

The battle had been fought on June 14, and the Spanish army remained inactive at Veurne until June 26 and then withdrew eastwards to Nieuport. Meanwhile Dunkirk fell to Turenne and was handed over to England. This was generally regarded as a blow to French prestige, but Turenne compensated for it to a large extent by taking Veurne, Dixmude, Gravelines, Ypres and Oudenarde in rapid succession.

The Spanish army was in an unhappy state. Its morale had been shattered on the sand dunes, and when Don Juan at a Council of War suggested defending the Veurne Canal between Nieuport and Dixmude, and thus inviting another battle, James argued vehemently against such a plan. He said that the army was in no condition to fight in the field and should be dispersed to defend the more important towns. After much discussion James's alternative plan was adopted: Caracena was to hold Nieuport, Condé was to go to Ostend while Don Juan went to Bruges and the Prince de Ligne to Ypres—where he was again defeated. Coming away from the Council, Condé said to James: 'Why did you venture to contradict Don John, as you did?'

James replied: 'Because I have no desire to run again, as we did so lately at Dunkirk.'

In James's simple philosophy one stood up to one's enemies and fought back; only a coward ran away, and James was no coward.

James and the British infantry units remained with Caracena at Nieuport and, as James had foreseen, this was Turenne's next objective. The French army approached and simultaneously James discovered that his incompetent Spanish allies had provided the garrison with only enough ammunition for fifteen days. Fortunately the expected attack did not develop. Louis XIV, then at Calais, suddenly became dangerously ill and for ten days in July it was feared he would die. In this emergency Mazarin told Turenne to suspend operations until further notice, and when Louis at last recovered completely, Anne of Austria said that in gratitude to the Almighty for her son's return to health, Mazarin must make peace with her brother the King of Spain.

Two months after the Battle of the Dunes, on September 16, when James returned to Nieuport after a series of marches between towns which Don Juan believed to be threatened by Turenne, he 'received the well-come news of Cromwell's death'.

In his diary, Evelyn wrote: '3rd September. Died that arch-rebel, Oliver Cromwell, called Protector.' It was the anniversary of Drogheda, Dunbar and Worcester; the Day of Destiny.

James, wanting to see Charles urgently, asked Don Juan to relieve him of his command, and he says that 'on the 21st of September I immediately made what haste I could to Brussels'.

The two brothers discussed the news from England exhaustively. None of it was encouraging. Cromwell's son Richard—Tumbledown Dick—seemed to have taken his father's place without any of the expected upheavals: the army and the fleet had declared for him, and so had General Monk who was governing Scotland. There had been ninety loyal addresses from counties and corporations, and foreign ministers were paying him the usual compliments.

Apparently firmly established, Richard summoned a parliament which, on January 7, 1659, undertook not to change the government.

To Charles and James, who had been so elated by Oliver Cromwell's death, the restoration seemed further away than ever and their fortunes were at their lowest ebb. But Oliver's enemies began to unite against his son. Army officers who had been dismissed by Oliver met at the apartments of General Fleetwood, the arch-republican and husband of one of Oliver's daughters, and became known as the Cabal of Wallingford House. General Lambert, 'roused from his retreat', as Hume says, 'inflamed all these dangerous humours and threatened the nation with great convulsions'.

Richard simply could not cope. He was a gentle, generous and humane man, genuinely horrified by a suggestion that the assassination of Lambert would solve his problems, and all he really wanted to do was go back to his country estate, his horses and his gardening. He revered his father and burdened himself with an enormous debt in providing him with what Evelyn considered to be a superb funeral. 'But,' adds Evelyn, 'it was the joyfullest funeral I ever saw; for there were none that cried but dogs, which the soldiers hooted away with a barbarous noise, drinking and taking tobacco in the street as they went.'

The parliament summoned by Richard Cromwell was frightened of the military cabal, there was no one of Oliver's calibre to knit together the fast-unravelling strands of authority, and the country sensed its own decline into a state summed up by Evelyn's entry in his diary against April 25: 'A wonderful and sudden change in the face of the public; the new Protector, Richard, slighted; several pretenders and parties strive for the government: all anarchy and confusion: Lord have mercy on us!'

James remained in Brussels with Charles until it was too late to return to the army because the soldiers of both sides had gone into winter quarters. Then he went to stay with Mary at Breda, 'where', he says, 'I continued for some time'.

The year 1659 dragged on. The exiled Royalists spent much time and energy over a plan, code-named 'The Select Knott', which was to be a carefully concerted rising all over England, led by Charles and James and timed for August 1. But it was betrayed by Sir Richard Willis, a man who had made with Cromwell a peculiar arrangement to reveal any Royalist plots but at the same time protect those who were involved in them. Thus all the conspirators, except one, were warned that the rising had been postponed, and Willis, unsuspected of treachery at this stage, sent a message to Brussels to tell Charles and James not to come over to England.

The one accidentally unwarned conspirator, Sir George Booth in Cheshire, put his part of the plan into effect and took possession of the City of Chester*—but not the castle, which was still held by its parliamentary governor.

James had just started off on a visit to Mary at Honslaerdyke and was a day's journey from Brussels when he received a letter from Charles, written in Brussels, giving him the news about Booth's rising and telling him to follow him to Calais. Accompanied by Charles Berkeley and one 'Trumpeter', and riding day and night, James caught his brother up at Hazebrouck. Charles told him to go to Boulogne, provide himself with a boat, and wait there for further orders which would be sent to him from

* A few weeks later Booth's rising was crushed without any difficulty by General Lambert near Nantwich, largely because Booth was a little unsteady on logistics and had failed to provide his men with any ammunition.

Calais. Fully believing that he and Charles were about to cross the Channel, James rode on to Boulogne. He assumed that he and Charles would soon be raising the Royal Standard in England. In fact, as James discovered later, nothing was further from Charles's mind. He had never imagined Booth's little insurrection in Cheshire would be anything but abortive and he had no intention of repeating the sort of adventures he had endured after the defeat at Worcester.

A day or two later, Charles went to Boulogne from Calais, on his way to Abbeville, and saw James. He told him he had not heard of any other rising in England but he proposed to go along the coast towards Dieppe and Rouen and, 'if he heard better news', to slip across the Channel. In the meantime James was to 'hover about those quarters where he was', and open any letters that came from England for Charles.

Since his real plans were so very different, Charles must have had some reason for telling James all this, but whatever it was he kept it to himself. He knew that as a result of Anne of Austria's sudden determination to stop fighting her brother, Mazarin and a Spanish envoy, Don Luis de Haro, were meeting at Fuenterrabia on the 'Isle of Pheasants' at the Bay of Biscay end of the Pyrenees, to discuss ways of bringing this about. He had decided to go himself to Fuenterrabia to persuade France and Spain to help him exploit the confusion in England. He travelled there by way of Abbeville and Rouen, Saint-Malo, Toulouse and Saragossa.

*

While England seemed to be sliding down a steep slope into anarchy and civil war the nations of Europe were slowly climbing up out of the dissension and conflict which had distracted them for so long. Turenne's campaign of 1658 which, had he possessed more time and artillery, might have ended with the capture of Brussels, had made Philip IV realize he was in grave danger of losing all the Spanish Low Countries. The failure of his two generals Don Juan and Caracena had been complete, and peace with France was no longer a bargaining counter but a necessity.

Mazarin, on his part, had never given up hope that he might one day be able to arrange a marriage between Louis XIV and the Infanta, his cousin Maria Theresa, daughter of Philip IV. There was, he felt, a chance that if this could be achieved it would end permanently a war which had been bleeding France for twenty-four years.

Thus, when Mazarin and Don Luis de Haro met at Fuenterrabia, both had good reason to hope the negotiations would be successful. The arrival of Charles, penniless and a suppliant, introduced a jarring, unwelcome element. Don Luis was exquisitely polite, respectful and entirely non-committal. Mazarin, on the grounds that France was allied to the English Commonwealth, would not even see him. For Charles, the situation seemed desperate. Every attempt to win support for the English monarchy had failed and no one, trying to pierce the gloom, could feel confident that even if the people of the Three Kingdoms regained a little of the liberty they had possessed in the time of Charles I, they would allow his son to return to the palace of Whitehall.

There was no fighting in France or the Low Countries in 1659, and the year was spent tidying up the loose ends of loyalties and all sorts of administrative problems left unsettled when the Fronde ended. The outcome of many months of negotiation at Fuenterrabia was the Treaty of the Pyrenees, under which France retained many of the places Turenne had captured, and at the same time a marriage contract was made between Louis and the Infanta, on condition that she gave up her right to the Spanish crown. They were married in the spring of the following year.

The Prince de Condé regained all his honours and estates, and the governorship of Burgundy;* even the duc de Lorraine, returning from custody in Spain, at last was given back his duchy but forbidden to fortify his capital or employ any soldiers. Turenne was offered by Louis XIV the highest office in his gift, that of Constable of France, but Turenne declined it because it could only be held by a Catholic and he was not yet prepared to change his religion. Instead he was created Marshal General of His Majesty's Camps and Armies, and made Governor of Limousin.

*

And so it was through a country in which the dank mists of civil and international war were at last lifting in the warmth of peace and hope that Charles travelled wearily back to Brussels. It had been made clear to him that he had now lost even the small nuisance value he had once possessed as a pawn in international politics. On the Continent, men's minds were occupied with rebuilding and renovation, and in their plans an uncrowned king without a kingdom played no part at all. What made everything so much worse was the knowledge that even if a majority of his countrymen

* He restored, and went to live in, the magnificent Château of Chantilly—about twenty-six miles due north of Paris—where, after many more battles, for he was a soldier who lived for fighting, he spent the last years of his life. He died in 1686, at the age of sixty-five. Perhaps one of his greatest achievements—second to the winning of the battle of Rocroi—was in 1675, after Turenne had been killed in the battle of Salzbach, in which the army of the Holy Roman Empire was defeated. Condé took over in Turenne's place and prevented the Imperialist troops, vastly encouraged by Turenne's death, from invading France.

was prepared to restore the monarchy in preference to the tumult of rival political and military factions, there was no group nor single individual with power enough to call him back.

James had been very busy while Charles was away, and he was not in the least depressed by the constantly disappointing news from England. Herein lies perhaps the basic difference between the brothers. Charles, the astute, mind-reading student of character, saw the problem of his restoration as essentially political and complex—which it was. James, the soldier, saw it in the straightforward context of invasion and military strength: nothing that could not be solved by resolute action, good communications and proper man-management—provided he had an adequate, well-balanced force to start with.

When Charles went off on his secret journey to Fuenterrabia he left James at Boulogne, and a few days later James went up to Calais to discover the latest news from England. It seems there were some Frenchmen who were not at all sympathetic to the English Royalist cause at this time, because James, who since Cromwell's treaty with Mazarin should not have been in France at all—he had adopted a disguise when he left Brussels—narrowly escaped considerable embarrassment while he was in Calais. An officer of the local garrison, described as 'an over-officious Captain', who had served with James in the French army commanded by Turenne, told the Lieutenant Governor, M. de Courtebonne, he had seen James in disguise in the town and knew where he was staying. Courtebonne shut the town gates and took a guard with him to arrest James. It turned out that the informer had been mistaken, for the man he thought was James was the Earl of Derby's brother, Edward Stanley, who, like many Royalists, had just arrived and was waiting to go over to England with King Charles.

In the search that followed, James, duly warned, lay hidden in Sir John Berkeley's lodgings, and when Courtebonne gave up and opened the gates again, an hour before nightfall, James was advised to slip out of the town and go back to Boulogne. He refused; the opening of the gates could be a trap, and he returned to the inn where he had been staying.

That night, between midnight and one o'clock, there was 'a hott alarm at his lodgings, and he verily beleev'd they were come to take him, for he was waken'd with great knocking and bouncing at the door of the Inne'. Going to the window and listening to the noise in the street he knew from experience that the men outside were soldiers, and for a moment or two he must have wondered what on earth he was going to do. But the soldiers had not come for him. They were bringing back the master of the house 'who was dead drunk and brought home betwixt four of them'.

Next morning James went back to Boulogne and, very sensibly, 'return'd no more to Calais'.

A little while later, his mother in Paris sent a Captain Thomas Cooke with a letter saying that Turenne, now at Amiens, wanted to 'speak with the King in reference to his affairs in England'. James sent Cooke away to find Charles, and when the Captain returned saying Charles was believed to be miles away in Saint-Malo he went to see Turenne himself.

Turenne's feelings for his English protégé were very different from those of the over-officious French Captain or M. de Courtebonne in Calais. He knew Charles and James were trying to raise an invasion force, and he offered his own Regiment of Foot, 1,200-strong, and the 'Scots Gendarmes'. He also promised to provide 'three or four thousand spare armes, six field pieces with ammunition proportionable, and tooles, and as much meale as would serve for the sustenance of five thousand men for the space of six weeks or two months'. In addition, ships would be found to convey all this to England, and the British contingent in Flanders (which had been defeated at the Battle of the Dunes) would be allowed to march to Boulogne and embark as soon as transports could be made available. Since this force would have to be financed, and neither James nor Charles had enough money even to pay their own households, Turenne offered to 'pawne his plate and make use besides of all his interest and credit' to raise enough money 'for the carrying on of the business'.

James 'accepted this noble Offer with great Joy', and at once began to make detailed plans. The landing would be at Rye, and 'if the Country came in to him' he would push on inland as quickly as possible, through Maidstone to Rochester. If there was no support initially from the men of Sussex and Kent he would strengthen the defences of Rye against an attack by Lambert, and 'by giving him work enough in that Siege divide the forces of the Rebells and disorder all their methods'.

Preparation began in earnest, and James found much satisfaction in all the work involved. Etaples, on the eastern side of the Canche estuary opposite le Touquet, was chosen as the port of embarkation, and troops began marching towards it. James was then joined by two of Turenne's nephews who wanted to serve with him as volunteers: the young duc de Bouillon whose father, Frédéric Maurice, had died at Saint-Denis soon after the battle in the Faubourg Sainte-Antoine, and his brother the comte d'Auvergne. James told them he had given orders for embarkation to begin on the following day.

At the very last moment a letter arrived from England telling of Sir George Booth's defeat, and everything was halted. No one knew where Charles was, though James was certain he had 'slipped across the Channel' and was either in the West Country or somewhere in Wales, and Turenne refused to allow James 'to hazard himself when there was no probability of Success'. He advised James to return to Flanders and wait for news from Charles and from the various intelligence sources in England. To help with the expenses of the journey he lent James 300 pistoles and gave him a 'Pass' to travel through France.

James was perfectly capable of making a military appreciation and he knew Turenne was right, but once again all his great hopes had come to nothing and, with great restraint, he says, 'thus an end was put to this design'. Bitterly disappointed, he set out for Brussels, wondering what had happened to Charles.

There was perhaps some compensation for being in Brussels. Mary was within fairly easy reach, and James was by now enormously attracted to her Maid of Honour, Anne Hyde.

Charles returned from Fuenterrabia, hopeless and disillusioned, just before Christmas. On his way back through France the general opinion of his total unimportance in European politics had been underlined by Mazarin's refusal to let him stay for a time with his mother, and he had been forced to return to Brussels after seeing her for only a few days. In the French and Spanish courts the feeling was that the English throne had been set aside, and since Charles Stuart would never be allowed to return to England, the most sensible thing to do would be to forget about him.

But though the Spaniards had no interest in Charles, they were well aware of James's abilities as a soldier and a leader. He could be useful. He was young, good-looking, industrious, a good linguist, charming and extremely popular. Above all, he was not only prepared to act on his own initiative but to inspire others to accept responsibility and get things done. Though unorthodox when measured against 'Spanish methods of proceeding', he was now an international figure who could breathe new life into the stiffening military body of Spain.

At the beginning of 1660 James was offered a job. Philip IV wanted him to command the Spanish army against Portugal and at the same time accept the office of High Admiral, with the title of 'Principe de la Mare'. James was told that this appointment had never before been held by any but a son of the King or a close relative; it included command of the Galleys and the Ships, and the automatic status of Viceroy of any country where the High Admiral landed, for the time he was there. The office carried 'a great Salary' and the right to one-fifth of all prizes, 'besides other considerable perquisites'. James was delighted. He badly needed employment which would exercise his talents and he was heartily sick of forever trying to make ends meet in an aura of genteel but desperate poverty.

Charles gave him permission to go, and James, in the early spring of 1660, began to make his preparations for the journey to Spain by sea.

From England there was no sign of any rift in the black clouds. In November 1659 the nation refused to pay taxes and the army and navy were ragged and starving, their pay years in arrears. The whole country seethed with discontent and apprehension. 'We had now no government in the nation', wrote Evelyn. 'All in confusion, no magistrate, either owned or pretended, but the soldiers, and they not agreed. God Almighty have mercy on us, and settle us!'

Then, quite suddenly, when Charles had almost resigned himself to a life in exile, everything began to happen at once. 'And when the motion was once begun,' says James, 'it went on so fast that his Majesty was almost in his own Country before those abroad, especially the Spaniards, would believe there was any Revolution towards it.'

FOURTEEN

As soon as the activities of General Monk in England became known in the courts and embassies on the continent, and it was clear to them that the impossible had actually happened, the complete reversal of their previous attitude to Charles must have given that affable cynic a great deal of amusement.

It seems unlikely that James knew very much about the comings and goings of Sir John Grenville, the emissary travelling between Monk, who was his kinsman, and the exiled court in Brussels. Edward Hyde prepared the Declaration of Breda, Charles's answer to Monk's request for 'a conciliatory letter he could lay before Parliament', and it may be that James, busy with arrangements for the journey to Spain, was left out of these delicate and complicated affairs until the outcome was apparent.

At the end of March 1660 Charles moved his court to Breda, telling Caracena he was going to Holland to visit his sister; but his real reason was that Monk had advised him to leave Spanish territory because it was known in England that the Spaniards were about to detain him as a hostage for the return of Dunkirk and Jamaica.*

Caracena let Charles go because he either knew nothing, or did not believe what he may have heard, about any return to England, but when the Declaration of Breda was issued on April 4 and news of reaction to it in England made the Restoration certain, he tried to persuade Charles to return to Flanders. According to James, he said 'he had business of importance to acquaint his Majesty with, from England' and that various 'persons' had come specially to Brussels with 'great offers' to make to him.

During his long exile, Charles had learned not to trust anyone, Caracena least of all, and now the return to England was certain, he would not take any risks. But, with his innate diplomatic sense, he did not intend to give Caracena 'cause for complaint', so he told James to go and find out the facts. James, intrigued by these stories of persons from England and great

* After an abortive attempt on San Domingo, Cromwell had taken Jamaica in 1655.

offers, does not say whether he was diverted or disappointed to find 'it was only Colonel Bampfield who was come over with some ayry proposition from Scott* and some of that Party'.

Out of politeness James stayed with Caracena for a day or two, then he went back to Holland and told Charles 'he had done wisely not to stir from Breda'. A little while later Charles went to The Hague 'where he was very well received'.

Meanwhile, on May 8, the House of Commons had voted 'presents' to the royal brothers: Charles was given £50,000, James £10,000 and Henry £5,000. These sums, in cash—more money than any of them had seen for many years—were brought over by Sir John Grenville,† and within a week local tailors had provided new clothes for the whole court, to replace the patched and ragged garments they had been wearing. Hitherto, credit had been a constant problem, and it was a great relief to James, the soldier, at last to be able to appear properly dressed.

On May 14 Admiral (ex-General) Montagu, anticipating orders from the 'free' parliament which had replaced the self-dissolved, twenty-year-old Long Parliament, arrived off Scheveningen with the English fleet, and James was received aboard the flagship as Lord High Admiral. With James in formal command the fleet sailed to Dover where 'Honest George' Monk, who had brought all this to pass, was waiting for the King to come into his own again. Charles landed on May 25 and with his brothers on either side of him began the triumphal progress to London. Nothing like it had ever been seen before. All the fear, all the foreboding, all the distress of the years of uncertainty had at last been blown away by the wind that brought the son of the martyred King back across the narrow waters to his people. The people's joy was really relief and satisfaction. The Commonwealth business had not worked; here, thank God, was the symbol they understood.

Against the date of May 29, 1660, Evelyn wrote in his diary: 'This day, his Majesty, Charles the Second came to London, after a sad and long exile and calamitous suffering both of the King and Church, being seventeen years. This was also his birthday, and with a triumph of above 20,000 Horse and Foot, brandishing their swords, and shouting with inexpressible joy; the ways strewed with flowers, the bells ringing, the streets hung with tapestry, fountains running with wine; the Mayor, Aldermen and all the Companies, in their liveries, chains of gold and banners; Lords and

* One of the regicides who was later executed.
† As a gesture of gratitude for all his tact and travelling, and for all he had done in restoring the monarchy, the Commons voted him the sum of £500, 'for the Purchase of a Jewel'.

Nobles, clad in cloth of silver, gold and velvet; the windows and balconies all set with ladies; trumpets, music, and myriads of people flocking, even so far as from Rochester, so as they were seven hours in passing the city, even from two in the afternoon until nine at night. I stood in the Strand and beheld it, and blessed God.'

James, riding with his brothers along roads thronged with people, many of whom wept and shouted with hysterical joy at the sight of returning royalty, must have felt he was riding into a new world and a new life, in which all the privation and despair of the long years of exile would soon be forgotten. He had at last come home, and he would from now on be among his own people whose loyalty to the monarchy had been tempered in the fires of despotism and anarchy. They wanted a king; they wanted the throne to be secure. Charles was their acknowledged King, and so his brother could now banish from his mind that awful feeling of personal insecurity.

As they rode across Blackheath, where the Ironside army, polished and glittering in the May sunshine, was drawn up in review order, James may well have looked at the long, silent ranks with more than mere professional interest, for they were the hall-mark of authority. This was what lay behind real political power. If his father had possessed such a force before 1641, there would have been no rebellion and no exile. The question now was, what would happen to this magnificent army?

The Declaration of Breda had been as vague on this point as it had been on many others. In it, Charles had promised he would be ready to consent to 'the full satisfaction of all arrears due to the officers and soldiers of the army under the command of General Monk: and that they shall be received into our service upon as good pay and conditions* as they now enjoy'. Nothing definite had been said about a standing army, or about demobilization. James was well aware of the difference between authority, which is merely the right to command or act, and power, which is the strength needed to enforce authority. Yet now was hardly the moment to discuss such things with Charles. This was a time to thank God for what had happened, not to start worrying about what was going to happen.

So, in his new clothes, mounted on a 'richly caparisoned horse', and waving and smiling as the cavalcade passed through the almost tangible warmth of this tremendous welcome, James came back to London.

In May 1660—the 'Annus Mirabilis' as that staunch Royalist John

---

* 'The Foot were paid 1/- per day and the Horse two and sixpence, so that many gentlemen and younger brothers of good family inlisted in the protector's cavalry. No wonder that such men were averse from the re-establishment of civil government, by which, they well knew, they must be deprived of so gainful a profession' (Hume).

Evelyn so emphasizes—James was twenty-six. The formative years of his life were behind him and had moulded his character and opinions. Tall, with a lean, powerful figure, his movements were swift and well coordinated. He was fit, strong and athletic. His rather long face, with the pronounced cleft in his chin, the large Stuart nose, and eyes set wide apart, was, as Macpherson says, 'engaging', but, as in so many portraits, it is possible to 'read' from the face watching immovably from the canvas, almost any interpretation from the expression given to it by the painter. In all the portraits of him the eyes have the same calm, level appraisal, honest and direct. The mouth is 'generous': sensual, one might say, but only with hindsight. 'He was,' wrote Burnet, 'through the warmth of his constitution, given to women, but never their slave.' James himself never attempted to hide his pleasure in female companionship, and no doubt like many a soldier before and since the one of whom Kipling wrote, he 'took his love where he found it', particularly during the long campaigns he fought in France and the Low Countries. By all accounts he was not very fussy, but fastidiousness where casual bedfellows are concerned is so much a matter of personal opinion that condemnation is often no more than a difference in taste. Burnet seems to be the authority—or source— for most of the stories about this side of his life. For example, the remark by Charles to the French ambassador, Courtin, 'I do not believe there are two men who love women more than you and I do, but my brother, devout as he is, loves them more'; and another remark which he also attributes to Charles, that he believed his brother had his mistresses given to him by his priests for penance. According to Burnet, James 'was perpetually in one amour or another without being very nice in his choice'. Presumably by this the Bishop meant that he would not have liked to go to bed with the ladies himself—again, purely a matter of personal taste.

James was easy to get on with, certainly as affable and almost as accessible as Charles. No man who has held high military command, and its responsibilities, can ever be entirely accessible to everyone because the very fact that he possesses the authority to send men into battle, and therefore perhaps to their deaths, tends to isolate him. If he tries to overcome this isolation and deliberately makes himself more approachable, he tends to undermine his whole authority. James had commanded men for long enough to know this, and it may well account for what Macpherson describes as 'his uncomplying disposition which prevented him from being ever loved'. He had all his father's natural dignity and this, added to a reticence which may perhaps be traced to his lonely childhood, created an indefinable 'distance', an 'aura of majesty' in his personal relationships. It was this which enabled him to command respect all his life, and, as Hume says, those of his enemies who reviled him behind his back seldom had the courage to be anything but obsequious to his face.

James never lost his stammer, and this gave him a psychological disadvantage in dealing with people. On those subjects which he had studied and understood, 'his observations', says Burnet, 'were judicious and solid', and Evelyn comments on his ability to speak on them fluently and with assurance. There is no doubt he was quick-tempered and, when sure of his ground, intolerant with those who could not see his point of view. This was because he hated procrastination, dilatoriness and uncertainty—he had seen too much when soldiering with the Spaniards. He believed in doing, not arguing and putting off what he felt had to be done, and the characteristics which probably lay at the root of the trust and affection he had inspired among brother officers and soldiers, were his passion for the truth and his habit of keeping his word. Throughout his life men knew exactly where they stood with him for he never attempted to conceal his feelings, believing that to dissemble was to be dishonest, and his constancy in enmity was equalled only by his firmness in friendship. Above all, he was honest. Naturally, against men like Shaftesbury, Sunderland and William of Orange, his principles were his vulnerabilities.

He was addicted to order and method—this made for a very happy relationship with Samuel Pepys—and he was industrious and painstaking. He was entirely without avarice. Extremely abstemious in an intemperate age, he disliked gambling and other open vices of his brother's court.

Perhaps the most repeated criticism of James is that of his obstinacy; but obstinacy is usually only applied to a man firmly pursuing a course with which others do not agree. If they do agree with it, they describe him as resolute and determined. A man may be admired for his determination and disliked for his obstinacy, yet the difference is often a matter of opinion.

All James's problems and all his misfortunes, as Duke of York during his brother's reign and as King, stemmed from his strength, not weakness, of character. There was always, even in his darkest hours of persecution and despair, what appeared to many people to be an easy way out. All he had to do, without any explanation or excuse, was to accept the Sacrament in accordance with the rites of the Protestant Church, for his conversion to Catholicism was the ruin of his fortunes. He spent his life among men— and women—not over-scrupulous in the observance of declared principles and for whom expediency justified almost any shift of allegiance. It would all have been so easy. The temptation must, at times, have been almost overwhelming, but he never succumbed. He loved honesty and truth, he did only what he honestly believed to be right, he kept his word and never deserted either his principles or his friends.

As a result he was thrust from his throne by the blackest treachery and deceit, and all but a handful of historians have vilified him and poured contempt upon him ever since.

*

In all the joy of his home-coming there was no hint of the troubles to come. He was a Protestant prince—heir to the throne until his brother married and produced a legitimate child—brave, young, handsome and unmarried. All his financial problems were solved, he no longer had to earn his living, and as he rode down the Strand from the City the world and life must have seemed very good.

As soon as Charles arrived at the palace of Whitehall he found himself immersed in the business of government, but James, whose only direct responsibility was for the fleet, was in no mood for work. Life had not been particularly easy for the past twelve years and now, determined to enjoy himself, he spent a great deal of his time hunting—when he was not with Anne Hyde. Then, within a few months of their return, James presented his brother with a problem.

Anne Hyde was pregnant and James was unquestionably the father of a child expected towards the end of October. This would have been quite unremarkable had not James complicated everything by promising marriage. This promise was apparently made in the dark days of 1659* when there was so little hope of a restoration that it really did not seem to matter very much who James married. Macpherson, among others, says 'it was only under the faith of a solemn promise that she admitted James to her bed', but it is reasonable to suppose this was a subject which James and Anne discussed privately, and no one can possibly know what they said to each other: but there is no doubt that James did want to marry her, and when he asked Charles for permission, it was at first refused.

Reasons for refusal are not hard to find. Charles, who was apt to look further ahead than his brother, did not particularly want to be related by marriage to the man who might one day be his chief minister. Mary, the Princess of Orange, had no wish to find herself suddenly ranking below the girl who had been her Maid of Honour. Henry, Duke of Gloucester, did not like Anne at all, saying 'she smelt so strong of her father's green bag that he could not get the better of himself whenever he had the misfortune to be in her presence'. Henrietta Maria disliked her father, Edward Hyde, intensely. But all these objections became merely personal

---

* Clarendon's biographer, Lister, says there was a secret contract made at Breda on November 24, 1659.

134

and unimportant when considered after the Restoration and in the light of the probable reaction of Parliament and the people of England. James, Duke of York, was a Prince of the Blood, and as such he was expected to marry a princess who would bring money and lands, or at least some valuable diplomatic asset, with her. There would be little public enthusiasm for an alliance with a girl by all accounts but sparingly endowed with beauty, and only the daughter of a man who was once no more than a lawyer and Member of Parliament for Wootton Bassett.

But there were two facts which tended to offset all this. First, in the opinion of the people, James was regarded as the temporary heir to the throne, for Charles was only thirty and it was simply a question of time before he married and James found himself several rungs down the ladder of succession. Therefore James's choice of a wife was not perhaps so important, and in any case, the girl was the daughter of a fervent Protestant. The royal brothers had spent a long time in a Catholic country and there had been a good many rumours. From the point of view of religion, this marriage might be no bad thing.

Secondly, James had given his word. He had promised Anne he would marry her, and marry her he did, despite all arguments and objections and the initial opposition of her father to whom, oddly enough, her pregnancy came as a distressing shock. It was a quiet wedding. It took place late at night on September 3, 1660, at Worcester House where Anne was then living with her parents; and Dr. Crowther, James's Church of England chaplain, conducted the service. Lord Ossery, eldest son of the newly created Duke of Ormonde, gave the bride away, and apart from him the only other witness was Anne's maid.

The first child of the marriage, Charles, Duke of Cambridge, was born seven weeks later, on October 22, and died seven months afterwards, on May 5, 1661. James and Anne had eight children;* only two survived childhood and they both became Queens of England.

Although the marriage was not made public until December 22, in court circles it did not remain a secret for long. Early in October Evelyn wrote in his diary of Henrietta Maria's attempts to 'break the marriage

*	Born	Died
Charles, Duke of Cambridge	22 Oct. 1660	5 May 1661
James, Duke of Cambridge	12 July 1663	20 June 1667
Charles, Duke of Kendal	4 July 1666	22 May 1667
Edgar, Duke of Cambridge	14 Sept. 1667	8 June 1671
Mary (Queen Mary II)	30 April 1662	28 Dec. 1694
Anne (Queen Anne)	6 Feb. 1665	29 July 1714
Henrietta	13 Jan. 1669	15 Nov. 1669
Katherine	7 Feb. 1671	5 Dec. 1671

of the Duke with the daughter of Chancellor Hyde', but apparently everything was amicably sorted out, largely because Hyde offered to 'befriend the Queen, who was much in debt, and was now to have the settlement of her affairs go through his hands'.

*

Inevitably, before Charles had been long in London, there was an outcry for revenge against the men who had condemned and killed his father, but there was nothing vindictive in Charles's nature and neither he nor Hyde, created Lord Chancellor, had any wish to celebrate the Restoration with a blood-bath. Charles, the politician, knew that the transitory satisfaction of revenge is often followed by regret for having given cause for lasting bitterness, but the Convention Parliament—so called because instead of being summoned by the King it had come together to summon him—took matters out of his hands.

James took no part in the campaign against the regicides, who in any case were more representative than guilty—he probably shared Charles's disgust for the horrible scenes on the scaffold at Charing Cross and at Tyburn—and after the ten who were executed in September 1660, only two more were condemned to death: Sir Harry Vane—whose skill in oratory and unanswerable argument had once moved Cromwell to remark in exasperation 'Sir Harry Vane, Sir Harry Vane! The Lord protect me from Sir Harry Vane!'—and General Lambert. In appealing to Charles for mercy, Lambert found unexpected but firm support from James, who held strong views on the duty of soldiers to obey and not question the orders given to them by their superiors. This had been the basis of Lambert's defence. He was pardoned, and he died at a ripe old age* having devoted the rest of his life to painting and the cultivation of a garden.

Vane scorned any such appeal, and the brilliance of his defence might well have gained him an acquittal had he not, many years before, been instrumental in bringing the Earl of Strafford to the block. This was recalled and decided his fate. He practised his oratory until the very last moment but the Sheriff protected the crowd from what he·felt was sub-version by ordering the drummers to drown the scaffold speech. But, when Vane met his death, it was felt the debt had been paid and there was no more talk of retribution or revenge.

In the years of exile, Charles had had plenty of time to think about the causes of his father's downfall and now, at the beginning of his reign, he

* So did Richard Cromwell—removed from power in 1659—who had the sense to travel abroad for a few years immediately after the Restoration. He died peacefully, in extreme old age, towards the end of Queen Anne's reign.

tried to avoid any semblance of firm government. He wanted to restore peace and a sense of security in the country which had been so torn by political and religious factions. He was reluctant to make decisions, hoping to be able to slide along on the tide of public favour until order and confidence had been regained. Yet, from the very start, events either compelled him to decide on a course of action or undermined with unhappiness his own peace of mind.

A few weeks after James's marriage his youngest brother, Henry, died with frightening suddenness, on September 23, of smallpox. Burnet, seldom entirely accurate in his reporting, says that 'the mirth and entertainments of that time raised his blood so high that he took the small pox; of which he died, much lamented by all, but most particularly by the King, who was never in his whole life seen so much troubled as he was on that occasion'. James was equally distressed, and he described his brother as 'a Prince of the greatest hopes, undaunted courage, admirable parts, and a clear understanding. He was in short possessed of all the naturel qualities, as well as acquired accomplishments, necessary to make a great Prince.' He was twenty-one.

Mary, Princess of Orange, had come over from Holland just before Henry died, and on October 28, Charles went to Dover to meet his mother, returning to the country from which she had been driven by Pym and his colleagues nearly twenty years before. She brought her youngest child, Henriette-Anne, with her. Henriette, to whom Charles was devoted, calling her by the nickname 'Minette', had been born in Exeter at the time of Essex's advance into the West Country, during her mother's brief visit in the civil war, and she was now sixteen. The unfortunate family, its reunion spoiled by Henry's death, was now even more distressed when Mary died, also of smallpox, four days before Christmas. 'This,' says Evelyn, 'entirely altered the face and gallantry of the whole court.' She had done so much for all her brothers, 'supporting them very liberally',* throughout her long widowhood, and Charles at once informed the Dutch that he would be happy to provide a home for her son William. How different James's life might have been if the boy, now ten years old, had grown up in London! As it was, his Dutch grandmother 'took care both of his estate and his education'.*

Soon after Mary's death the Queen Mother and her daughter decided to cut their visit short and return to the less infected air of France. They left London on January 2, 1661, and travelled to Portsmouth. Charles went with them, to escort them to the ship which was to carry them across the Channel, and while he was away from London there took place

* Burnet.

137

what appeared at the time to be an insignificant rising of a few fanatics, calling themselves Fifth Monarchy Men. Yet this little insurrection was to have far-reaching effects for which his brother James had hardly dared to hope and which no one could have foreseen.

FIFTEEN

EVEN before they left the Continent to come to England Charles had made it clear to James that since he was Lord High Admiral he would have the overall responsibility for the navy, whereas General Monk, whose army from Scotland was the instrument which had brought about the Restoration, was to have command of the land forces. Both James and his brother Henry, before the latter's death, were given command of regiments, but George Monk, created Duke of Albermarle, became the Lord-General and commander-in-chief.

James had not been long in England before he realized that although Parliament and the people regarded the fleet as an essential and permanent feature of the national scene—despite their extreme reluctance to provide for its upkeep—they had an almost atavistic antagonism to any form of 'standing' or regular army. This antagonism had been intensified by Cromwell and the Rule of the Major Generals—which left a permanent scar on the relationship between civilians and soldiers—and thus General Monk's command was likely to become no more than a title.

The Convention Parliament had made extravagant protestations of loyalty and subservience to the King, but they had no intention of allowing him to have an army. Monk was made to draw up a plan for general demobilization, which they approved, and the extremely dangerous and difficult task of disbanding an army of 65,000 men began. Many of the men could see no future for themselves in civilian life and they understood very well the latent power of a disciplined, armed force to change not just the course of government but the government itself. Monk, a supremely able leader, was probably the only man in the country capable of doing what was eventually achieved, for within a few months what Churchill describes as 'this omnipotent, invincible machine which might at any moment have devoured the whole realm and society of Britain', had crumbled away. The soldiers received their pay, an Ordinance was passed to enable them to take up trades without first serving an apprenticeship, and they were peacefully absorbed into the life of the country.

139

By the end of the year 1660 very little of this splendid army was left. In Monk's plan the order in which units were to disband had been decided by drawing lots, but the two taken over by James and Henry, and his own regiments of Horse and Foot,* were to be the last. The process of disbandment reached Monk's own cavalry regiment in the first week of January 1661, and with great reluctance James had by now accepted the fact that there was to be nothing left, even as a personal bodyguard for the King.

When Charles went off to Portsmouth with his mother on January 2, James, who was feeling unwell, remained in Whitehall with his wife, and early in the morning of Monday, January 7, General Monk came into his quarters in the palace to tell him that during the night there had been a 'rising' in the City. James had by this time recovered, and in reply to his questions Monk said that when the alarm was raised in the middle of the night he had immediately sent off one of the troops of his Horse, commanded by Sir Philip Howard, to deal with the situation.

Apparently what had happened was that a man called Thomas Venner, a wine-cooper and fanatical preacher, who kept a conventicle† in Coleman Street had spent the whole of Sunday, January 6, preaching and praying and fasting, and then, at about eleven o'clock at night, he and his congregation of some thirty 'saints', well-armed, had marched down to St. Paul's Churchyard shouting 'Live, King Jesus!' and telling everyone they saw either to join them or stay at home. Grabbing some wretched bystander they killed him when he told them he was on the side of God and King Charles. The train-bands, called out to restore order, fled before them, and Venner and his supporters went up through Aldersgate and spent the rest of the night in Cane Wood, between Hampstead and Highgate, where Howard and his horse guards could not attack them.

Two days later, at seven o'clock in the morning, Venner and his misguided saints came out of the wood and stormed through Aldgate, proclaiming 'King Jesus' and indicating their determination to take up arms on his behalf against the powers of the world. They advanced along Leadenhall, past the Exchange to Woodstreet, and were there confronted by twenty horse guards, while the train-bands, much braver when operating in daylight, came up behind them from Cheapside. Barricading themselves in an alehouse, they resolved to defend it to the last.

James and Monk, told that Venner had returned, cantered down to the city with an escort of twenty troopers, 'no more being left on guard', and

* They had stayed with him, uncomplaining, in the village of Coldstream during the bitter December of 1659 awaiting the right moment for the march to London.
† A clandestine meeting-place for religious dissenters.

on their way the nobility and gentry flocked out to join them in such numbers that by the time they reached St. Paul's, James found he had some 1,500 horsemen behind him. Here, they were met by the Lord Mayor who caused great disappointment with the news that 'Venner's party were all killed or taken'. They had fought with ferocious tenacity. It had been deemed impossible to dislodge them without setting the building on fire, but this would have endangered the whole street. Finally a seaman called Lambert climbed on the roof, took off some of the tiles and got into the house that way. James, who always admired courage, particularly when it was allied with initiative, must have made a note of Lambert's name because a little while later he promoted him to the command of his yacht.

Venner's impossibly brave defiance of authority was a pathetic failure. He himself survived the attack on the alehouse but was wounded nineteen times, and the surgeons complained of their extremely difficult task in keeping him alive long enough to be executed. Of his followers only one asked for quarter and a wounded comrade immediately tried to kill him with his sword. Few survived, and all were executed except two 'reserved as witnesses' and two who were reprieved by the King. Venner's insurrection was in fact a curious blend of religious fanaticism and militant republicanism, for his few followers were mainly Cromwellian soldiers who, unable to accept the return of the Stuarts, became, as Macpherson says, 'utter enemies to all authority'. The strange incident of the Fifth Monarchy Men* did however hammer home a point James had tried to make but had been unable to press for fear of raising a storm of protest: there must be a small permanent force for the physical protection of the King's person.

Thus it is to the wild, deluded Venner that the British Army owes its first regular establishment.

Aware that his point had at last been taken, James suddenly found

---

* The origin of this term can be found in the second chapter of the Book of Daniel (Venner's preaching was centred on the more obscure passages of Daniel and Revelation). In the second year of his reign King Nebuchadnezzar began to have dreams so troublesome that 'his sleep brake from him', and he sent for Daniel to interpret one he had had about an image with a golden head, silver chest, brass stomach, legs of iron and feet of clay. Daniel's interpretation is a bit involved but he talks of four 'kingdoms': the one before Nebuchadnezzar's (gold), Nebuchadnezzar's (silver), a third kingdom of brass and a fourth of iron. Then he goes on to talk about a fifth kingdom—which is Venner's Fifth Monarchy—related to clay; and it is verse 44 which seems to have inspired Venner and his saints: 'And in the days of these kings shall the God of Heaven set up a kingdom which shall never be destroyed; and the kingdom shall not be left to other people but it shall break in pieces [like the clay] and consume all these kingdoms, and it shall stand for ever.'

there was no need for him to risk his popularity by pursuing it. The Lord Chancellor had been badly frightened by Venner's rising—perhaps his memories of the Fronde made him fear something similar in England—and it was at his instigation that Charles—and subsequently the new Cavalier Parliament*—reconsidered the whole question of a regular force. The outcome was that the disbandment of Monk's regiments was postponed and a new regiment of twelve companies of Guards, commanded by Colonel John Russell, was raised. There were also to be a regiment of Horse in eight troops commanded by the Earl of Oxford and a troop of horse-guards commanded by Lord Gerard. James's own troop of horse-guards which had charged with him at the Battle of the Dunes was recalled from Dunkirk. But, to comply with an Act of Parliament, the remnant of Cromwell's Ironsides still had to be formally disbanded, and so, on February 14 on Tower Hill, scene of so many far less inspiring sights, Monk's Regiment of Foot laid down its arms, and, to the immense satisfaction of every man on parade, including James, straightway took them up again as the Lord-General's Regiment of Foot Guards. Colonel Russell's regiment, which contained the last of the men who had stood firm when the line broke on the dunes at Dunkirk, took precedence, since its task was the protection of the King, and became the 1st (Grenadier) Guards, and the older, sole survivor of the New Model Army became the 2nd (Coldstream) Guards whose Latin motto, with justification, claims they are second to none.

The King's troop of horse guards, and James's troop from Dunkirk, the Duke of York's Own, took precedence over Monk's Life Guards, and after many years as independent troops—composed of 'men of birth and education' and known as the Gentlemen of the Life Guards—they became the First and Second Regiments of Life Guards. From the colour of its uniform Lord Oxford's regiment of Horse came to be known as The Blues.

This royal bodyguard of cavalry and infantry was still not enough to satisfy those who feared echoes or repercussions from Venner's rising, and in 1662 Douglas's Regiment, which had been part of the Scots Brigade of Gustavus Adolphus, King of Sweden, was also brought back from Dunkirk. It was granted precedence over a regiment raised by Lord Peterborough in 1661 to defend the new possession of Tangier, and these two infantry regiments became the 1st and 2nd of Foot: The Royal Scots† and The Queen's.

---

* The Convention Parliament dissolved itself in December 1660, and the 'Cavalier' Parliament, which lasted for eighteen years, assembled in May 1661.

† A very old and very great regiment, but not quite as old as its nickname of Pontius Pilate's Bodyguard might suggest.

James, naturally, was delighted by this complete reversal of policy—hitherto the Lord Chancellor had argued passionately against keeping any of Cromwell's men in arms, saying that 'with mutiny, excitement and rebellion the king would never be safe till they were gone'—but James was relieved not because he regarded this small force as a means for imposing the will of a ruler upon his people, but because he was convinced that a ruler had to be protected from the mob. He had, after all, a soldier's appreciation of relative strengths: this force could only be used for local defence. There was, of course, another aspect: his years of soldiering on the Continent had taught him to take a real interest and pleasure in soldiers and everything to do with them. He understood them, and because he led by example, they understood him. Later, when he came to the throne, his work for the army was such that the army's greatest historian, Fortescue, whose praise for administrators is sparing, has written, 'it is not too much to say that his expulsion was in this respect the greatest misfortune that ever befell the Army'.

But now, in the aftermath of Venner's rising, James had little to do with the army. Monk was carrying out an extremely difficult task of reorganization so efficiently that there was no possible justification for interference, and James's only official interest was in his troop of Life Guards. He turned his attention to the fleet.

Here, the problems were enormous. The navy consisted of a fleet of 157 ships in stages of disrepair which varied from bad to shocking. The stores in the great naval dockyards at Deptford, Rochester, Chatham and Portsmouth were empty and the naval accounts were nearly three-quarters of a million pounds in debt. Although Parliament voted money to clear the arrears of pay and meet the outstanding bills, no provision was made for repairing ships or replenishing stores. If the fleet was ever to put to sea, the money had to come from the meagre annual income of £1,200,000 which Parliament, genuinely believing it was being generous, allotted to Charles.

It was fortunate for the country that at this moment, when its fleet was in desperate straits and when England had been too preoccupied with her own affairs to counter or contend against the erosion of her overseas trade by the Dutch, there were two men whose patriotism and industry enabled the protective shield of warships to be rapidly restored.

The core of energy was undoubtedly that dark, sparkling little man with thick lips, broad nose and slightly bulbous eyes, Samuel Pepys. He was perhaps one of the first and certainly one of the greatest civil servants, though he was not as selfless in his devotion to duty as one might perhaps expect someone of his status to be today. He made a fortune, but it was built up over the years by methods which, in his time, were probably regarded as perfectly honest. Pepys was a very intelligent man and he realized that if he was ever to run so complex an organization as the navy, which he did, his authority must stem from respectability: for no one really has any respect for an official easily swayed by self-interest and from whom promotion or preferment can always be bought. Pepys was indefatigable, just, relentless and tenacious in the interests of the navy, and supremely literate. In his own way he was a very great man, rightly called the saviour of the navy,* but his origins were humble, he had no hereditary position in the society of government, and he had to fight hard to reach each ascending step in his career. Even such a man as he could not, in the political and social climate of the times, have achieved anything without a powerful patron. It was his good fortune that his patron was James, second citizen in the kingdom.

Yet the mere existence of so exalted a patron was not enough. If his plans and reforms were ever to be implemented, Pepys needed not only active but determined patronage by one who had a genuine interest in everything to do with the navy, from the tedious and basic administrative details to the excitement of a great ship's launching. James had this interest, and the determination needed to promote it, and it was of course of enormous value to Pepys that James was a member of the Privy Council and could thus raise naval matters at the highest level.

It would be as wrong to imagine that James himself initiated all the reforms and innovations introduced in the service at this time as it would be to assume that every government minister prepares the first draft of major measures for which he is ultimately responsible. Though Pepys must be given a major share of credit for the naval reforms and organization which were to create, in the British navy, the force which for the next two and a half centuries profoundly influenced international politics, it cannot be assumed that James only signed what his subordinates laid before him. New measures arise from ideas which are often inspired by the discussion of some incident or thought, and it is not always clear from whom an original idea comes. In his diary Pepys, not unnaturally, is apt to give the impression that he was the instigator of most of the plans, and James's detractors support this. Macaulay goes further and says that James would only 'have made a respectable clerk in the dockyard at Chatham', but the instances of Macaulay's apparently deliberate misrepresentation of well-documented facts are so numerous tnat he cannot be regarded as anything but a great writer.

There is no doubt that when James came back to England and took over

* By Sir Arthur Bryant.

the actual duties of the Lord High Admiral as opposed to merely possessing the title, effective control of naval affairs remained in the hands of Pepys and James's secretary, Sir William Coventry, and according to Pepys this state of affairs continued even after Coventry was replaced by Matthew Wren in 1667. But Pepys makes it clear that he regarded James as an invaluable 'departmental chief' who was prepared to use all the authority of his rank not only to support the work of the subordinates he trusted but to protect them when they were assailed by those who were envious or antagonistic. In the beginning Pepys certainly had to work to win and hold James's patronage—perhaps he was helped by there being only six months' difference in age between them—for after the struggle for existence during the exile James was prepared to leave the affairs of state to others. Yet, probably because of Pepys's personality and persistence, James became deeply involved in the navy's problems and, as Pepys himself says, 'concerned to mend things in the Navy himself and not leave it to other people'.

This involvement grew into a real affection for the service, evinced by James's frequent visits to and inspections of ships and dockyards. He really wanted to know what was going on and he made it his business to find out. But, as always, he was far more interested in meeting people, talking to them and walking with them through 'the building-yards, docks, timber-yard, deal-yard, mast-yards, gun-yard, rope-walks; and all the other yards and places, set apart for the works belonging to the navy',* than in the necessary committee work such as the weekly meetings of the Navy Board. At these, according to Pepys, his attendance was not as regular as perhaps it ought to have been.

He was learning all the time. There was nothing dictatorial in his chairmanship of the Navy Board, and he was apt to disappoint advisers who tried to make him decide an issue beforehand, by taking particular pains to hear both sides. Perhaps his attention to detail was the result of Turenne's teaching that no commander should allow himself to be hurried into a decision until he has all the available information.

If Pepys was lucky in his patron, James was equally lucky in his subordinate; and he knew it. Between them there grew up a mutual trust and understanding which was wholly to the benefit of the navy. When Pepys complained to James about problems arising from the lack of proper job descriptions and clear definitions of duties in the Navy Office, James told him to put his suggestions on paper. Subsequently Pepys was delighted to find that James had them copied 'without the alteration of a syllable' and presented the document to the Privy Council as his own, that

* Which so fascinated Daniel Defoe when he visited Rochester some years later.

is, with the full weight of his personal authority behind it—naturally no one assumed he had actually written it. It was Pepys, too, who compiled the 'Instructions to Commanders' which, unchanged in essence, is still the basis of naval discipline.* But the two greatest reforms which date from this time, the setting up of a regular naval establishment and the introduction of midshipmen, could well have emanated from James himself.

Hitherto it had been the custom to pay off a ship's company and lay warships up until they were needed for operations. Crews were mustered as and when the need arose, from such sources as discharged sailors, merchant shipping, the Press Gang and the gaols. In James's opinion there was the same need for a regular naval establishment as there was for a regular army. He knew from experience that men who have been working together for some time, learning their trade, are immeasurably better in action than a unit of individuals suddenly thrown together by necessity. Pepys may well have thought about this, but James knew about it, and to suggest, as Macaulay does, that James cannot be held responsible for any of the innovations which, for the first time, set the navy on a firm footing, is to ignore the fact that in service matters James was knowledgeable, experienced and extremely practical.

During these early years the major problem in rebuilding the navy was one of officers. They were not difficult to find because there was a generally held opinion—which persisted for more than a hundred years—that since it was the primary duty of an officer to lead, and by showing a fearless example probably get himself killed, he did not need any particular training. Furthermore, there appeared to be no reason why an officer who had proved his courage on land should not be just as effective at sea. Prince Rupert, George Monk, Duke of Albemarle, Sir Edward Montagu (now created Earl of Sandwich) and James himself, among many others, were all soldiers first and sailors afterwards.

As a policy, this could not work, and James, who had seen often enough how things went wrong when an enthusiastic but inexperienced officer was told to lay an ambush, or site trenches during a siege, knew it could not work. In many ways an officer at sea, trying to harness elements over which he has no control, needed more experience than his counterpart on land; and experience is the one attribute which cannot be taught.

It was for this reason that James, as Burnet says, 'began a method of sending pages of honour and other young persons of quality to be bred

* The manual known as *The Duke of York's Sailing and Fighting Instructions* was largely the work of that experienced seaman Sir William Penn, though it can be assumed that such a document, bearing his name, was carefully edited and approved by James before it was published.

to the sea'. But Burnet goes on to say that these young persons were 'put in command as soon as they were capable of it, if not sooner', and this so discouraged the seamen on the lower rungs of society that they left the navy and went off to command merchantmen. Burnet seems to have confused two quite separate categories of 'persons of quality'. On the one hand were the boys, sent to be bred to the sea, who were far too young to be promoted over the heads of the old 'tarpaulins'—the experienced seamen who had come up the hard way—but since both James and Charles held the opinion, not shared by Pepys, that the nobility and gentry made the best officers, it was of course their intention that in due course the boys would rise to command.

On the other hand, in the second category, were the Royalists and hangers-on of the court who managed to obtain commissions although they were hardly 'officer material'. Even so there was a good reason for bringing them into the navy. Neither Charles nor James had any illusions about that wonderful triumphal progress from Dover to Whitehall: both knew that all over the country there were many supporters of 'the good old cause', republicans who needed little or no encouragement to light the flame of rebellion. They also knew that all officers who had served under Cromwell were, to a greater or lesser extent, security risks. There was plenty of evidence: Venner's insurrection, another plot in which three Cromwellian majors were involved, and Bradford's Conspiracy,* and so James was to some extent compelled to replace officers whose loyalties were suspect, by those on whom he could count, even though such changes were not to the navy's advantage.

Charles possessed what Hume has described as 'a natural lenity'. All he wanted was to forgive and forget, and unite all his subjects in affection for king and country, but he knew this was a long-term, perhaps un-attainable aim. The knowledge of hidden disaffection was always at the back of his and James's minds. Both had much experience of civil war, in England and in France. Both knew how easily and from what apparently trivial causes it could suddenly erupt, and throughout both their reigns it is not difficult to see, like a broad band woven in the pattern of events, this uneasiness, this sense of insecurity rooted in an ever-present fear of sudden revolt which would sweep them back into exile and oblivion.

It was this fear that governed James's attitude to a standing army and an effective navy, and made Charles keep in such close touch with Louis

* This was a plan to kill Charles when he visited a militia unit by firing a ceremonial salute at him, using muskets loaded with bullets instead of just powder. It was betrayed by a preacher called Ridge who apparently succumbed to Charles's charm and kindliness during a personal cross-examination. Ridge turned Royalist and was later killed in a naval battle, serving as a muster master.

XIV, at the head of what was rapidly becoming the greatest power in Europe. It is reasonable to assume that nothing but the certainty that he did need money and the possibility that he might one day need outside military aid to preserve his throne, could have led Charles to retain, and sometimes strengthen, his ties with the man whom most Englishmen regarded as their natural and hereditary enemy.

The feeling was mutual, but on Louis's side his objective was to establish an unassailable north-eastern frontier, at the expense of Holland. To achieve this he needed freedom of action, and he could foresee that the English fleet could be a disruptive factor in his plans. He was prepared to pay, and pay well, to hold Charles under an obligation, while Charles, kept chronically short of money by a Parliament unwilling to increase taxes to keep pace with post-Restoration inflation, was prepared to accept a pension which gave him some measure of political independence.

The covert threat of rebellion affected the two brothers in quite different ways. Charles, the politician, dexterous, supple, and really very lazy, was unrivalled in his skill at paying out rope to his enemies with which they hanged themselves. In the end, after a reign which, largely because of James, was a hard battle, he won for himself the peace for which his heart longed. He achieved political mastery largely by apparent inertia. He had learned, perhaps from that disastrous episode with the duc de Lorraine at Villeneuve-Saint-Georges, of the dangers of taking sides, and he knew that the man most difficult to defeat is he who will not fight.

James, the soldier and sailor, was only too happy to take up arms against a sea of troubles—and surely no prince has ever created for himself a more turbulent flood—but, because these troubles were political rather than military, by opposing he tended to make them worse. Charles was prepared to appear yielding and conciliatory, unwilling to put a weapon in the hand of a potential rebel; James, far more like his father than Charles was, had all that misguided monarch's determination to enforce the royal prerogative, and he despised what he regarded as weakness in the face of the enemy. He must, at times, poor honest, forthright and courageous man, have been a great trial to his brother, yet, although there were occasional periods of coolness, they remained remarkably close to one another throughout Charles's life and there is little doubt that on many occasions Charles took courage and comfort from his brother's strength of character and will.

The principal events in the years immediately following the Restoration were Charles's coronation* in April 1661, somewhat marred by pouring

* At which James's old gaoler, Algernon Percy, appeared as Lord High Constable, but he had retired from public affairs and died in 1668, aged sixty-six.

rain, his marriage and the sale of Dunkirk—which contributed to Clarendon's fall; James's excursions in the world of commerce which perhaps brought nearer the war with the Dutch; and the restoration of the Anglican Church which began a new chapter in religious persecution.

As soon as Charles mounted the English throne he became Europe's most eligible bachelor, and it must have amused him, for he was the least spiteful of men, to be able to decline offers made by Mazarin with regard to his niece, Hortensia Mazarini, whom James enigmatically describes as 'cry'd up for the greatest beauty in Europe'. Only a short while before, Charles's tentative inquiries about marrying her had been rebuffed because Mazarin was not prepared to stake anything on the future of an insolvent exile.

Eventually, urged by Clarendon, he decided to marry John of Braganza's daughter Catherine, the Infanta of Portugal, whose dowry included the ports of Tangier and Bombay and £500,000—which was never paid in full. Lord Sandwich brought her to England, Charles met her at Dover on May 19, 1662, and she began a married life in which there can have been little happiness or joy. Both Charles and James found that faithfulness to their wives was a discipline they were incapable of imposing upon themselves, but at least James was never so grossly discourteous as to compel a young wife to accept one of his acknowledged mistresses as a Lady of the Bedchamber.* To seduce one of his wife's Maids of Honour† was perhaps rather a different matter. It is odd that Charles, so noted for his politeness and good manners, and who so well understood the human heart, should have been so consistently unpleasant to a girl who could not prevent herself from falling in love with him, and who endured two miscarriages in her efforts to provide him with the heir who would have solved so many of his problems.

Clarendon was unlucky in that the girl he advocated so strongly did not rapidly produce a son. It was even more unfortunate that she was a Catholic. In the opinion of most people no good had come from Charles I's marriage, and when his son also married a Catholic there were even more rumours of conversion to Rome.

The much criticized sale of Dunkirk in 1662 was no more than an act of common sense. English possession of it was a potential cause of war with either France or Spain; it had no harbour, was virtually indefensible against determined assault and cost £120,000 a year to maintain, without hope of any return. Clarendon advised disposing of it because for economic reasons a choice had to be made between Dunkirk and Tangier.

* As Charles did with Barbara Villiers, Countess of Castlemaine.
† Arabella Churchill.

A treaty with Portugal barred a sale to Spain, so Charles offered it to his cousin Louis for £900,000. Louis countered with £200,000 and it changed hands for £400,000. Tangier turned out to be a bitter disappointment. The Portuguese Ambassador had assured Charles that it was 'a place likely to be of great benefit and security to the Trade of England'. What he did not say was that it had no harbour either and was permanently besieged by the Moors who, with some justification, regarded it as their property. This essay at control of the Mediterranean had to be abandoned in 1684—but Samuel Pepys, as the Treasurer of Tangier, considered that the whole project had been worthwhile.

Although his denigrators claim that James did not take any direct or active part in commercial affairs, overseas trade was a subject he understood and he never underestimated its importance to a maritime nation. In his advice 'For My Son The Prince of Wales', in 1692, he wrote: 'Study the Trade of the Nation and encourage it by all lawful means, tis that which will make you at ease at home and considerable abroad.'

Within a few months of his return in 1660 he began discussing with the Earl of Pembroke the formation of a trading company in Africa, and this led to the Royal Africa Company, which he founded. In the autumn of 1663 he fitted out two ships at his own expense and sent them out under the command of Sir Robert Holmes with orders to seize the Dutch fort at Cape Verde, recapture the castle at Cormentin, drive the Dutch away and re-establish 'factories' all along the Gold Coast—where they had been before the time of the Commonwealth. These orders were obeyed.

James also found another way of taking trade from the Dutch when he learned that various merchants had, as he says, 'got the secret' from the Dutch 'of dying the Sayes* of such a colour as the Blacks liked, and of giving the smell in the packing them up like that which was used at Leyden, from which place formerly all the Sayes were brought that were sent into Guinea'.

In addition to establishing the Royal Africa Company James also invested in and gave much support to 'the severall trading companies of the East Indies, Turkey, Hamburg and Canary', and he had a considerable financial interest in the Hudson Bay Company.

Towards the end of 1663 Charles made a present to James of Long Island 'in the West Indies' and the 'tract of land between New England and Mary Land which had always belonged to the Crown of England since it was first discovered'. Here again, the Dutch had established themselves during the rebellion and had built a town and several forts in order 'to secure the Bever-trade to themselves'. In the spring of 1664

* A fine serge cloth which was apparently a profitable export to tropical Africa.

James sent two warships, commanded by Colonel Richard Nicholas, 'an old officer and a Groom of His Bedchamber', to take possession of his land. The Dutch settlers were in no position to resist the force of 300 infantry led by Nicholas, and James records that they gave up 'without stricking a Strok'. Most of them stayed where they were, friendly neighbours of the original English inhabitants, and Colonel Nicholas 'remained in peaceable possession of that country'. In James's honour the town, and the country round it, were named New York, and 'the Fort up the River was named Albany'.

Not surprisingly, the Dutch regarded these expeditions to the Gold Coast and North America as overt attacks on their vital trading interests.

*

Another restoration which had perhaps more far-reaching results than the return of the Stuarts was that of the Anglican Church which, during the Commonwealth, had lapsed into a state bordering on total eclipse. At the Savoy Conference, held on March 25, 1661, twelve bishops met twelve Presbyterian leaders with the object of seeing what could be done to resolve basic differences, and so put into effect that promise in the Declaration of Breda 'that no man shall be disquieted or called in question for differences of opinion in matters of religion, which do not disturb the peace of the kingdom'. Further, Charles had undertaken to assent to such an Act of Parliament 'as, upon mature deliberation, shall be offered to us for the full granting of that indulgence'.

The meeting at the Savoy was the beginning of this mature deliberation by the two main sects, while the Catholics, independents and other sectaries stood by, hoping that at last they would be allowed to worship God in their own way, without persecution.

Charles was well aware of his position as the Protestant king of a Protestant people, and he knew that to a very large degree the security of his throne depended on his attitude to religion. He had been away for a long time, living in Catholic countries where, as many people realized, he had been in contact with strong Catholic influences. It was thought that his experiences in Scotland, before the battle of Dunbar, might have urged him to the other extreme, and it was suspected that his mother had done her best to convert him. He might have been attracted by what no one could deny was a splendid and satisfying form of worship and the latitude which, to the uninitiated, the forgiveness and absolution of the penitent sinner seemed to encourage.

Yet, although his people had their fears and suspicions, the truth is that Charles, like so many who are young and fit and for whom life seems to stretch away into a future too remote to bother about, felt no need for religion. He had no strong views—if he had any at all—about dogma or practices or individual relationships with the Almighty. So far as he could see, there was no reason on earth why people should not be entirely free to go to God in their own way, or ignore Him if they felt so inclined. He was in fact an advocate of toleration at a time when religious bigotry and persecution were matters in which the majority of the clergy, and particularly the Anglican clergy, took an intense and enthusiastic interest. In the face of this attitude he had no chance whatsoever of being able to introduce any measures which would grant to minority religious sects the freedom to worship in their own way, even in private.

James, who shared his brother's views in so far as they related to what he described as 'liberty of conscience', was, when the time came, far more determined in his approach, and his cause was wrecked on the rocks of Protestant, not Catholic, bigotry.

When the Cavalier Parliament first assembled on May 8, 1661, there were only fifty-six members of the former all-powerful Presbyterian party, and power now lay on the side of monarchy and episcopacy. In the first five years of its long life this Parliament not only took from the hands of the King all control of Church affairs but passed a series of Acts,* called collectively the Clarendon Code after that unbending churchman, which destroyed the political supremacy, and thus much of the influence, of Puritanism, and divided religious thought in England into the two categories of Established Church and Dissent. Furthermore, in attacking 'Dissent' the Clarendon Code forged weapons of persecution which, morally, were as indefensible as any Spanish Inquisition and put into the hands of the Anglicans the power to make life intolerable for anyone who could not accept their views.

* The Acts which comprised the Clarendon Code were:
Corporation Act, 1661, participation in any local government authority was restricted to Church of England communicants.
Act of Uniformity, 1662, all clergy had to state their 'unfeigned consent and assent' to everything in the Prayer Book, or be expelled from their livings. (2,000 Puritans did lose their livings.)
Conventicle Act, 1664, attendance at any religious meeting, except of the Established Church, was punishable by imprisonment for the first and second offences, and by transportation, on pain of death if the convicted man returned, for the third.
Five Mile Act, 1665, every clergyman and schoolmaster had to declare that 'he would not at any time endeavour any alteration of Government either in Church or State', or be barred from coming within five miles of any city or corporate town. (Since Puritans tended to congregate in urban rather than rural areas this Act affected their education as well as their faith.)
The Cavalier Parliament insisted that these Acts were to be enforced without royal mercy or any other form of favour, and they were—with few intervals—until 1689.

It is interesting to speculate on what effect these penal laws had on James who, at this time, was still a practising Protestant but one whose mind had been for some time 'clouded with a doubt'. He must have discussed with his brother the Declaration of Indulgence* which Charles put forward on December 16, 1662, and was subsequently compelled to withdraw, and there is little doubt that he regarded the political pressures exerted on Charles as an attack on the royal prerogative. He also felt that the withdrawal was an act of weakness, but he was not yet ready to throw his cap into the arena of religious controversy.

Conscious of his responsibilities and aware of the part he would be expected to play if there should be war, he was busy learning about navigation and ships and the men who served in them. It was his industry, and that of Pepys and Coventry, with the support of Charles who had provided £800,000 he could ill afford, that made it possible to equip a fleet at all; and when the time came for him to command a fleet in action he was not, as has been suggested, merely a titular admiral, repeating like a parrot the orders of a subordinate. He was also busy with his commercial projects and he spent most of his spare time out in the open air, hunting. Indoors, when not with his wife, he amused himself with intimate friends such as Goditha Price or Lady Denham.

Charles, who so hated 'business', had plenty of problems, almost all of them connected in some way with money. James, who has been accused of parsimoniousness when in fact, like many Scots, he was thrifty and sensible about money, was enjoying life.

Then, four years after the Restoration, all the progress which he and Samuel Pepys and the Navy Board were making with the rehabilitation and reform of the navy was interrupted by an event which raised James to extraordinary heights of popularity and public esteem.

* The object of the Declaration of Indulgence, issued by Charles as Head of the Church, was to dispense with the penalties imposed by the Act of Uniformity.

SIXTEEN

ON the occasions when James went to Holland during the exile he had gone to see his sister Mary—and latterly, Anne Hyde too—and not because he liked either the country or the people. His prejudice probably dates from the time when Cromwell's ambassadors arrived at The Hague in 1651 and he had been compelled to withdraw to Breda. His opinion of the Dutch was confirmed when although the States-General did repeal the Act of Seclusion, which had deprived his nephew William of the hereditary position of Stadtholder, they did not allow him any of the civil or military rights attached to that office. In James's eyes the Dutch were no more than 'insolent republicans', and he said so; in his vocabulary the term 'republican' was a very dirty word.

Thus when the City merchants brought a string of complaints to both Houses of Parliament about the 'injuries, depredations and encroachments' of the Dutch during the period of anarchy before Monk restored the monarchy, and asked for 'a speedy redress thereof', James in the Privy Council argued for war. Albemarle took his side but his father-in-law Clarendon, Ormonde and the Lord Treasurer Southampton spoke for peace on the grounds that after what was euphemistically referred to as 'the late disturbances', the country was in no state to fight.

Van Gogh, the Dutch Ambassador, shared this view and refused to take the threat seriously even when James, in September 1664, warned him privately that the mood in the country was such that unless the Dutch made reparations of some sort there would be war. James himself was sure that when the Dutch realized how serious the situation was growing they would climb down, but the republican government in Holland felt that a successful naval war would do much to reduce the authority and prestige of the military faction which supported the House of Orange. And so, with neither side really believing the other would fight, the two great maritime powers slid slowly down into the bitter waters of the Second Dutch War.

In October, a few weeks after his conversation with Van Gogh, James saw that war was unavoidable and began to concentrate all his energy and very nearly all his time on preparing the fleet for active operations. At the beginning of November, forty-one ships, including *Royal Charles*, *Royal James*, *Swiftsure* and *London* of the 1st and 2nd rates,* which had been refitted in the Thames, assembled at Spithead, and James went down to Portsmouth to join Prince Rupert and the Earl of Sandwich. Although there had been no declaration of war it was known that the Dutch Admiral Opdam had collected a considerable fleet with which he proposed to force a passage through the Channel, escort a convoy to Africa and destroy the recently installed trading stations of the Royal Africa Company. James proposed to give battle in the Channel, but Opdam was held against his own coasts by contrary winds for several weeks and at the beginning of December, when the wind at last veered into the east, he felt it was the wrong time of year for operations and laid up his ships for the rest of the winter.

James, with Rupert as his second-in-command, had been at sea since the second week in November, cruising on a four-day turn-round between Dunnose, near Ventnor in the Isle of Wight, Cap de la Hague, at the tip of the Cherbourg peninsula, and Portland Bill. Manœuvring the fleet in these narrow waters required considerable skill and discipline but there were no accidents. Learning that Opdam had laid up his fleet, James and Rupert returned to London, leaving Sandwich in command at Portsmouth with orders to continue patrolling with 4th and 5th rates off the Isle of Wight and to bring in any Dutch ships they might find. The winter months were spent in refitting and trying to make sure the fleet would be ready for sea in the early spring; James took a close personal interest in this.

In November, Parliament had voted £2,500,000 for the war which Charles declared on March 4, 1665. On March 23 James went by water from London to the general rendezvous of his ships at the Gunfleet† where he found that despite all his efforts during the autumn and winter it would not be possible to put to sea for another five weeks. But this interval was well spent. James held daily conferences of all his flag officers on board his flagship *Royal Charles*, 'there to agree upon Orders of Battell and Rank', for though Cromwell's fleet had fought well 'they minded not any set order, and their victories were still more owing to their valour than method'. Hitherto naval tactics had been uncomplicated. There

* The actual number of guns, in tiers of gun-decks, determined the 'rate' of a ship: a 1st rate had 90 guns or more, and so on, down the scale.

† The Gunfleet is a long bank on the northern side of the Thames estuary, off Brightlingsea and Clacton, at the mouth of the Blackwater estuary.

was an initial contest to 'gain the wind', in other words, to get to windward of the enemy so that with the wind astern, or at least in a favourable quarter, one side could bear down upon the other and yet retain some degree of manœuvrability. Thereafter a naval battle was largely a matter of each captain seeking out an enemy of comparable rank and size and, having inflicted as much damage as possible with one broadside after another, to 'lay alongside' and physically take over the ship with cutlass, pistol and musket in a hand-to-hand battle.

The broadside of, for example, a hundred-gun ship must have been appalling. Fifty great cannon, loaded with iron shot weighing something in the region of 24 pounds, fired simultaneously at a range of fifty yards or less, with the simple object of smashing a ship to pieces and sinking it, must, with their thunder, smoke and tremendous shock of impact, have had a terrifying effect. Yet, like the 'fatal discharge' of the infantryman's musket, they seem to have done much less damage than one might expect. On June 30, 1665, John Evelyn had dinner with Lord Sandwich in the *Prince*, a 90-gun ship with a crew of 700, where he was given an excellent meal of 'meat of all sorts' served on silver plates, and he was surprised 'to behold the good order, decency and plenty of all things in a ship so full of men', which, in a battle only some three weeks before, had 'received a hundred cannon shot in her body'.

Undoubtedly some ships did suffer terrible damage in the sea battles of this period but it is only rarely that one reads of a vessel being so badly holed that it sank. They blew up, certainly, and it is astonishing that this did not happen more often, for the fire risk would hardly be acceptable to modern underwriters. The ships were made entirely of wood, food was cooked over naked flames and light was provided by oil lanterns. In action, all weapons were fired by the smouldering 'match', from which, as James said when describing the infantry advance to the relief of Arras, the sparks flew in the wind. There was always plenty of gunpowder lying about, in kegs, barrels, bags or just loose, having been spilt during loading, and it could be ignited by any number of mishaps.

The best guns were made of brass which was comparatively easy to cast and, unlike ferrous castings that were liable to crack or split, expanded in the heat of firing. Non-ferrous metal must also have slightly reduced the risks of fire from sparks when an enemy shot came through a gun-port and struck a gun.

In battle, the theory was to manœuvre so as to be able to fire all the guns on one side in a devastating cannonade and then go about or wear round and fire all the other guns on the other side. In practice this was seldom possible, largely because ships were difficult to manage and needed

156

plenty of sea-room, and therefore all the guns were normally only in use when a ship was attacked from both sides. This, in the 'in-fighting' of those days, happened often enough.

There were several reasons why so little damage was done by these guns in relation to the noise, smoke and weight of shot. Ballistically they were inefficient and had a low muzzle velocity. When loading, a charge of powder, usually in a calico bag, was thrust down the barrel with a ram-rod and held tight by a leather wad. This was followed by the shot, held in by another wad. If there was no wad, and the ship rolled, the shot was liable to slide out and fall into the sea, causing much disappointment and frustration to the sweating gunners. It could not fit tight in the barrel because otherwise it would have been impossible to ram it down to the far end. Thus, when the powder in the touch-hole was ignited, and the main charge fired, a high percentage of the explosive force rushed out of the barrel round the shot—a waste of energy known as 'windage'. The force behind the shot threw it out of the piece relatively slowly—there was no difficulty in following the flight—and it sailed through the air as a heavy sphere of metal with little penetrative power. Such penetrative power as it did possess was further reduced by the yielding nature of the target, and the thickness of its planking; a ship would 'give' slightly under such an attack—unlike the stone walls of a besieged town—and the famous 'wooden walls' were made of massive oak timbers between nine and twelve inches thick. These timbers were strengthened internally by ribs and knees and the heavy cross-beams which supported the decks, so the effect of cannon shot striking these tough, resilient hulls, was much the same as that of a heavy hammer pounding a plank.

Since this fact was appreciated, a naval captain in action had two main objectives: to put his enemy's guns out of action by accurate broadsides aimed at the gun-ports—no easy task—and to bring him to a standstill by destroying his masts and rigging. He could then be boarded. To damage rigging, guns had to be fired at their maximum elevation, but this was extremely limited, particularly for guns in the lowest tier. Elevation could sometimes be increased by timing the firing to coincide with the rolling of the ship in a swell, but this was unreliable and the aiming of cannon was not an exact science.

As always, with any weapon using an explosive charge, there was the problem of recoil, and it was disastrous on a cramped gun-deck, often with less than five feet of headroom, if guns got out of control. They were secured by blocks and tackles attached to the carriage and either side of the gun-ports, with a system which, when the gun fired, allowed it to run back far enough for the crew to swab out the encrustation of burnt powder and reload, and then haul the gun back until it protruded through the open port. The rate of fire depended entirely on the skill and strength of the crew, and could be as much as two rounds a minute.

Apart from the guns of warships and the boarding parties there was another weapon which had long since proved its value: the fireship. Loaded with inflammable material it was sailed by a skeletal crew who took to the boats when the ship was set on course and the tiller lashed. Launched against enemy ships either in harbour or lying disabled in battle, the ship bore down on them in a terrifying pillar of flame setting fire to everything in its path, but they were used sparingly and usually as a last resort. A disabled ship could be repaired and treated as a prize, one that was gutted by fire, sank.

During April of 1665 James sat for long hours every day with his captains in the great cabin of the *Royal Charles*, while outside the windows seagulls planed and dived among the anchored fleet and water lapped against the carved and gilded sterns. He listened and studied and questioned and worked out with them how they were going to defeat the Dutch. He does not, as some have said, lay claim to having invented the 'line ahead' formation, only to having made a practice of discussing tactics, and all he says is that the battle he was soon to fight was 'the first wherein fighting in a Line and a regular Form of Battell was observed'.

It is indeed extremely unlikely that he invented the new formation. Round the table with him sat many experienced sailors, Prince Rupert, Lord Sandwich, William Penn—knighted after the battle—and many others. James co-ordinated the ideas and took the main decisions from which the plan of battle emerged; and this is perhaps one of the more important functions of a commander. He set an example which many great sailors, particularly Nelson, were to follow. He got to know, personally, the commanders who were to receive his orders in action. He was able to judge their characters and capabilities—as at least one instance will show—and they were able to form their opinions of him. His confidence and determination must have been reassuring. But, just as important, they got to know each other.

Here again is the effect of Turenne's teaching. James had been taught the value of building a 'team' in which everyone, so soon to be dependent on each other, knew what he could expect and what would be expected of him. Of all the great naval traditions, this is not the least and it is directly attributable to James.

He put to sea at last, at the beginning of May, with a fleet of ninety-eight ships. As usual, the force was divided into three squadrons, the Red, the White and the Blue. James, in *Royal Charles* with the Royal Standard and the arms of England at his maintop, led the Squadron of the Red, and his Vice-Admiral was Sir John Lawson. Prince Rupert, Vice-Admiral of the Fleet, flying the Union Flag, led the Squadron of the White with Sir Christopher Minns as his Vice-Admiral, and the Earl of Sandwich, Rear-Admiral of the Fleet, was Admiral of the Blue.

There was no sign of the Dutch. James made for the coast of Holland and found the whole enemy fleet at anchor in Texel harbour. His appearance caused intense alarm and the English fleet saw a line of beacons fired along the coast, warning the country of invasion. Hoping to draw the enemy out to sea he stood off ten leagues, but there was no pursuit. Rather by accident a fleet of ten chartered Bordeaux merchantmen, carrying Dutch cargoes and escorted by two Dutch warships, came within his reach, and despite fog and worsening weather the merchant ships were captured. A few days later, still hoping the Dutch would appear, several of his ships were dismasted in a gale and, in need of fresh water and repairs, he took the fleet back to the Gunfleet.

At the end of May he again ordered the fleet to sea and almost immediately the wind swung into the east and, even making full use of the tide, the ships had difficulty in clearing the sands in the estuary. James knew that the change of wind would bring out the Dutch and he made for Southwold Bay, south of Lowestoft on the Suffolk coast. He dropped anchor there on the morning of June 1 and at about one o'clock in the afternoon the Dutch fleet came up to windward of him. Commanded by Admiral Opdam, a man of what James calls 'quality' and great personal courage, the enemy had 113 warships of all rates, divided into seven squadrons, and with them were eleven fireships and seven yachts. The Dutch flag officers were Cornelius Evertz, his son John Evertz, Stillingwert, Tromp—the famous Tromp's son—Schram and Cortenaer.

The English fleet got under way at once but could not take up the agreed battle stations because some of the 1st and 2nd rates had not returned from intercepting a large fleet of colliers, which had passed by *en route* from Newcastle to London, to make up their complement of men. Fortunately the Dutch held off and showed no signs of attacking. At dusk the easterly wind dropped and both fleets began manoeuvring to get to windward of each other—to 'win the wind'. In the morning the Dutch had disappeared and they were not sighted until ten in the morning. James, with a fresh gale at his stern, then stood towards them with thirty of his fastest ships and kept two leagues away until he was joined by the rest of his fleet. Sorting out his order of battle he moved in and by sunset the two fleets were only a few miles apart. They were now just off Lowestoft; the sea was calm and there was hardly any wind all night.

In the darkness of two o'clock in the morning James was told matches were being lit on the enemy ships and they were preparing for battle. At first light the wind began to blow from the south-west, and James 'with great care and labour made shift to gain it'. The Squadron of the White formed the Van, with Sir Christopher Minns in the leading ship, and he fired the first shot. The Dutch, also in line ahead, were led by three flag-ships commanded by Tromp, Cortenaer and Stillingwert.

The battle began at three in the grey light of the June morning, some forty minutes before sunrise. The two fleets opened fire, and when the Dutch Van was opposite the English Rear James ordered the signal to be made for the whole fleet to go about; but the sailor sent up the masthead took so long to break out the signal flag that Minns, forced to use his own initiative, went about, and as ship after ship followed suit James cancelled the signal because it would have caused chaos. Even so, it took six hours to get things sorted out—an indication of the unhandiness of Stuart ships —but, as soon as he could, James signalled for the whole fleet to go about simultaneously and this brought both fleets together, close hauled on the starboard tack.

In these two 'passes' neither fleet did much damage to the other, al-though the 50-gun *Charity*, captured from the Dutch in Cromwell's time, which had been escorting the colliers and was a slow sailer, was unable to weather the Dutch and was retaken—but not without a fight in which her captain, Dickenson, and half his crew were killed as he tried to break through the Dutch line.

The problem now was to win the wind—the Dutch to gain it and the English to keep it—and during the manœuvring the English fleet changed its order because James in *Royal Charles* moved faster than Sandwich in *Prince*. 'The Red had the Van, the Blue the Battle and the White the Rear.' Then James, seeing that Sir John Lawson in *Royal Oak* 'had got the length of the headmost of the Dutch', signalled him to bear in towards the enemy, and the whole line followed.

The close engagement began at ten o'clock, in ideal conditions. The sea was calm, the wind steady in the south-west, not a cloud in the sky and no sign of any change in wind or weather—a perfect June day. James bore down on the rival commander-in-chief, Opdam, and the two ships opened a furious fire on each other and went on shooting for no less than four hours, until the Dutch began to give way. Shortly afterwards, Lawson in *Royal Oak*, 'one of the bravest seamen of his time', was hit in the knee by a cannon ball, a terrible wound from which he soon died, but not before he had sent off a boat to tell James what had happened. James ordered Captain Jordan, commanding *Saint George*, to take over Lawson's ship and command of his Division, but when Jordan went aboard *Royal Oak* he found her so badly damaged that she had to be taken out of the fight for immediate repairs.

Unfortunately, acting strictly in accordance with 'Fighting Instructions' as then framed, the whole Division 'lay by to look after their Flag', and James, now in the Van with only four or five of his Division's ships ahead of him—led by Sir Thomas Allen in *Plymouth*, found himself very much exposed. At this moment three Dutch men-of-war away to windward, which had been looking for an opportunity to rejoin the Dutch line, suddenly made towards it; one being 'a great ship of 80 guns'. On the way to the head of the Dutch fleet Cornelius Evertz, 'a mettled man', who was commanding the big ship, decided to run *Plymouth* down and sink her. Sir Thomas Allen, reading Evertz's intention from the way he handled his ship, hove to and Evertz missed him, but only just, for their yardarms touched in passing and both ships poured a broadside into each other. Evertz sheered off with the other two vessels and rejoined his fleet, and Allen remained at the head of the English Van until the damage he had suffered forced him to pull out of the line. Two other ships, *Fountain* and *Mary*, had to do the same for the same reason.

As these three ships were turning away, a 2nd rate called *Old James* sprang her luff (developed a leak in her bows where the timbers begin to curve in towards the stem) and went out of the line too. On board James's flagship Sir Allen Apsley, a great friend of the Earl of Marlborough who commanded *Old James*, not seeing how badly damaged she was, turned to James and said how sorry he was to see his old comrade do such a thing. James, who knew the men he commanded, said he was sure the Earl had been killed. He was right. Both the Earl and his nephew the Earl of Portland, a volunteer on his uncle's ship, had indeed been killed and now James had only the 50-gun *Happy Return*, commanded by Captain Lambert,* ahead of him, so that 'the enemy had the more leisure to ply his Royall Highness'. And ply him they did.

Within a few minutes Charles Berkeley (now Earl of Falmouth), Lord Muskerry and Richard Boyle, a younger son of the Earl of Burlington, all standing beside James on the quarterdeck of *Royal Charles*, were killed by one cannon shot, and James, appalled and deeply distressed, was splashed with their blood.

Charles Berkeley had been James's intimate friend for years, Captain of his Guards and his close companion in France and Flanders when they had campaigned together first for Turenne and then Don Juan. Berkeley

---

* Who had risen far since the day he took the tiles off the roof of the ale house Venner was defending.

repaid the real affection that both Charles and James had for him by being both devoted and entirely trustworthy; 'having never made a false step to either of them'. When he died, being almost penniless, he left nothing to his wife and daughter. Needless to say, James made proper provision for the widow, but he was more deeply affected by this loss than by any other during his lifetime.

Lord Muskerry, one of James's Gentlemen of the Bedchamber, was another old friend who had fought beside him in France and at Dunkirk. Young Richard Boyle was a volunteer on James's personal staff, and it was the first time he had been in action.

At about two in the afternoon it became clear that the Dutch were getting the worst of the battle: the fire of Opdam's ship had slackened to two or three guns at a time instead of broadsides, and this gave James an opportunity to take stock, 'waiting till the great smoak had cleared a little'. He could then see that *Royal Oak*, *Mary* and *Plymouth* had tidied themselves up and come back into the battle ahead of him, and *Royal Catherine* and *Swiftsure* were now astern. These reinforcements—what he describes as a 'seasonable Rejoyning'—alarmed the Dutch. Those astern of Opdam began to move away, though Opdam himself and those ahead of him still held up into the wind. Reassured, James who was now within musket shot of Opdam resolved to try something he had seen Turenne do with musketry fire. He ordered his Master Gunner to fire all the guns on the side facing Opdam but in succession, and to lay each gun himself, beginning with those on the lower tier.

At the third shot Opdam's ship blew up, and the explosion so disheartened his fleet that it turned and fled, leaving behind only the *Orange* of 84 guns. Her captain, a Scot called Sebastian Seaton whom James says was 'a lusty, proper man', stood on his poop waving a two-handed sword, clearly determined to lay his ship alongside *Royal Charles* and board her. But *Mary* and *Royal Catherine* raked him with their guns, setting *Orange* on fire. He and all the survivors on his ship were taken off, and he subsequently admitted that he had wished to distinguish himself either by boarding James's ship or being taken by him. He died of wounds a day or so later.

James set off in pursuit of the fleeing, battered Dutch, and half an hour later he destroyed four tangled enemy ships, fallen foul of each other, with one of his fireships. The sea was full of enemy sailors who were rescued by English ships. The chase continued for the rest of the day and into the night; several more ships were captured but twelve of the Zealand Squadron under John Evertz, making for the Texel, managed to escape because of a curious incident during the night.

162

At dusk James ordered the captain of the *Norwich* to carry lights and keep just ahead of him during the night, closing right up on the Dutch. Remaining on deck until it was too dark to see, James then went down to his cabin to rest. It had been a long, exhausting day—he had been on deck since two in the morning—and he was now eager to turn a resounding victory into what Nelson would have called a 'conquest'. Coming on deck again to 'reinforce his orders' he returned to his cabin at eleven p.m. and lay down on a quilt, fully clothed to be ready for immediate action.

While he was asleep a man called Henry Brounker, a Groom of the Bedchamber, tried to persuade Captain Cox, Master of the ship, to shorten sail so as not to endanger James by running into the enemy squadron in the darkness. He pointed out that at dawn they might be attacked by fireships or find themselves surrounded by the enemy, and he reminded Cox that James was the Heir Apparent and the King's only brother. Cox, very rightly, told him to go away. James had left perfectly clear orders before he went below. Brounker then addressed the same remarks to Captain Harman, the First Lieutenant, who was an old hand with whom he got nowhere, but he made no approach to Vice-Admiral William Penn who was the captain of the ship. Perhaps Penn, having handed over to Cox, was also asleep below.

Brounker then went below himself, hung about for a bit and then came up to Harman and told him James had given orders to shorten sail. Captain Harman could not believe that a man in Brounker's position would tell a deliberate and dangerous lie, and took in sail. In normal circumstances he might well have been suspicious but after such a day it is more than likely he was tired out and in no mood to argue. At first light, when the enemy could be seen well ahead, the sail taken in during the night was hoisted again and so when James came on deck all he saw was that the enemy had gained about half a league on him. He chased them right into the Texel and not until they were safe in their own harbour did he stand out to sea again.

It was now June 4. James led his fleet back to the Buoy of the Nore to refit and make ready for sea again. Unknown to him, Brounker had robbed him of his conquest. 'Came news of his highness's victory,' wrote Evelyn, 'which indeed might have been a complete one, and at once ended the war, had it been pursued, but the cowardice of some, or treachery, or both, frustrated that.'

When James did eventually find out about Brounker he wanted him to be tried by court martial, but being a member of the House of Commons he claimed privilege of Parliament. He was however expelled from the House and from James's household and escaped to the continent before any other action could be taken. He was a notorious character with a bad reputation and it seems probable that fears for his own safety made him take the grave risk of doing what he did; but there were stories that he was in the pay of the Dutch. It was also rumoured that James's wife had given strict orders to all her husband's personal staff that their first duty was to make sure he came back alive, and Brounker was merely obeying her instructions. This seems most unlikely, for though she was able to exercise considerable authority over James himself it did not extend to his staff.

Nevertheless, despite the lost opportunity on the second day of the battle, the first day had been a complete success. The Dutch had lost twenty warships, 'the least of which was 40 guns', and of these, eight were destroyed by fire and the remainder brought in as prizes. 4,000 prisoners had been taken and James estimated that Dutch casualties, in all, amounted to some 10,000 men. The figure was certainly between five and six thousand. Opdam, Cortenaer, Schram and Stillingwert had all been killed.

On the English side, casualties in killed and wounded amounted to about 900. The only ship lost had been the *Charity*, before the real battle started.

While anchored off the Nore James kept his scouts out, as Turenne had always done, and frigates patrolled continuously right up to the Texel, to give instant warning of enemy moves. One of these patrols provides another example of James's clemency, for one frigate captain, when his ship was approached by two larger Dutch warships, told his crew that the only thing to do was run for it. They disagreed, locked him up and attacked, capturing one of the enemy and driving off the other. The court martial ignored the mutiny, found the captain guilty of cowardice in the face of the enemy and sentenced him to death. As commander-in-chief, instead of confirming the sentence James sent for the captain, pardoned him but gave him a musket telling him that since he was unable to perform the duties of a captain he must now be a soldier and serve in the ranks.

Having spent several days supervising the refitting of his fleet James went off with Rupert to report to Charles, leaving Sandwich in command. He was welcomed as a hero.

'I waited on his Royal Highness,' says Evelyn, 'now come triumphant from the fleet, gotten into repair.'

James had commanded the French and the Spanish armies, and he had been offered high command in Italy and Spain, but all this was over-shadowed by his victory at the head of the English fleet. From this opening phase in the Second Dutch War he gained much glory and enormous popularity.

SEVENTEEN

THE summer of 1665 was perhaps the zenith of James's popularity, personal happiness and achievement. For the last few years his steady support for his father-in-law, that cold autocrat who was now the target of attacks from all sides, and the much resented arrogance and extravagance of his wife, had done him a great deal of harm. Now, returning from the great battle, all animosity seemed to have vanished and he had the satisfaction of knowing that this sudden upward turn in his fortunes was largely the result of his own industry and leadership. But the glory, the admiration and the affection were all transient. From now on, the path of his life-story slopes downhill, sometimes only very gradually, sometimes even rising a little as it crosses a narrow crest, but the trend is downwards.

It has been said that so far as his leadership in the battle of Lowestoft was concerned, since he was too young to have been able to exercise effective command, he was merely extremely lucky in the flag-officers whose orders he claimed as his own. But it is impossible to believe that James, as Lord High Admiral on the quarterdeck of his flagship, really took no active part in directing operations. After all his experience in continental warfare, and possessing as he did the natural authority inherited from his father, it is probable that he asked seamen as experienced as Penn, Cox and Harman for advice if and when he needed it, but highly unlikely that he encouraged unsolicited suggestions on the action they felt he ought to take.

James was well aware that responsibility for victory or defeat rested on his shoulders alone. It was not in his nature to transfer that burden with the intention of only accepting it after the battle had been won. Far from being too young to command he was, at thirty-two, not only of an age to exercise his authority as Lord High Admiral but well-equipped to do so by his previous high military commands—the principles of war which he had learned from Turenne are the same at sea as they are on land—and his careful study of the techniques and details of naval warfare.

James was no fool, and he was extremely conscious of his royal position. He knew, because he had seen, what happened when incompetent commanders made a mess of things, and if he had thought that he might bring the royal house into disrepute, he would have let Rupert lead the fleet.

There is no doubt that his contemporaries were aware of the part he had played not only in winning a victory but in the mobilization of the fleet before it, and the death of his two old friends and the young volunteer as they stood beside him suddenly made everyone take note of the risks he ran. James had never shirked danger in battle*—he knew what effect a commander's personal example had on morale. While he held command he considered it to be his duty to 'remain where the service was hottest'. He enjoyed a good fight and he seems to have had no fear of death, perhaps because since he had emerged unscathed from so many battles, sieges and cavalry actions he had come to believe that what had happened to Charles Berkeley would not happen to him.

During the exile nobody was particularly concerned about the risks he took because for years there appeared to be no future at all for the House of Stuart. Now, five years after the Restoration, there were political considerations attached to his death in action which no one seems to have thought about before. The Queen had not produced an heir and though Charles appeared to keep extremely fit, taking exercise with his mistresses at night and going for long walks every morning at a speed which exhausted the few of his courtiers able to keep up with him, he was just as vulnerable as anyone else to smallpox, the plague and all the unexplained diseases: and in the summer of 1665 the plague was raging in London.

If anything happened to Charles, James would wear the crown, and if James had been killed in action the crown would go to his infant daughter Mary, born in April 1662 and now three years old. Charles knew very well that as things were, the monarchy could not withstand a strain such as that. Until the country was more united and republican ardours had cooled there must be no deliberate risk to the succession.

To James's dismay, at a General Council of flag-officers presided over by Charles himself on board *Royal Charles* on July 1, 'it was determined', as Evelyn says, 'that his Royal Highness should adventure himself no more this summer'.† James, deprived for reasons of his personal safety

* Evelyn says James told him that 'when we were in a fight his dog sought out absolutely the very securest place in all the vessel', but he does not say where this place was. Surely James must be one of the few Admirals ever to take a greyhound on active service.

† Evelyn attended this Council and 'came away late, having seen the most glorious fleet that ever spread sails'.

of the active command of this fleet he had helped to build, and in which he took so much pride, was very upset. He foresaw, rightly, that the ban would extend far beyond the summer and autumn operations of that year, but he was a monarchist: the succession must be secured, and he could not argue with the Council's decision.

Returning to London from the Buoy of the Nore, Charles and James were so alarmed by the rising death-rate of the plague* that Charles at once moved the court first to Hampton Court and then to Salisbury a few days later. The Duke of Albemarle with half the Foot Guards and a troop of Horse Guards stayed behind 'to keep things quiet in London'. From Salisbury Charles sent James up to York, ostensibly because there were strong rumours of a rising in the north by Cromwellians and republicans in league with the Dutch; but Charles may also have thought it wise to separate the King and his Heir in case both died of the plague. Soon after arriving in Salisbury the plague broke out there too and Charles moved to Oxford where both court and Parliament assembled.

Still enveloped in the glory of his naval victory James set off with his duchess on what was a most enjoyable holiday. Everyone turned out to see them go by. Sir George Savile—who became Viscount Halifax three years later—entertained them magnificently at his seat, Rufford Abbey, and at York the reception was both splendid and generous. The Mayor, a little long-winded in his appreciation of James's naval achievements, paid for the time he had taken up with a purse containing a hundred pounds in gold for each of his visitors, and with no public duties to perform, James as usual spent as much of his time as possible during the next seven weeks out in the open air. His main occupations were coursing and shooting, but he also began to teach one of his wife's young Maids of Honour to ride.

The girl's name was Arabella Churchill. She was seventeen years old and had joined the Duchess's household earlier that year. One afternoon she joined a large mounted party, led by James, to go greyhound-coursing, and the story is that at some stage or other her horse bolted and then threw her. James, perhaps feeling responsible for his pupil, galloped in pursuit, and in Lord Wolseley's words, 'gallantly dismounted to help her, and, struck by the grace and beauty of her figure as she lay half-unconscious on the grass before him, his susceptible heart took fire and ere-long she became his acknowledged mistress'—a charming, imaginative picture.

---

* The rate rose sharply from 1,000 a week in August to 10,000 in September and the total number of deaths in this last outbreak of the scourge was in the region of 100,000.

One person not in James's party was his wife. She apparently was coming along behind in her coach accompanied by a gentleman whom Burnet describes—without naming him—as 'a very graceful young man of quality that belonged to her court, whose services were so acceptable, that she was thought to look at him in a particular manner'. One cannot help feeling almost relieved that she was able to get a little of her own back. The young man was Henry Sidney, afterwards Earl of Romney, the brother of Algernon Sidney who was executed some years later for his alleged involvement in the Rye House Plot. Henry Sidney may well have been the Duchess of York's lover; James seems to have thought so because according to Burnet 'he put him out of his court with much precipitation' and from that time Anne began to lose the hold over her husband which she had maintained since her marriage.

Despite what has been said about James's mistresses, from her portrait Arabella appears satisfyingly sensual. Anthony Hamilton* says that although her face possessed no more than 'the ordinary feminine charms', she had a beautiful figure. But, no matter how she managed, either deliberately or unintentionally, to 'inflame' her riding instructor, and regardless of her looks, her role in history was not unimportant.

She was certainly largely responsible for arranging for her younger brother John to join James's household as a page after a plan to get him into the Badminton establishment of the Duke of Beaufort had fallen through, and it was James's patronage and personal interest that launched the future Duke of Marlborough on his spectacular career. John Churchill repaid his patron with treachery and deceit which have been a challenge to the ingenuity of his loyal biographers.

Arabella† remained James's mistress for some seven or eight years—when she was replaced by Catherine Sedley—but the date of the beginning of this relationship is not known. Her first child by James was Henrietta, born in 1670, but there may have been other children before her who died in infancy. Arabella certainly bore James four children. The first was subsequently married to Sir Henry Waldegrave; the second was James FitzJames,‡ the Duke of Berwick and a Marshal of France who fought brilliantly for Louis XIV in the War of the Spanish Succession and won the battle of Almanza in 1707. The third child was Henry FitzJames, born in 1673, created Duke of Albemarle by his father and made Grand Prior of France by Louis XIV. According to Wolseley he was 'a useless

* In his *Memoirs of the Life of the Count of Grammont*.
† Arabella married Colonel Charles Godfrey, who had been a Captain in the Guards with her brother John, in 1677. He died in 1715. She died in 1730 and was buried in the tomb of her brother George Churchill near the quire door in Westminster Abbey.
‡ Fitz indicates the bar sinister, as in 'Fitzroy', natural son of the King.

and debauched drunkard' who died in 1702. The last child was Arabella, born in 1674, who became a nun.

In producing all these healthy children Arabella proved how ill-founded were the accusations of all those enemies of James who claimed he was incapable of begetting one that would live. Their argument was that the excesses of his youth had really been the reason why six out of Anne Hyde's eight children had died in infancy. Burnet tells all sorts of stories to imply that James was either diseased or otherwise afflicted. Writing of his children by Anne Hyde he says 'they were born with ulcers, or they broke out upon them soon after: and all his sons died young and unhealthy'. Then he goes on to make his real point. 'This has, as far as anything that could not be brought in the way of proof, prevailed to create a suspicion that so healthy a child as the pretended Prince of Wales could neither be his, nor be born of any wife with whom he had lived long.'

Burnet was one of the faction who believed, or pretended to believe, the ridiculous story that the son of James's second wife, Mary of Modena, was brought to her bed in the notorious and non-existent bed-warmer. It was all nonsense, for James's children by Arabella Churchill were healthy enough, but there have been historians, far more recent than Burnet, who have developed this theme of 'excesses'. It has been suggested in all seriousness that James's great interest in copulation as a young man led in later life to a mental disorder made out to have been a blend of paranoia, schizophrenia, and no doubt a syndrome or two, which provides the complete explanation for his autocratic behaviour when he came to the throne. In other words, James's fondness for women when young led to insanity in middle age.

This allegation would be understandable if there was anything to suggest that James suffered from syphilis—which he certainly did not—but to claim that normal untainted intercourse, albeit frequent, can lead years later to paranoia is perhaps a little extravagant. James was not mad, but he has been accused of insanity because he was wont to regard explosive political issues as straightforward objectives which he attacked with abrasive determination.

*

In the middle of September Charles called his brother back to Oxford to attend a Parliamentary session. The sum of £1,256,347, according to James, was voted for continuing the war, and Parliament also voted a present of £120,000 to James 'in token of the great sense they had of his conduct and bravery in the late engagement'. It is unlikely that they would have given such an enormous sum to a mere figurehead. They also formally thanked Charles for refusing to let James expose himself to further danger at sea.

In November the number of deaths in London from the plague fell sharply but the court remained at Oxford until well into the new year, returning first to Hampton Court at the end of January 1666 when it was plunged in deep, formal mourning for the death of Anne of Austria, the French Queen Mother. Charles came back to Whitehall on February 2.

James returned to the Navy Office, where the loyal Samuel Pepys had remained on duty throughout the worst of the plague, and at once became immersed in all the problems of refitting the fleet. Much to the disappointment of the Earl of Sandwich, who had taken over command when James left the fleet at the Buoy of the Nore, Albemarle had been given command over his head, with the title of General at Sea. There was, unfortunately, considerable animosity between the two men—Albemarle had been making aspersions not only about the way in which Sandwich had disposed of certain prizes but about his personal courage—and bickering among the high command could only harm the navy, particularly at a time when the war had suddenly become more complicated. Having tried to prevent the Second Dutch War, Louis XIV had decided to intervene on the Dutch side.

In June a far greater battle than Lowestoft was fought by Prince Rupert and Albemarle against the Dutch. After putting to sea from the Buoy of the Nore the English fleet divided. Rupert went off to attack the French before they could join the Dutch, while Albemarle remained off the North Foreland on the Kent coast, where, in Rupert's absence, he was attacked by a superior force under de Ruyter. The Dutch had not only learned a lesson from Lowestoft and now carried heavier cannon but they had devised a new type of ammunition: chain shot. This consisted of two cannon balls joined together with a length of chain which, when fired from the same gun at maximum elevation, cut through sails and rigging like a scythe. As a weapon used against men on crowded decks it was murderous.

Albemarle and his fleet fought with desperate gallantry for two days. Burnet says that 'the English fleet was quite unrigged, and they were in no condition to work themselves off'. Fortunately Rupert, off the Isle of Wight, heard the thunder of the cannon and came back to restore the balance. Evelyn in his garden at Wootton at six o'clock on June 1, heard 'the great guns go thick off' and on June 3 'the guns were still roaring very fiercely'. On the fourth day Rupert and Albemarle after heavy losses withdrew to the Buoy of the Nore and the Dutch returned to their harbours.

On June 17 Evelyn 'beheld the sad spectacle, more than half that gallant bulwark of the kingdom miserably shattered, hardly a vessel entire but appearing rather so many wrecks and hulls, so cruelly had the Dutch mangled us'. Yet, after prodigious efforts by James, Pepys and the Navy Board, the English fleet, in no way daunted by the 'Four Days Fight', put to sea and on July 25, St. James's Day, won a victory.

Not until the Dutch had recovered from this battle and were again at sea did the French fleet join them, but by this time the City of London between the Tower and the Temple had been burned to the ground and Charles and his ministers had more to worry about than naval operations in the Channel. The Great Fire raged from September 2 until September 7, not only destroying a vast number of buildings but purging the last vestiges of the Great Plague. 'The King and the Duke,' says Burnet, 'were almost all the day long on horseback with the Guards, seeing to all that could be done, either for quenching the fire, or for carrying off persons and goods to the fields all about London.' 'It is not indeed imaginable,' wrote Evelyn, 'how extraordinary the vigilance and activity of the King and the Duke was; even labouring in person, and being present to command, order, reward or encourage workmen.'

Parliament, meeting soon after the Fire, was, as James says, 'in evil mood'. Everything seemed to be going wrong, and the Puritan element was convinced that the Plague and the Fire were reflections of the opinion of the Almighty on what was going on in Charles's court. The war, which James had so nearly won in the first engagement, now looked as if it would drag on for years. Swinging right round, the men who had been so insistent two years previously now refused to vote supplies for the war they had demanded. Clarendon, Lord Treasurer Southampton, Sir William Coventry and other ministers persuaded Charles to save money by laying up all the 1st and 2nd rates and, becoming defensive, keep in commission only the smaller vessels which could interfere with the enemy's trade.

James was appalled by this proposal and put forward as arguments against it the enormous boost to enemy morale if they were allowed to feel they had swept the English fleet from the seas, and the danger of giving them time and encouragement to refit with no threat of attack. He said that money saved on the fleet would in any case have to be spent on militia and other forces to guard the coasts, but what really upset him was the thought of 'permitting the Dutch to ride Masters of the Seas just under our noses'. He was overruled. A programme of heavy retrenchment began and moves were made towards negotiating for peace. The Dutch, who were gaining nothing from the war, shared the feelings of the English

Parliament, and, to encourage definite action towards peace, in June 1667 a Dutch fleet under de Ruyter sailed without opposition into the Thames, captured Sheerness, broke through the chain at Upnor and went up the Medway to Chatham.

Here they burned seven warships, including *London*, *Royal Oak* and *Old James*, and towed away *Royal Charles*, James's flagship at Lowestoft. Albemarle, not wanting to outlive this national dishonour, stood in the open on the quay at Chatham amid the flight of Dutch cannon shot when they bombarded the dockyard, but his time had not come. Having blockaded the Thames, almost unmolested, for four weeks, the Dutch sailed away, and the Peace of Breda was proclaimed in London on August 24.

James had done all he could to warn the Privy Council against adopting defensive measures, and the result was far worse than he had ever imagined. At the time, the blame was laid squarely where it belonged, on those who counselled defence and those who would not vote the means to fight the war, but James has since been blamed for failing to ensure that the defences at Upnor were adequate. They were not his responsibility and there was no money for such things anyway, so this seems a little unfair.

The three great national disasters, the Plague, the Fire* and the Dutch raid in the Medway, had a profound effect on politics in England for the next twenty years, and on James personally. James himself felt that his victory at Lowestoft was the start of the long chain of events which led to the loss of his throne—he thought that thereafter the Dutch were determined on revenge, and there may have been something in this—but if this was the beginning, the triple calamities were the next step.

Apart from the fact that many people regarded them as a threefold revelation of the wrath of God, they also claimed to see behind them the dread hand of 'Popery'. The Fire, though blatantly caused by an accident, was said to be the work of 'Papists', and French Papists at that. There were all sorts of stories of Papists throwing incendiary bombs—or their equivalent—into houses, and French and English Catholics were roughly handled by the mob. The 'Popery' behind the Dutch raid was equally far-fetched, for though Louis XIV had temporarily allied himself with the Dutch he contributed nothing whatsoever to their cause, either by land or at sea; but, because he was the Catholic head of a Catholic power, he

---

* When the Fire burnt out the Plague which annually for generations had, in Trevelyan's words, 'relieved Society of its proletariat', the increasing number of the poor in London made them a potent force. This was methodically employed by Shaftesbury at the time of the Popish Plot to bring about a second 'Rebellion'. He was wont to refer to the mob as his 'brisk boys'. Pym, at the time of Strafford's impeachment, had used the mob as a political weapon—no doubt this was what gave Shaftesbury the idea.

was looked upon as a far more dangerous enemy than the Dutch. Therefore, in the limited reasoning and twisted logic of the times, he must have been the real instigator of the raid.

The Papist was an enemy. The hideous atrocities of the Irish Rebellion of 1641 had not been forgotten. Both sides had been equally barbaric but in the wave of feeling against the Catholic Queen Henrietta Maria more publicity had been given to the revenge of Catholic Irishmen on the Protestant landowners and settlers.

In short, the prejudice against Catholics, which was bad enough already, was enormously increased by the Plague, the Fire and the Raid, and when James became a Catholic he automatically and inevitably provided a focal point for that prejudice. In 1667 there was already a great deal of public uneasiness about James's religion—though allowance must be made for contemporary historians such as Burnet writing with hindsight.

It was in 1667 that the enemies of James's father-in-law finally achieved his downfall. Despite his unswerving loyalty to the crown during the exile, and his great gifts, Clarendon had succeeded in making himself extremely unpopular, even with Charles. For this he had only himself to blame. Possessing an infinitely quicker mind and far greater intelligence than most of his contemporaries, and being incapable of suffering a fool gladly, he never bothered to conceal his impatience and sometimes his contempt. He made mistakes; the mob broke his windows when the Dutch came up the Medway, and scrawled:

> Three sights to be seen,
> Dunkirk, Tangier and a barren Queen

on his door. He had antagonized Charles over the ill-fated Declaration of Indulgence, for when this was proposed in the House of Lords it was vehemently opposed by Clarendon and the Bishops and 'others of the zealous Church of England men'.

James, no doubt under some pressure at home, had always supported Clarendon, even to the extent of incurring Charles's acute displeasure and creating an open rift at the time of his dismissal. It was left to James to break the news to Clarendon that he was required to 'deliver up the Seal', but just after this James went down with a mild attack of smallpox and could not do all he wanted to vindicate his father-in-law publicly. Clarendon was extremely grateful for all James's sympathy and help at a time when nearly all his other friends had deserted him, but James could not save him. To avoid impeachment he fled to France in November 1667 and was formally banished in April 1668. Yet, when no longer young and when a lesser man would have been broken by the distress and dislocation of his fall, flight and exile, he began and completed his great literary achievement, his *History of the Rebellion*.

Seven years later, on August 29, 1674, weakened by violent attacks of pain from gout and feeling a premonition of death, he wrote a pathetic appeal to Charles asking if he might be allowed to return to die among his children. His petition was not granted and he died at Rouen, with his eldest son Lord Cornbury beside him, on December 9 of the same year. He was sixty-five.

James was very angry with the members of his own household who had been open enemies of his father-in-law. His secretary, Sir William Coventry, was dismissed—to be replaced by Matthew Wren, later killed at sea on James's flagship in 1672—and he even sent away that old and faithful friend Colonel Sir John Werden who had ridden with him through the gateway of the palace of Saint-Germain on that April morning so long ago when James, a boy of eighteen, had started off to join the army of Turenne. But the ties of friendship were strong, the estrangement was not permanent and the Colonel returned to be James's private secretary.

The departure of Clarendon, apparently the result of popular demand, somewhat paradoxically placed Charles in a strong position: having apparently bowed to the wishes of Parliament and people he was now able to choose his own ministers without interference. Among them were Henry Bennet, returned from his diplomatic post in Madrid and created Lord Arlington, and Buckingham. Between James and Arlington there had long been deep animosity, and James had no time at all for the dissolute and treacherous Buckingham, 'full of flashy witt and nothing of steady or solid in him'.

The sustained opposition to James in court circles which led, ten years later, to the movement to exclude him from the succession, was originated by these two and dates from this time. Things were made much easier for them by Charles's resentment over James's support of Clarendon, for James was virtually isolated from the court and his enemies were encouraged to attack him. An example of this isolation which gave James great distress was the success of the Buckingham clique in arranging with Charles for Sir Thomas Osborne and Sir Thomas Littleton to be appointed Treasurers of the Navy without any reference to James who was head of the department. The clique was also successful in blocking James's nominee for promotion to Commissioner of the Navy, Sir Jeremy Smith, 'a man of long experience' as James says, who had commanded *Mary* at Lowestoft.

These calculated slights are an interesting sidelight on Charles's character. Clarendon, with characteristic penetration, once wrote that

Charles 'had in truth a just affection for the Duke and confidence in him, without thinking better of his natural parts than he thought there was cause for; and yet, which made it the more wondered at, he did very often depart in matters of the highest moment from his own judgement to comply with his brother'. Charles for the sake of peace may well have yielded to James's insistence often enough, and there must at times have been a good deal of friction. Perhaps Charles's attitude after the business over Clarendon was the outcome of an accumulation of petty irritations, and having chosen to slight his brother to the advantage of his enemies, a reconciliation may have been made more difficult by some misgivings felt by Charles when he realized he was in fact treating his most loyal subject with unjustified harshness.

James's isolation lasted for nearly two years and during that time Arlington and Buckingham set in motion their two-pronged attack against him. On the one hand was a design to persuade Charles to divorce Catherine of Braganza and marry someone who would give him an heir, and on the other was the plan to have James, Duke of Monmouth, Charles's natural son by that 'brown, beautiful, bold but insipid creature' Lucy Walters,* declared legitimate. The motive behind this attack was purely personal. Both men were frightened of James and they were afraid that if he ever succeeded to the throne he would stop at nothing to gain his revenge.

The fact that Charles could not be moved on either point in no way discouraged the plotters. He had ill-treated his poor wife often enough but he was not prepared to inflict upon her so final an insult and disgrace. As far as his son Monmouth was concerned, he was extremely fond of him and he showed extraordinary magnanimity in forgiving his pretensions and trusting him beyond sensible limits. But he knew, and never hesitated to affirm, that the boy was a bastard. To a Stuart King, even one so indolent as Charles, imbued with the Divine Right and Royal Prerogative, it was quite impossible that anyone with so insuperable a disadvantage could ever sit on the throne of England.

It was unfortunate that at this time, when his enemies were plotting against him for personal reasons, James should have played into their hands by giving them cause to raise a private vendetta to the level of a national issue.

* Lucy Walters—or Mrs. Barlow—was the daughter of Richard Walters Esq. of Haverfordwest. Evelyn first met her on August 18, 1649—when Charles was nineteen —at Saint-Germain. She was sitting in a coach with Lord Wilmot, the soldier who accompanied Charles on his adventures after the battle of Worcester. She bore Charles two children, James and Mary. Mary married a William Scarsfield of Ireland and, after his death, William Fanshawe. In France her son James joined the household of Lord Crofts and was known as Mr. Crofts.

EIGHTEEN

LOOKING back across three hundred years it is very difficult to imagine or assess the real attitude towards Roman Catholicism in James's time. It is extraordinary that a nation perfectly well aware that the proportion of Catholics was less than one in a hundred could ever have become reduced to the apparent state of hysterical terror which gave credence to the palpable inventions of the Popish Plot. That a genuine dislike, hatred or fear—possibly a combination of all three in varying strengths—did exist is an indisputable fact, and there were two reasons for it. One rested on events since the Reformation and the other was propaganda.

In the fifteenth century the English people had long regarded themselves as quite separate from the rest of Europe: thus 'interference' by the Pope in what they—or perhaps more accurately, their leaders—considered to be their own domestic, as opposed to spiritual, affairs, was bound to be resented. With one exception the Popes had always been foreigners, and this did not help. There were some laymen who reasoned that since Jesus Christ had never possessed nor sought temporal power, why then should a man who was only His elected representative not only claim but exercise it? Futhermore, all the Pope's representatives had followed his example until the Church as an institution not only kept a tight grip on men's minds with the promise of a holocaust for heretics in the hereafter, but possessed vast lands and great wealth. The fact that the great abbeys and other religious foundations provided social security benefits on a very large scale was so awkward that the reformers could only ignore it.

The power—in its fullest sense—of the Roman Catholic Church was resented by men who were jealous of it, but the isolation created by twenty miles of sea water was a primary factor in the waning of papal influence. The Church of England was established—with, initially, very few differences of dogma or practice—and the power of the Church in England declined rapidly and has never recovered.

Except for those to whom the charity of the monasteries meant the difference between life and death, the majority of the people more or less agreed that it was a far more tidy and convenient arrangement—which above all preserved their independence—to owe spiritual allegiance to their own king who was on the spot, rather than to someone who lived far off in Rome and never came near them.

Queen Mary's disastrous marriage with His Catholic Majesty Philip II of Spain, and the smoke rising from burning heretics in Smithfields, were nasty shocks to her people who began to realize that differences of religious opinion could be fatal. The appearance of the Armada in the reign of her half-sister awoke men to the fact that all this was much more—or could be made much more—than a religious quarrel. This was aggression wrapped up in ideology, and before they knew where they were they would find themselves acting as a target for a Catholic crusade. Thus 'Popery' came to mean two separate but closely related things: enforced acceptance of religious dogma, practices and discipline imposed by a distant authority they were not prepared to acknowledge, and the positive threat of invasion by Catholic troops who would, by force, 'turn the country to Rome'. If this happened, the fires in Smithfields would hardly ever go out. The people were aware that given the right conditions there could be an invasion, and they also realized that if their leaders inclined to Popery a religious 'revolution'—with or without assistance from Catholic countries —could be brought about from within, and ever since the Irish Rebellion, Popery was indissolubly associated with violence.

The Anglican clergy had not enjoyed the rule of Cromwell and his Puritans. The career structure of the Church, with its possibility of promotion to the rank of Bishop—perhaps even Archbishop, had been broken up and they found themselves persecuted and denigrated. On its restoration in 1661 the Anglican Church, supported in strength by the Cavalier Parliament, did its best to ensure that this traumatic experience was never repeated. Enforcement of the Clarendon Code changed the direction of persecution but it was aimed at all those who did not conform to the Established Church and not at Catholics in particular. Of all the religions in Europe Catholicism was by far the most powerful and it was backed by large armies of the Catholic states. With its underlying threat of violence and invasion, Catholicism was regarded as the real threat to the Anglican Church and the Anglican clergy did not hesitate to say so.

In the days when few could read but everyone could hear what the parish priest said in his pulpit, the churches were the main medium of mass communication, and the word of the preacher carried weight. It was easy to inflame the minds of a congregation with anti-Catholic propaganda—particularly since the persecuted Catholics could not answer back—and the theme was fear: the most potent persuader of all. Many priests left their congregations in no doubt about what would happen to them if the 'Papists' had their way because they felt, with justification, that the most effective safeguard against Catholicism was a people united in fear of it. Thus events within living memory, combined with propaganda, created a real fear, albeit at the back of men's minds, that Catholicism would, and might at any time, bring about a massacre as bad as, if not worse than, anything in Ireland. It was against this background that James made up his mind to be, in his own words, 'reconcil'd to Rome', and he failed completely to understand the strength and determination of the Protestant forces opposed to him.

There has been much speculation on the reasons why James took this step which he must have known would make life extremely difficult for himself and for Charles. He had long been 'exposed to Catholic influence' in France: he had been extremely impressed by the piety of Turenne's troops who made a practice of taking the Sacrament and making their confession before going into action, and it is more than likely that when Turenne himself became a Catholic—and he had been a strong Calvinist who had declined the highest post in France on the grounds of religion—James began to think about it seriously. Hitherto, he had not apparently been particularly interested in the subject.

On the reasons for his decision the consensus of opinion seems to be that since he was so enthusiastic a monarchist, and since, like his father, he held that the first duty of a subject was to obey his sovereign unquestioningly in all matters, it was only logical that he should turn to Catholicism. This was the only faith compatible with such obedience because it acknowledged the infallibility of its temporal head, the Pope. Thus, since Protestantism encouraged some freedom of thought and argument, it was, to him, the religion of rebels and republicans. Perhaps there is some truth in this—certainly he must have noticed that as a general rule the Cavaliers who fought for his father were Catholics while republicans were usually Protestants. But it could have been that he found Catholicism, with its emphasis on faith and discipline, its majestic ritual and comforting assurance, was more satisfying and answered his questions more fully than the creed of the Anglican Church—for which his father had died.

He said, some years later, in a long letter written in Edinburgh, that his first doubts about the Protestant faith had arisen from reading the tract of a learned bishop who sought to clear the Anglican Church of the guilt of schism. It had been the first time James had ever read anything like this and it had completely the opposite effect to the one intended by the bishop. He began to investigate the whole subject, reading such works as

Dr. Heylin's *History of the Reformation* and Hooker's *Ecclesiastical Policy.*
As a result he became convinced that neither the Church of England nor
Calvin nor any of the reformers 'had the power to do what they did'.

He always denied that any attempt had been made to persuade him to
change his religion when he was in France. He tells a story of a meeting
with a nun who spoke to him on the subject but when he said he was too
young to argue with her she told him to keep an open mind and pray for
guidance.

No one can possibly know what went on in James's mind and to make
any assumption at all is to run the risk of treating surmise as fact and using
it to substantiate a theory. The only facts not in dispute are that James,
for reasons known only to himself, changed his religion, and having done
so remained steadfastly faithful to it in conditions which give the impression that his conversion was genuine and deeply felt.

Rumours about the leanings of both brothers towards Catholicism had
been current for years, but whereas James underwent a genuine conversion from which nothing moved him it is not possible to judge the depths
of Charles's feelings. 'Attached to no system of religion,' says Macpherson,
'he seemed favourable to them all.' But whatever he may have felt about
Catholicism he had 'too much good sense to throw away by wantonness
and folly what fortune had unexpectedly bestowed'; and so it is very difficult
to imagine what was really in his mind when he made his extraordinary
announcement at a meeting in James's quarters in Whitehall on January
25, 1669—by an odd coincidence, the day of the conversion of St. Paul.

Round the table with him sat his brother, Lord Arundel of Wardour
who was a Catholic, Sir Thomas Clifford who soon afterwards became
one, and Henry Bennet, Lord Arlington, then Secretary of State, who
died a Catholic but was not at that time prepared to prejudice his career
by any public statement. Charles announced that in principle 'he adhered
to the Church of Rome' and that the object of the meeting was to decide
how best to 'settle the Catholic religion in England'. He also asked for
advice on how and when to make his conversion known.

It soon became perfectly clear that there could be no question of any
outward and visible sign of a change of religion. The fiasco of the Declaration of Indulgence seven years before had shown how strongly the tide of
opinion ran against Catholicism, and Charles would have had good reason
to fear another rebellion which would 'send him again on his travels'. But
it was at that meeting that the Grand Design—to convert the country to
Rome—was first mentioned, and this led to the Treaty of Dover.*

* In brief, the terms of the secret treaty were that England and France would unite
to defeat and divide Holland between them, and that Louis would provide money and,

It is very hard to believe that a man so astute as Charles could ever have imagined that a country in which 'Popery' was anathema to ninety-nine per cent of the population would ever be persuaded, by force or example or any other means, to accept Roman Catholicism as the Established Church. His motive in negotiating this infamous treaty may have been little more than his perpetual need for money which he felt his cousin Louis, under certain conditions, would supply. But no matter what may have been in Charles's mind, it has been said that his statement at the meeting on January 25, and the formulation of the Grand Design, gave James his mission in life.

There is no doubt at all that James at times was impetuous; he was sometimes misguided and often ill advised. He had what were regarded as old-fashioned and unworkable ideas about Divine Right, Royal Prerogative and Absolute Rule, and some of his actions—as they have been reported—appear to justify the statement that he was determined to press forward with the Grand Design. But there is another point of view. If Charles knew that wholesale conversion of the people was impossible, James knew it too. Furthermore, as a soldier he had gained by experience an ability to gauge what was and what was not feasible. He did not deliberately undertake what he knew to be impossible.

It is perfectly true that he had a mission, and he stated it clearly on several occasions. His concept of Christianity was that all men should be free to worship God as they thought fit, and that there should be complete 'Freedom of Conscience' and toleration for all beliefs. 'Our blessed Saviour whipped people out of the temple,' he wrote, 'but I never heard He commanded any should be forced into it. Tis by gentleness, instruction and good example, people are gained, and not frightened into it, and I make no doubt if once Liberty of Conscience be well fixed, many conversions will ensue, which is a truth too many of the Protestants are persuaded of.'

In this way he was generations ahead of his time. The Established Church of England, slowly recovering from its horrid experiences under Cromwell, was not going to allow anyone, least of all a Catholic prince or king, to encroach on its preserves or set up a rival establishment. James realized too late that in pursuing his policy of toleration he was in fact removing from the Established Church the weapon of persecution: the means by which it held on to its position in the face of 'Dissent'. If

if necessary, troops to enable Charles to declare his conversion to Catholicism and establish the Church of Rome in England. Signed in May 1670, the secret treaty was covered by the overt Treaty of Dover in the following year, made for the benefit of Protestant ministers. In it there was no mention of Catholicism.

dissenters could not be persecuted they might rise again in strength and throw the Anglican Church once more into the wilderness. Toleration must be resisted; and the Established Church was determined to resist it to the death.

Yet in fact all the religious fervour, indignation and opposition James allegedly aroused was, as he said himself, only a cloak for something quite different. The religious issue was seized on and blown up out of all proportion by those who wished to destroy the Stuart monarchy. Charles realized this after he had been on the throne for fifteen years, and it was not until he suddenly woke up to the very real danger threatening him personally that he began to exert his political genius. His loyal support of his Catholic brother was not inspired by his affection for James but by the knowledge that the exclusion of the rightful heir would destroy him. The one subject on which Charles was immovable was the succession, and the enemy of the monarchy whose target was the succession was the brilliant, twisted, utterly unscrupulous politician Lord Shaftesbury, so devious and crafty in duplicity that Charles and James nicknamed him 'Little Sincerity'.

James had two great enemies. One was Shaftesbury who regarded him as the first of his objectives in his campaign against the monarchy, and the other was William of Orange. William, that sour silent man, forcing his way remorselessly up the steep path of his ambition, was hailed in Europe as the only man who stood between the Protestant faith and the all-engulfing Catholic power of Louis XIV. He inspired no affection but he possessed a cold, hard authority which, supported by the fear of 'Popery', enabled him to establish himself as the Protestant Champion.

Burnet, who thought it best to leave England towards the end of Charles's reign, came back with William at the time of the revolution. He says of William that 'he had no vice but of one sort, in which he was very cautious and secret', and contemporary poets, who wisely forgot to sign their work, indicate that they knew what the secret was. One poem—if one can call it that—purporting to be written by a frustrated courtesan, bewails the lack of any requirement for her talents at William's court. But he appears to have been attached to his mistress, Elizabeth Villiers, the cousin of Charles's friend Barbara. In his own way, William was a great man, and great men have always had their denigrators.

William was clever, ruthless and far-sighted. He planned ahead, thinking out his moves and advancing with caution. England was a Protestant country with a great potential. Her wealth, her manpower and her resources could be of infinite value in the struggle against his real enemy, Louis XIV. It is impossible to say when the idea of tapping these resources first came into his mind, but his plan became apparent to many people long before James realized what was happening.

While Charles, the Protestant King, sat on the English throne and there was an outwardly Protestant heir, the English monarchy seemed secure, but when James became a Catholic he gave Shaftesbury the opportunity he had been waiting for and it is possible that at the same time he put all sorts of ideas into William's head. If James had possessed his brother's political acumen he might have postponed his downfall, but it is doubtful whether he could have withstood for any real length of time the forces which were assembled to exploit his decision to change his religion.

He himself obviously had misgivings about the effect it would cause, for in 1668 he asked the Jesuit priest Simons if he could become a Catholic while outwardly appearing to remain a Protestant, until he could make a proper declaration at a suitable time. When Simons said this was impossible James wrote to the Pope, and received the same answer. Being honest, he wanted to make the declaration there and then, but Charles and his ministers persuaded him to delay it. For the next four years, until 1672, he went on taking the Sacrament at Easter and Christmas and attended Church of England services until 1675.

In September 1669, while James and his brother were staying at Southampton and hunting in the New Forest, they heard that their mother, now nearly sixty, had died at Colombe near Paris at the end of August. She was buried in the cathedral at Saint-Denis with all the magnificence appropriate to the daughter, wife, mother and aunt of kings. In his Memoirs James says that 'she excelled in all the qualities of a Good Wife, a Good Mother and a good Christian': exaggerations which are customary in epitaphs.

On January 3, 1670, George Monk, Duke of Albemarle, died too, at the age of sixty-two, and James advised against promoting anyone to replace him because the tiny army hardly amounted to a general's command. He said that if there should be a war it would always be possible to promote some suitable officer when the time came. Charles agreed.

Four months later, in May, Henriette-Anne who had married Louis XIV's brother Philippe, duc d'Orléans, in the year of the Restoration, came over to England as Louis's representative in the negotiations for the Secret Treaty of Dover. Charles, very fond of 'Minette', had not seen her for a long time and looked forward to her visit. James did not. Minette had spent most of her life with her mother, and Henrietta Maria never attempted to conceal her antipathy towards James. Minette seems to have taken her mother's side, and the polite coolness between her and James was not improved by James's feeling that women should not meddle in affairs of state. Louis, knowing of Charles's fondness for her, had sent his sister because he felt her influence would keep Charles to the terms of the treaty; but at the same time he planted an agent in Charles's court on whom he could rely to promote French interests. The agent was the lovely Louise de Querouaille—known to Londoners as Madame Carwell —who became one of Charles's mistresses and subsequently was made Duchess of Portsmouth.

The secret treaty was signed, and after spending nine days with her brothers in Dover, Minette returned to France. She rejoined the French court on its way back to Paris after a progress through Louis's recent conquests in Flanders, and went to her house at Saint-Denis. Ten days after saying goodbye to Charles, she was dead. It was all rather suspicious. Her husband had violently opposed her visit to England, and when overruled by Louis, insisted she was to go no further than Dover. Then, soon after coming back, after drinking a 'glass of succory' (chicory), she 'died of a sudden and violent distemper', and Charles was sure her husband had arranged for her to be poisoned. A post-mortem revealed an abscess on her liver but no poison; physicians then were not pathologists and they seldom found anything that was not obvious. Yet it seems highly unlikely that Charles's accusations were true: certainly no one in the French court —where Minette had been well-loved—believed that little Philippe, despite his preference for his friends the chevalier de Lorraine and the marquis d'Effiat, had enough character to murder his wife.

Her visit to Dover had alarmed the Dutch considerably and their Ambassador in London asked for assurances which he could convey to his government. These were given, because Charles was not enthusiastic about undertaking another war, despite the treaty with Louis. As James pointed out, a war cost money, and one with Holland would leave Charles at the mercy of Parliament. Arlington and Clifford, both of whom were in the secret of the treaty, disagreed, saying that a fleet of fifty ships could be mobilized for £600,000 and this sum could be found from Customs and Excise revenue. James did not argue with this, he said it would be impossible to secure the overseas trade routes, replace ships damaged in battle or keep the fleet at an operational level. No one, except the Navy Board who knew what the problems were, agreed with him.

James became ill that summer, but only with a bad cold—one of the few occasions in his life when he was anything but active and healthy— and it was at this time that his wife decided to become a Catholic. Burnet says her conversion was an attempt to regain some of her old authority over James after the Henry Sidney affair, but this can only be his private opinion. It is improbable that Anne, with her intelligence and independence of mind, allowed herself to be influenced by anyone or anything but her own judgement. At the end of 1670 it was noticed that she no longer took the Church of England Sacrament and had broken a regular monthly practice followed since childhood; then, when she was ill, no prayers were said to her by her chaplain, as was normal. Charles, with troubles enough over the growing public fears of 'Popery', raised the matter with James and was told that Anne had 'determin'd to be reconcil'd to the Roman Church'. He asked James to keep the whole thing as quiet as possible, and only the Franciscan Father Hunt 'who reconcil'd her', Lady Cranmore of her household, and Dupuy, one of James's servants, knew about it. But others guessed. When Anne died three months later, on March 31, 1671, her elder brother Lord Clarendon, 'a violent Church of England man' like his father, refused to come and see her on her death-bed because of his suspicions.

She died of cancer, begging James not to leave her before she was dead, and her last pathetic words to him were, 'Duke, Duke, death is very terrible, death is very terrible.' Burnet's description of her body as 'a mass of corruption', to which he adds unpleasant details, is one clue to the unhealthiness of her children—but he, of course, attributes her condition to disease imparted by James. She had been ill for the past twelve months and her death at the age of thirty-four may well have been hastened by the birth of her last child, Katherine, six weeks before it. The baby lived for ten months. James was now thirty-seven.

On the grounds that Charles still had no legitimate heir and the Queen showed no signs of producing one, James was urged to marry again, in his Memoirs he says 'by his friends'. Charles, always concerned about the succession, supported the idea. The daughter of the Archduke of Innsbruck was suggested and after prolonged negotiations with the court of the Holy Roman Empire the Earl of Peterborough, as an Ambassador Extraordinary, set off to marry the Princess by proxy. When he landed at Calais he was told the arrangements had been cancelled. The Empress had just died and the Emperor was going to marry the girl himself.

*

Preparations for the war against the Dutch began in earnest in 1672, the year of the formation of the famous 'CABAL' of ministers—Clifford, Arlington, Buckingham, Ashley Cooper, later Lord Shaftesbury, and Lauderdale. Once again, James was extremely busy fitting out the fleet, and early in the year he had a major disagreement with the Cabal, of which he was the sixth and usually unmentioned member. They wanted to place an embargo on all outward-bound merchantmen in order to find enough sailors to man the fleet. James opposed this successfully on the grounds that it would affect the country's trade and so have serious repercussions on the revenues from Customs which were the source of income for the war.

The ban which had been imposed on James after Lowestoft was no longer in force and he was again to command the battle fleet. He asked for sixty warships and twenty fireships which, with the promised French contingent of thirty men-of-war and ten fireships under the command of Admiral d'Estrées, would be a sufficiently strong force to deal with the Dutch fleet and yet still allow enough ships and crews for routine merchant convoys. With his enthusiasm for commercial enterprises and the country's trade James was determined not to allow war to interrupt them.

Early in March news came that the Dutch Smyrna fleet, escorted by six warships, was approaching the Channel, and Sir Robert Holmes—who had led James's little expedition to the Gold Coast in 1665—was ordered to sail at once from Portsmouth with all the ships he could muster, call upon any other English ships he might find at sea, and intercept the Dutch. He put to sea* and met Sir Edward Spragge off the Isle of Wight with six men-of-war homeward bound from the Mediterranean. Disobeying his orders about calling on other ships for assistance, because he did not wish to let Spragge 'share in his enterprise', he made contact with the Dutch and attacked 'with more courage than conduct'. Having so small a force 'he had little advantage'. His own ship was disabled and only four merchantmen were captured: only two of these were of value.

This act of what was nothing less than piracy was the principal cause of the war which was declared on March 17, 1672. Towards the end of April James gave orders for the English and French fleets to rendezvous off St. Helens in the Isle of Wight, but before the fleets could combine, he was told that de Ruyter with seventy warships and additional fireships was already at sea. Almost at the same time he heard that Estrées had sailed from Brest, and reckoning from the wind that the French must by now be in the Channel, James sailed from the Nore with forty warships and twelve fireships—all that were then ready for sea.

A fresh westerly gale took him down the King's Channel and when he was off Long Sand Head he saw several Dutch 'scouts'. From the signals they made he concluded that they were in contact with their main

* Holmes himself was in *St. Michael*, a 2nd rate, Ormonde's son the Earl of Ossory was in *Resolution*, Sir Fretcheville Holles in *Cambridge*, Captain George Legge, later the Earl of Dartmouth, was in *Fairfax* and Captain John Holmes in *Gloucester*. All these were 3rd rates, and they were accompanied by four smaller vessels of 5th and 6th rate. Hardly adequate to take on armed merchantmen and their escort.

battle fleet away to the east, but haze reduced visibility, he could see nothing and so stood away to the south. When darkness came, the wind rose, threatening bad weather; the fleet hove to and anchored until dawn, but the wind moved into the east, bringing a thick fog, and James, heading for St. Helens, sailed past de Ruyter's far larger fleet without seeing or being seen. He had been lucky.

At eleven in the morning the weather cleared and James saw he was to the west of Dover, close inshore. Staying on course he joined the French at St. Helens early next morning, May 4.

The Dutch fleet came into Dover roads only two hours after James had left. After two days at St. Helens, going over with Estrées the order of battle and tactical plan, James led the whole fleet eastwards, first to collect the ships left behind at the Nore and then to look for the Dutch.

His flagship was the 100-gun *Prince*, on her maiden voyage, and he led the Squadron of the Red with Sir Edward Spragge in *London*, 100 guns, as his Vice-Admiral; Captain Sir John Harman—who had been officer of the watch at the time of the Brounker incident in *Royal Charles* after Lowestoft—was Rear-Admiral in *Charles*, 90 guns.

The comte d'Estrées was Admiral of the White, Vice-Admiral of France, in *Saint-Philippe*, flying the White flag at his foretop since no one but the Admiral of France was allowed to wear a flag at the main.

The Rear-Admiral of the Fleet and Admiral of the Blue was the Earl of Sandwich in the 100-gun *Royal James*. His Vice-Admiral was Sir Joseph Jordan in the old *Sovereign*, 100 guns, and his Rear-Admiral Sir John Kempthorne in *St. Andrew*. Lord Sandwich, whom Evelyn describes as 'that incomparable person and my particular friend', had a strange foreboding. A few days before he went to join his ship he had said goodbye to Evelyn. 'Shaking me by the hand,' wrote Evelyn, 'he said he thought he should see me no more, and I saw, to my thinking, something boding in his countenance. "No," says he, "they will not have me live. Had I lost a fleet I should have fared better; but, be as it pleases God—I must do something, I know not what, to save my reputation." ' As Evelyn points out, the whole trouble was that Sandwich, as a thoughtful, prudent commander who 'always governed his affairs with success and little loss' was, by men such as Albemarle and Clifford, considered to be timorous. 'He was for deliberation and reason,' says Evelyn, 'they for action and slaughter without either.' There had been a whispering campaign against him, and 'this it was, I am confident, grieved him, and made him enter like a lion, and fight like one, too, in the midst of the hottest service, where the stoutest of the rest seeing him engaged, and so many ships upon him, durst not, or would not, come to his succour, as some of them, whom I know, might have done'. Evelyn voiced what was a general opinion after the battle.

Beating into the east wind, the fleet reached Dover where James was joined by his ships from the Nore and told that the Dutch were off Ostend. The Dutch fleet was sighted there at ten a.m. on May 19, and with the wind now westerly James bore down upon it; but Sandwich sent his Captain, Richard Haddock, 'an old experienced man', to warn James that there was a danger of running on a bank called the Rumble, 'known only by a few of our Pilots'. Haddock reckoned that the Dutch had anchored just to leeward to draw their enemies on it, and though none of James's pilots had ever heard of the Rumble, his Master Gunner, Captain Lecke, who had cruised off the coast often enough in Cromwell's time, knew it well and confirmed what Haddock had said.

Sounding forward from a small 4th rate proved Haddock and Lecke to be right. James stood away to the north. A thick fog came down that night and next day the fleets came closer together, manœuvring almost within range, but no shots were fired. The Dutch avoided an engagement because de Ruyter, faced with all sorts of problems, could not afford to hazard his fleet. A major naval defeat might ruin his country, already in desperate trouble from Louis's invasion and conquests, yet he had to stay at sea to keep up the morale of his countrymen, prevent his sailors from deserting and also stop them from becoming as frightened of the war and its effects as were the people ashore. James considered him to be the greatest sea commander of his time.

Already short of victuals and fresh water because of the hurried departure, James went off to Southwold Bay while de Ruyter stood into his coast. Anchoring in the bay, James took on food and water, and ballast for his fireships. He felt reasonably secure while the wind was in the west but he warned his captains to be ready to stand out to sea and anchor in order of battle if the wind changed to the east.

The wind did change, and de Ruyter, knowing he had the weather, moved up to attack. James ordered Sir John Cox, his flag-captain, to make the signal to the fleet to stand out to sea, but Cox said there was no cause for alarm. The enemy were in no position to attack: Captain Finch, in command of a patrolling vessel, said he had just come through the Dutch fleet anchored off the Goree with yards and topmasts down, taking in supplies. There was bound to be a delay of at least twenty-four hours. This information was confirmed by the French, and James, against his better judgement, allowed himself to be persuaded that there was no urgency. Captain Cox was so confident there could be no immediate attack that he careened his ship to carry out minor repairs.

Next morning, May 28, James was warned of the approach of the Dutch by Capitaine Cogolin, commanding a French 4th rate. He had been out on patrol with Captain Finch but since his ship sailed more slowly than the English frigate and he had been unable to rejoin the fleet before dark, he had anchored a few miles to the east. When the tide turned he made sail to return to the fleet, and seeing two Dutch vessels close by, which did not attack, he at once assumed that the rest of their fleet was not far behind them. He fired warning guns all the way back to the allied fleet.

At first light James saw the enemy fleet to windward of him and bearing down fast. He was completely caught against a lee shore, with a leeward tide running hard against him and the east wind in his face. From the Dutch point of view conditions were perfect for the use of fireships, and de Ruyter, unlike Opdam seven years before who had delayed his attack, gave James no chances but came straight in.

The battle began soon after seven o'clock: de Ruyter opened fire on James's ship *Prince*, broadsides were exchanged and de Ruyter sent in two fireships, 'hoping to make short work with his Royal Highness'. Sir Edward Scott, one of James's 'old Land officers', saw them coming and told the flag-captain Cox. Cox was giving orders about dealing with them when he was killed by 'a great shot which struck him dead and at the same time carried off the head of Mr. Bell, a volunteer'. Scott then told James who immediately issued orders which caused the despatch of the first ship and put the second one out of action. De Ruyter and his 'seconds'—ships detailed to act in close support of the flagship—closed in to hammer *Prince* mercilessly, and by eleven o'clock 200 of the men on board were casualties, her main topmast had been shot by the board, the foretopsail, the starboard main shrouds and practically all the rest of her running rigging and fighting sails were shot through and torn to ribbons. James could no longer fight the ship so he told her captain to tow her out of the line and try and refit or at least save her from enemy fireships.

He then, taking with him Lord Feversham'* Henry Savile, Mr. Ashton, his servant Dupuy and his chief pilot, moved his flag to *St. Michael*, commanded by Sir Robert Holmes. *St. Michael*, being ahead of him and slightly to leeward, was 'not much damaged'. During this time the French Squadron of the White had got away, close-hauled, to the south and tried to stay clear of danger. De Ruyter said afterwards that if the French had fought like the English he would have been beaten.

The brunt of the Dutch attack was borne by the English Squadrons of

* Louis Duras, marquis de Blanquefort, first Earl of Feversham, who was one of Marshal Turenne's nephews. Henry Savile was the brother of George Savile, Earl of Halifax.

the Red, led by James, and the Blue, commanded by the Earl of Sandwich, and the real trouble was that having been taken by surprise, only twenty ships of these two Squadrons were able to manœuvre into line to take the Dutch attack. The remainder could not take up their positions until the afternoon, and so James and Sandwich were forced to fight a desperate battle all morning. Of the two, Sandwich suffered most.

He was first attacked by the Dutch Captain Braakel* in the 90-gun *Great Holland*, with a fireship in attendance, and this was followed up by van Ghent's whole squadron. Braakel, coming alongside Sandwich's ship *Royal James*, grappled her, but Sandwich's men, led by the gallant old Captain Haddock who was wounded in the thigh by a musket ball, boarded and took *Great Holland*. During the fierce hand-to-hand fighting 'with swords, halfpikes and pistols' on the decks of *Great Holland* van Ghent came up on the other side of *Royal James*, thundering his broadsides into her, but he himself was killed almost at once by a cannon shot. Three Dutch fireships and another man-of-war which tried to lay her alongside were sunk by the guns of *Royal James*, and she was at last able to free herself from Braakel's ship which was now almost a wreck. Braakel was wounded, all his officers were either killed or wounded, and two-thirds of the crew were casualties. Having defended himself with the utmost gallantry for five hours, causing havoc among his enemies, Lord Sandwich might now have withdrawn from the battle, but he refused to disengage. Then another enemy fireship, concealed by the smoke from the guns, grappled *Royal James* and set her on fire. Captain Haddock—soon to become Sir Richard Haddock—told Sandwich of the danger, 'but he answered that he saw how things went and was resolved to perish with the ship'.

Royal James burned almost to the waterline while watchers on the cliffs overlooking the battle, and men on ships around her, waited in fear for the explosion when the fire reached her powder magazine. But there was no explosion: her gunners had fired all their ammunition.

James, unable to help, watched the great ship die, but he ordered *Dartmouth* to pick up survivors. Between two and three hundred out of a crew of 1,000 were rescued—600 men had been killed on her decks—and these included Captain Haddock, Lieutenant Majo the Master Carpenter, and Sandwich's servant Lowd, who was made a Page of the Bedchamber by the King a few days later. Lord Sandwich was drowned. Ten days later, a vessel trying to recover anchors lost when cables were cut in the struggle to get under way, picked up his body, identifiable by the George round his neck and the Star of the Garter on his breast. He was

* Who had distinguished himself by leading the raid up the Medway to Chatham.

buried in Westminster Abbey with all the pomp and magnificence of a state funeral.

The death of van Ghent led to considerable confusion in his squadron and this created an opportunity for the Blue Squadron to join the Red. Some of the pressure on James in *St. Michael* was taken off, for he had been pounded by a double line of Dutch warships and soon had five feet of water in the hold. Yet the leaks were stopped and the ship pumped out without there being any slackening in the fire of her guns. At five o'clock in the afternoon Sir Robert Holmes told James he could fight no more: apart from all his casualties and enormous damage, the hold was once again so full of water that unless the ship was taken out of the line and some of the holes filled, she would sink.

James then moved his flag once more, into Sir Edward Spragge's *London*, but she was soon disabled after a fight with Rear-Admiral van Nesse.

Finally, at seven in the evening, de Ruyter bore away to join his Zealand squadron which had engaged the French squadron to windward, and in the manœuvring that followed, James collected between twenty-five and thirty of his warships, and several fireships, to windward of the enemy. He then joined the French. Thus, at the end of the day, after a battle lasting more than twelve hours both fleets were still capable of operating and neither could claim a real victory.

In the English fleet, feeling against the French ran high: 'They were wanting in their duty, and only fought at a distance after they had separated from the fleet.' One account says that 'the French, notwithstanding their great caution, lost two men-of-war'. One reason given for their behaviour was that Louis had given secret orders to Estrées not to 'expose the French ships too much' but to let the English and Dutch fleets destroy each other.

Losses were fairly even. The English had lost five ships and the Dutch four. Fortunately the night was calm with only a slight breeze, and both sides, despite exhaustion after the battle, spent it repairing damage. James was determined to continue the battle next day but when he had taken stock of the damage and found that any ships able to engage had no ammunition left, he decided to return to Sheerness. On the way, the Dutch suddenly threatened another attack. The English fleet took up battle stations to protect the damaged vessels and cover their withdrawal, and when de Ruyter saw that James was apparently prepared to fight he changed his mind and went away southwards with fifteen ships in various stages of disrepair limping along behind him.

James returned to the Nore, and despite the appalling damage done to hulls and rigging in the battle, the fleet was ready for sea again by the end of June. Charles came down from London to plan the next moves in the war, and he brought Clifford and Ashley Cooper, now Lord Shaftesbury, with him. James, whose simple tactical creed was based on finding and destroying the enemy, proposed to make for the Weelings where de Ruyter and his fleet lay, and either fight or force the Dutch into harbour where they could be penned up by blockade. Shaftesbury persuaded Charles that the best course of action would be to intercept the Dutch East India Fleet now on its way home round the north of Scotland—if James went for the battle fleet this rich merchant convoy might reach Texel or Vlieland safely and escape. James and his flag officers said the only way to make sure of the East India Fleet was to destroy de Ruyter who was not yet strong enough to withstand a concentrated attack. If the English fleet was dispersed to catch the merchant convoy, de Ruyter, able to collect ample information from fishermen and privateers about the stations of widely scattered enemy vessels, would be able to mop them up at his leisure.

But Charles and the Cabal disregarded the suggestions of the sailors who had to do the job, and James was ordered to find and bring in the East India Fleet. He sailed from the Nore on June 27 and began cruising off the Frisian Islands, but he was defeated by the weather. The gales were so strong that at one time he was forced to strike his topmasts and yards and anchor for a fortnight: the Dutch merchant fleet slipped safely into the Ems. Hearing this, James returned to England, anchoring in Burlington Bay at the beginning of August and putting ashore 3,000 men, mostly scurvy cases, too sick too remain at sea. From Burlington Bay he took the fleet to Yarmouth Sands, anchored off Lowestoft and was told de Ruyter had been there two days before. The weather, which had been extremely bad ever since the end of June, showed no signs of improvement. He therefore decided that his battered ships and depleted crews had had enough, and went back to the Nore to lay up the ships for the winter. As soon as he arrived there, Charles, Rupert and Shaftesbury came to see him and urged him to go out and attack de Ruyter. This time James was quite firm. He said no, and all his experienced flag officers supported him. Old Sir Jeremy Smith got up and reminded the Council that in Cromwell's time a fleet of twenty Dutch ships had been lost in one night off the East Anglian coast, and weather conditions had been very much the same. Charles listened to the voice of experience and sent all the big ships back to Chatham to refit for the following year's campaign.

So ended the summer campaign at sea in 1672, and so ended, too, James's career as an active naval commander. From now on and until just before his brother's death, his battles were to be fought against his personal enemies.

NINETEEN

WHILE de Ruyter had been waging war at sea to defend his country from sea-borne invasion, Louis XIV's cavalry swam the Rhine and, trained by General Martinet and armed with the new bayonet which was clipped to instead of plugged into the barrel of the matchlock, 100,000 French troops tramped into Holland. Essentially a maritime people, the Dutch had no land force with which to bar their way. Four provinces were occupied and Holland, as a country, faced extinction.

The government of the de Witts* fell before the frenzy of a mob which literally tore the brothers to pieces in the streets of the Hague, and the Orange party brought the young William of Orange—he was twenty-two —to power as Stadtholder. He, with the famous remark, 'we can die in the last ditch', halted the French by opening the dykes. From now on, William ruled Holland, and so one can perhaps say that the Treaty of Dover, designed to destroy Holland, in the end only succeeded in destroying James.

Towards the end of 1672, Charles asked Clifford and Lord Arundel to tackle James on the question of taking the Sacrament with him at Christmas, but James 'was not to be moved in his resolution of not going against his conscience'. Charles was well aware that anti-Catholic feeling was increasing throughout the country. His second Declaration of Indulgence, made in March 1672 during a parliamentary recess, had suspended all penal laws against dissenters of all kinds, and allowed Protestants to attend special places of worship and Catholics to celebrate privately in their own houses. Thus, when Parliament assembled in February 1673, they were naturally in a mood to inquire into the apparent encouragement of Popery, particularly since only eighteen months previously they had passed the Conventicle Act.

It was becoming more and more difficult to conceal that James had

* There were two brothers, Jan and Cornelius. Burnet says that one of them—he doesn't say which—'had the honour to be thought the inventor' of chain shot.

become a Catholic; and Charles's Declaration indicated the direction in which he too was moving. Popular feeling against the treaty with the French had been mounting since their conduct at Sole Bay and those who feared Catholicism seemed to have good reasons for their alarm. Parliament, with its control over Charles's income, was in a strong position. The war with the Dutch was still going on and Charles was warned by Arlington, and even by Louis, that insistence on a policy of religious toleration would gravely prejudice the outcome of it. On March 7 Charles withdrew the Declaration and Parliament immediately passed the Test Act. This required all holders of public office not only to take the Sacrament according to Anglican rites but to declare their disbelief in the doctrine of Transubstantiation. Some compensation was offered to Protestant dissenters by an Act which gave them freedom of worship, but this was stamped on rapidly by the bishops in the House of Lords.

James took an active part in the debates on the Test Act. He was not a professed and open Catholic; in fact he made no declaration of his beliefs while Charles was alive, largely because Charles had been emphatic about the embarrassment it would cause. But he could not possibly abjure Transubstantiation nor could he take the Sacrament in the Anglican Church.

The Test Act became law, and his enemies waited and watched. He resigned all his offices: returning to his brother his commissions as Lord High Admiral, Lord Warden of the Cinque Ports and Governor of Portsmouth. It was a tacit admission that he had changed his faith. He says in his Memoirs that 'his enemies had got him at last out of all commands and out of all business under the pretence of securing the Protestant religion', but this is not strictly true. Although Prince Rupert* took over command of the fleet, James was still all-powerful at the Navy Office. In any case, Charles had decided in January, two months before the Test Act was presented as a Bill, that the Heir Apparent must not be allowed to risk his life again, and the French Ambassador had been told of this.

James remained a member of his brother's inner council and was largely responsible for the appointment of Sir Thomas Osborne—later to be the Earl of Danby—to replace Clifford, compelled by the Test Act to resign from the post of Lord Treasurer. Osborne, who owed his position as one of the Treasurers of the Navy Board to the anti-James faction led by Buckingham at the time of Clarendon's dismissal, had proved his worth.

* Rupert fought three indecisive naval actions in the summer of 1673, on May 28, June 4 and August 11. Van Tromp expressed relief that James was at none of them.

In the campaign now developing against James a familiar topic was again revived: the question of Monmouth's legitimacy; and Charles, aware of what was going on, spoke to James about making serious efforts to find another wife. He took the view that since it now seemed unlikely that he could assure the male succession himself, this function devolved upon James. After much searching and deliberation, Mary Beatrice, daughter of the late Duke of Modena and his wife Laura Martinozzi, was chosen—and the choice was approved by Louis XIV as well as James and Charles. Unfortunately there were unexpected complications. The little Princess, who was only fifteen, had no intention of getting married because she had decided to become a nun. She had never heard of England, nor of the Duke of York, and she was a Catholic while James, apparently, was not. She was quite happy where she was; she was frightened by the thought of 'so high a place', and she was very worried about being able to worship God properly in a Protestant country.

All these objections were eventually overcome, even though her mother, the Dowager Duchess of Modena, had to write to the Pope and ask him to persuade her daughter to do what was so obviously the right thing. In due course, though he may have been slightly apprehensive of a repetition of the affair of the Archduchess of Innsbruck, Lord Peterborough set off for Modena where he acted as proxy for James at a wedding ceremony on September 30, 1673.

When this became known, the House of Commons made no attempt to conceal their anger and concern. Charles's marriage to a Catholic had not been popular but it had happened during the upsurge of loyalty after the Restoration, and Catherine was, after all, the daughter of the ruling house of Portugal who brought a good dowry with her. Mary Beatrice, Princess d'Este, seemed to have no advantages to compensate for her faith. Parliament met on October 20, and the Speaker had hardly had time to take his seat before the Commons voted an address to the King 'to prevent the consummation of the marriage between his Royal Highness and the Duchess of Modena'. The address was not read because Charles, warned of it, prorogued Parliament for a week—while Mary Beatrice was on the road between Paris and Calais.

The address, when it was read, had no effect on the marriage but it was unsettling in court circles and only a few people went with James to Dover to meet the girl when she arrived with her mother on November 21. Nathaniel Crewe, Bishop of Oxford and subsequently Bishop of Durham, seems to have been quite prepared to accept the proxy wedding in a Catholic church, for although in James's Memoirs there is mention of a marriage 'according to the rites of the Church of England', the actual ceremony must be one of the briefest on record. The Bishop asked Lord Peterborough if he had authority to contract the marriage. Peterborough said he had. The Bishop then asked James if he had his brother's permission to marry, and he asked Mary Beatrice if she was prepared to marry James. When they both said yes, he pronounced them Man and Wife in the name of the Father, the Son and the Holy Ghost.

It must all have been an intimidating experience for the Princess who had seldom before been outside the walls of her home or a convent. When she saw James's long, rather sad face for the first time, she burst into tears. He was now forty, old enough to be her father, yet she seems to have grown very fond of him. He was delighted with her. Lord Peterborough, who had written a eulogistic description to James, was enormously attracted by her, and he was ten years older than James. Evelyn may well have felt as antagonistic towards her as did many other loyal Protestants, for though he spared a long paragraph for Catherine of Braganza he does not describe Mary Beatrice at all. He says that he saw her for the first time on St. Andrew's Day (November 30) with her mother, and on December 9, 'I saw again the Italian Duchess and her brother the Prince Reynaldo.' It is unlike Evelyn to be so cool.

Mary Beatrice d'Este—Londoners corrupted her name to Madam East—was tall and slim, and she moved with elegance and dignity. Her dark eyes, according to Peterborough, 'so full of light and sweetness', were set in a face 'of the most graceful oval', and her hair, 'black as jet', contrasted with a very fair complexion. Macpherson says she settled down well, 'giving herself up wholly to innocent cheerfulness and amusements', and that gradually the prejudice against her disappeared until 'she was universally esteemed and by many beloved'.

This may be an exaggeration: in court circles she was undoubtedly and deservedly popular, for she was witty, charming and intelligent—as well as her own language, Italian, she spoke and wrote French and English and had a good knowledge of Latin—but elsewhere the antipathy and distrust aroused by her faith were deliberately encouraged by James's enemies. Inevitably, since she was deeply religious, she has been accused of bigotry—a term which 'good' Protestants seemed to regard as always applicable to 'Papists' and not to themselves—and of being the driving force behind James's 'Catholic' policy.

There is little evidence to show that she exercised any authority over James in what he regarded as state affairs which did not concern women, but it must be assumed that, as a good Catholic, even if she did not actively inspire him she must have given him her encouragement. She was entirely in favour of liberty of conscience since it offered relief to persecuted Catholics, and she undoubtedly supported his efforts to remove the social inequalities brought about by Anglican bigotry. Like him, she must also have seen that in so firmly Protestant a country there could never be any compulsory conversion to Catholicism.

To the people at large, the fact that she was a Catholic was bad enough, but feeling against her was intensified by strong rumours that the marriage had really been arranged by Louis XIV, who was underwriting her dowry. It was regarded as another move in the Catholic plan against England and so put another weapon in the hand of the 'little limping peer' Lord Shaftesbury.

Anthony Ashley Cooper, first Earl of Shaftesbury, had been made Lord Chancellor in the summer of 1672, replacing Orlando Bridgeman who had held the post since the fall of Lord Clarendon. No matter what one may feel about Shaftesbury's principles or methods, and his relentless attack on the monarchy through the unfortunate James, it does seem that his adherence to the Protestant faith was genuine and unwavering. He was so totally opposed to Charles's policy of religious toleration that he could not continue as his loyal minister, and since it was not in his nature to resign, he had to be dismissed. When this happened, in September 1673, just before James's proxy marriage, he felt free to concentrate his considerable powers on bringing down the Stuarts. His plan was to exclude James altogether from the succession, arrange for James, Duke of Monmouth to be declared the legitimate heir and, when the time came, ensure that in mounting the throne Monmouth was no more than, in modern terms, a 'front' for his dictatorship.

It was Shaftesbury's misfortune that he over-estimated his own abilities and under-estimated those of Charles. He thought—with good reason, for up to now Charles had made little attempt to assert himself—that he was a far more able politician than Charles, and he also thought that Charles could be lured into making the same sort of mistakes as his father. But Charles II had no Henrietta Maria to hiss her scorn and browbeat him into going down to the House of Commons to arrest his enemies; as a politician he was a great deal better than Shaftesbury, and he understood very well the strange pendulum of public opinion. He knew what Shaftesbury failed to realize: that throughout the country, support for the monarchy ran deep and wide, and sooner or later the attack on the monarchy would produce a reaction which might well destroy Shaftesbury. Charles played for time, knowing, too, that if Shaftesbury and his 'brisk boys' were seen to be revolutionaries threatening to overthrow the government by force, their support in the country would ebb away. There had been too much revolution, civil war, dictatorship and anarchy in the

The *Prince* (1670), by Van de Velde

Sovereign of the Seas renamed *Royal Sovereign* by
Charles II, built by Peter Pett in 1637, accidentally
destroyed by fire in 1696

Mary Beatrice, by Wissing

Charles II, by Hawker

Anthony Ashley Cooper,
Earl of Shaftesbury,
after Greenhill

The Coronation of James II

Judge Jeffreys

John Churchill, first Duke of Marlborough,
after Kneller

past thirty years: the people had no wish to disturb what appeared to be a settled and acceptable order.

Feeling against 'Popery' ran strongly, but largely because of the looming menace of Louis XIV and his armies. The great Catholic power of France appeared to be sweeping across Europe: Protestant Holland had been invaded, at any time this could happen to England, and if there was a Papist King on the throne it was reasonable to assume there would be little or no organized military resistance. Few realized that James was far too great a patriot and far too jealous of his country's independence and position in the world, ever to invite the forces of another power into England.

After their rapid wedding at Dover, James and Mary Beatrice returned to Whitehall on November 26 and were met by Charles and most of the court at the Privy Stairs. James's daughter Mary was now eleven, four years younger than his wife, and his other daughter Anne was eight. Mary Beatrice and Mary became very fond of each other and their friendship survived Mary's wedding to William of Orange. This throws a little doubt on the alleged 'bigotry' of Mary Beatrice, for she made no attempt to persuade Mary to reconsider her religious beliefs.

James's second marriage, to a Catholic whom many believed was another of Louis's 'agents', marked the beginning of a very unhappy period in his life. He said himself that all the troubles from now on, and all the 'storms raised against him' originated from the suspicion he had become a Catholic. This suspicion, much enhanced by his reaction to the Test Act, became a certainty when he married Mary Beatrice for 'till then his enemies had little to catch hold of'. Up to now he had been popular and respected, the latter perhaps to a greater degree than the former, for he had 'so often ventured his life for honour and interest of King and Country, and had always been active and industrious for the Navy and the Country's Trade—all to the advantage of the people. Yet, no sooner was the alarm given of his being turned Papist when all these merits were blotted out of their memory, and he sett upon on every side as the common Enemy.' It was all true enough.

Shaftesbury began his attack in January 1674 by trying to persuade the House of Lords that no less than 16,000 Catholics in the London area were preparing to take desperate measures to assert themselves, and he urged his colleagues to be ready for the massacre which was likely to begin at any moment. Since, in a population of some five million, there were only about 12,000 adult Catholics in the whole country, Shaftesbury had resorted to exaggeration for emphasis, and, bearing in mind his support for Charles's Declaration of Indulgence only a few months before, he must have known perfectly well that, so far from being a threat, the great majority of Catholics wished only to live in peace and be allowed to practise their religion in their own way.

It was, at this time, impossible for Catholics to do anything right: if they openly professed their religion they were accused of insolent pride in something shameful; if they tried to be unobtrusive it was said they were plotting the ruin of the Anglican Church and the country. Shaftesbury fostered this attitude of total unreason, exploiting with skill the fears and feelings of the people until his campaign reached its point of maximum pressure five years later, when Titus Oates spread the story of the Popish Plot.

Peace with the Dutch was signed on February 9, 1674, and announced in London on February 28. The House of Commons followed up this news at once by exerting pressure on Charles to declare war against the real enemy: France. But there was marked reluctance to vote any money for it. The country was in no state to take up arms against France. The French had twice demonstrated their reluctance to fight at sea and England had no land forces capable of confronting the great armies of Louis, but whatever the Commons may have felt about war, the major domestic issue was enough to distract their attention.

At Shaftesbury's instigation an attempt was made to introduce a second Test Act, barring Catholics from the King's presence. It was passed by the Commons, but James's friends and the court party in the Lords managed by a majority of two votes to defeat its whole object by inserting a proviso making an exception of the Duke of York. Shaftesbury, furious, took no further interest in the Bill, and he then tried to revive the hardy perennial of Monmouth's legitimacy. He had the effrontery to say to Charles that knowing of his great affection for his son, if he would make a declaration of legitimacy, witnesses would be produced to prove it.

It was Charles's turn to be extremely angry. He said he would rather see Monmouth hanged at Tyburn than make any such declaration. The plotters were not discouraged, nor was Monmouth. All sorts of ideas had been put into his head by a man called Ross, appointed his Governor by the King after the Restoration, who was ambitious too. Ross had tried to persuade the old Bishop of Durham, almost mad in his dotage, to sign a marriage certificate relating to Charles Stuart and Lucy Walters on the grounds that such a certificate would do a great service to the Church of England by 'keeping out Popery'. The Bishop, who had known Lucy in Paris when she pretended to be penitent and converted by him from her way of living, refused. He was not mad enough to sign what he knew was a false certificate presented to him surreptitiously by someone who was obviously up to no good. He told Charles about it, and Charles, with his usual insight and caution, said nothing to anyone, but he dismissed Ross. It was this certificate that formed the basis of the famous 'Black Box' story some years later.

James, Duke of Monmouth, had been brought up as a Catholic by Father Goff, a priest in the household of Lord Crofts where Monmouth lived as an ill-defined 'relation'. He was a boy of eleven when his father was restored to the throne, well-grown and very good-looking. Charles then owned him as his son, created him Duke of Monmouth and three years later arranged for his marriage to the only daughter and heiress of the wealthy Earl of Buccleugh, then a child of twelve.* Renouncing Catholicism, Monmouth was educated as a Protestant—James says that this change of religion was made at an age when the boy was too young to understand what it all implied—and he grew up to be a tall, handsome young man with beautiful manners. Unfortunately, he was hopelessly spoilt, particularly by his father. With his good looks, excellence as a dancer and well-merited reputation for bravery, women loved him, flattered him and so encouraged him that he began to think of himself as the rightful heir to the throne. James was very fond of him until he realized that under the charm lay cunning and treachery; and being weak, conceited, rather stupid and easily influenced he became the perfect tool for men like Shaftesbury and William of Orange to use in their carefully built plots against James.

Of his courage, the essential requisite of every young courtier, there is no doubt at all. He had been with James on his flagship in the fight against Opdam, he went to sea again in 1672, and was then sent by his father to France where he served in Louis's army as a Lieutenant General at the siege of Maastricht. Here, he and young Churchill greatly distinguished themselves in a desperate counter-attack to retake a defence work. On his return he persuaded his father to give him command of the English army—such as it was—and take over the post of Lord-General left vacant, on James's advice, when Albemarle died. The posting would have been of no significance had there not been all manner of trouble in making out the actual Commission. Sir Joseph Williamson, Secretary of State, through whose hands the Commission passed before being signed by Charles, at Monmouth's instigation deleted the word 'natural' before 'son' in the description of Monmouth. It angered Charles and put James on his guard, for Monmouth's aims were becoming clear.

Life was not made any easier for James by the problems which arose

* Charles, writing to Minette to tell her he was going to the wedding, explained it would only be a ceremony, 'for they are both too young to lie all night together'.

over the marriage of his daughter Mary. She was a Protestant and James does not seem to have made any attempt to influence her towards conversion. In fact, when Dr. Compton, the Bishop of London, told him it was high time she was confirmed, James said he had not tried to make either of his daughters change their religion 'because he knew if he did they would at once be taken from him'.

Three years before, when Mary was only nine, there had been rumours of a possible marriage with William of Orange, and by the spring of 1674, when peace was signed with the Dutch, it was the general opinion that negotiations would start at once. But in the previous year there had been suggestions from France that a match might be arranged with the Dauphin. James, as a Catholic, naturally welcomed this, but with the state of feeling in England as it then was, such an alliance would have caused a political explosion.

In November 1674 a special mission consisting of Arlington and Ossory went to Holland to see William on business connected with the treaty signed earlier in the year, and the question of the marriage cropped up. William was not enthusiastic: the English court was known to be in a close alliance with France, with whom Holland was still at war. Negotiations starting at this stage were liable to cause trouble in Holland, and so, for the moment, nothing further was said.

Then, on October 9, 1677, William landed at Harwich and went straight to Newmarket where Charles and James were staying for the racing. He brought with him a proposal for an alliance against France if his present peace negotiations with Louis broke down, and on October 18 he abruptly raised with James the question of marrying his daughter. Both James and Charles were surprised and annoyed, and Charles said there was much else to be considered before there could be any talk of marriage. He did not propose to discuss the subject until William had agreed on peace terms with France. James realized that there could be no marriage with the Dauphin and since he liked William he had no objection to letting Mary marry him, but neither he nor Charles could afford to antagonize Louis by so blatantly friendly a gesture towards the Dutch.

Both the brothers wanted to use Mary as a lever to push William into making peace with Louis; William wanted things to be arranged at once, so that his alliance with England would strengthen his hand in dealing with France. One cannot help wondering whether this was all that was in William's mind. James was under attack by the 'anti-Popery' party who had long accepted the marriage as a matter of policy. Mary was the only Protestant heir. If Shaftesbury's plans for James's exclusion were successful, William could see that by marrying Mary he would, with luck and if James could be got out of the way, be at least the consort of the Queen of England. The whole idea must have been very attractive.

William, determined to have his own way, found Charles and James equally resolute. Then Danby, whose popularity was diminishing rapidly because he was not a competent Lord Treasurer, intervened. He knew how welcome the marriage would be to all those who wanted a strong link with a Protestant power, and he saw a chance of rising a little in public esteem. He persuaded Charles that refusal now might lead to such an outcry that he would have to change his mind. If he agreed now to the marriage he would gain credit which he could not otherwise claim.

Charles agreed; James was horrified; William was very pleased indeed. On the following day, October 21, James told Mary: she cried all afternoon and all the next day. She was fifteen, William was twenty-seven.

That evening James gave the news to the Privy Council, saying that his main interest, as always, was the security of the kingdom, and that he would never seek to change the religious beliefs of his children. Two weeks later, on November 4, William and Mary were married. The ceremony took place late in the evening, in her bedroom, with Charles and James and his wife as the only witnesses. At eleven o'clock Charles drew the curtains of the bed remarking, 'Now, nephew, to your work! St. George for England!' It seems he was rather drunk.

Having achieved his object, William, who never made any attempt to acquire social graces, could not be bothered even to be courteous to his wife. All he wanted was to return to Holland and get on with more important business. Yet the marriage, apparently considered by William to be no more than a limited but necessary political objective in a far greater design, turned out well enough in the end. Even though Mary rapidly became, and remained, completely dominated by him, she never resigned herself to being merely the Princess of Orange: until she became Queen she always insisted on her English title of the Princess Royal.

Delayed by contrary winds, William was not able to leave at once for Holland, and when he could wait no longer and was determined to put to sea, there were mournful scenes at parting. It was bad enough when Mary had to say goodbye to her father, but there were floods of tears on both sides when she had to leave her dear friend and stepmother, Mary Beatrice.

James may well have felt that in raising no opposition to the marriage he had done the right thing for his country. He knew Louis would be very angry and he realized it might have been more sensible to have postponed everything until the Franco-Dutch war was over; but he had, as usual, given way to Charles. He could not have foreseen that doing so was a fatal step from which there was no going back.

*

Danby, the Lord Treasurer, must have been disappointed to find that his successful persuasion at Newmarket did not mitigate the attacks on him by his enemies at court. The 'anti-Popery' gang which consisted of Monmouth, the figurehead, Shaftesbury, Lord Russell, Sir Henry Capel, Ralph Montagu and their hangers-on, had the exclusion of James from the court and the succession as its principal aim, but the removal of Danby was also one of its objectives. Danby tried vainly to protect himself by urging Charles to issue proclamations and Orders in Council for enforcing the penal laws against Catholics, banishing them from court and offering rewards to those who caught priests. Being a man of no principle he turned against James, whose influence and recommendation had secured his post for him, and advised Charles to banish his brother.

James, who probably was not aware of Danby's duplicity, remained loyal to him, and when Russell and Shaftesbury indicated that they were prepared to do anything he wanted, such as restore him to Lord High Admiral and his other offices, if he would help them to get rid of Danby, James said he was prepared to take any action which would benefit the King and the country, but he was not willing to use his considerable influence with his brother to intrigue against a senior minister whom Charles had appointed. The activities of what James describes as 'the Factious party' were typical of the court intrigues with which he and his brother were plagued. One moment full-scale attacks were being launched against James in Parliament and in the country, and a little while later efforts were made to enlist his help. But though James was still the focal point for anti-Catholicism, as yet, in the summer of 1678, there was nothing to concentrate the fears, suspicions and hatred of those who regarded Popery as a force to be destroyed before it destroyed them.

Then, in August, Titus Oates provided the catalyst, and round James's tall, lonely figure, proud and steadfast in his faith, the storm broke in earnest.

TWENTY

JAMES has been held responsible, indirectly, for the horrors of the Popish Plot on the grounds that if he had not changed his religion there would have been no Titus Oates and no Plot. One might just as well say that the man who, choosing between a Picasso and a Goya, decides to hang the Picasso in his house, is indirectly responsible for his wife's action in ripping the canvas with a kitchen knife.

It is interesting to note the lengths to which James's detractors are prepared to go. To him have been assigned motives which were or are the inventions of his enemies or hostile historians, and it has long been customary to blame him for almost anything that went wrong or was unsuccessful in the years between the Restoration and the Revolution. The two tragic and inexcusable events in these years, events which came about through ignoring or abandoning the dictates of commonsense and the rule of law, were the Popish Plot and the Dutch Invasion of 1688. The former was certainly one of the greatest crimes in the pages of English history, because not only were harmless and innocent men butchered* publicly by executioners, but those who sent them to the scaffold, and those who watched them die, knew they were harmless and innocent. The latter, the result of bigotry and treachery on an unprecedented scale, destroyed James utterly, and naturally he is held responsible for that too.

It is undeniably true that James became a Catholic. It is also true that Catholics were persecuted abominably, but this persecution had been going on for generations and was not, as is sometimes implied, the result of James's change of faith. The Plot was a development of this persecution, seized upon by Shaftesbury not to destroy Catholicism but to bring down the monarchy and so make way for his dictatorship. It was to be the prelude to James's exclusion. Shaftesbury and his 'Green Ribbon Club' and well-organized 'brisk boys' fanned, and continued to fan, first the spark and then the flames of anti-Catholicism because he realized that

* Half-strangled on the gallows, disembowelled and castrated while still alive, and then cut in pieces. Butchered is perhaps too mild a word.

only by keeping alive an hysterical frenzy of hatred, based on fear, of 'Papists' could he create the political climate in which James could be hounded into permanent exile. It was of no concern to Shaftesbury that a few innocent Catholics might have to die.

He failed because Charles, despite all outward appearances, possessed an inflexible determination where the monarchy was concerned, and he was more than a match for 'the little Lord'. In all fairness to Shaftesbury, the suppurating internal cyst which tormented him for so much of his life may provide some explanation for his apparent resolve to make things so unpleasant for other people. It is not upon James but on Shaftesbury, and to a certain extent Danby, that blame for the success of the activities of Titus Oates must lie.

Oates, son of a ribbon-weaver who became a chaplain in one of Cromwell's regiments, began his education at Merchant Taylors School, went on to Cambridge and was sent down without a degree. He then 'slipped into orders', as Macpherson says, became curate to his father and after 'officiating' in various livings, came to London where he indulged in every vice and reduced himself rapidly to a state of beggary. He was prosecuted for perjury but escaped to serve as a chaplain on a man-of-war, 'from which he was dismissed', says Burnet, 'upon complaint of some unnatural practices, not to be named'. He returned to London and, again reduced 'to beggary and rags', he had the good fortune to be befriended by a Dr. Tonge, according to Burnet 'a gardener and a chymist . . . a very mean divine, credulous and simple'. Tonge told Oates about various plots being made in England to 'introduce Popery', and suggested that if Oates became a Catholic and went abroad ostensibly to study at the Jesuit colleges at Valladolid and Saint-Omer, 'if he could discover the existence of a real plot, or even procure names upon which an imaginary one might be formed, his fortune and preferment were made'.* Oates went to Spain for six months, returned to England and then went to Saint-Omer, from whence he was rapidly expelled. He then came back to England with resentment added to 'his wicked designs', and in the house of a bell-founder called Lambert, at Vauxhall, he and Tonge and Kirby worked out all the details of the 'Popish Plot'. The motive behind it was solely Oates's own 'fortune and preferment' and, initially, there was no link with Shaftesbury and his anti-court faction.

On August 12, 1678, when Charles was going for one of his brisk walks in St. James's Park, Kirby came up, and speaking with deplorable lack of deference, told him to keep close to his companions because an attempt to kill him was soon to be made. Charles, who had heard this sort of thing

* Macpherson.

before, was not impressed, but Kirby told him that a certain Dr. Tonge, if permitted, would be only too glad to tell the whole story. Next day Tonge arrived, bringing with him what he said was the narrative of the plot 'reduced under forty-three heads'. The barest glance at such a document was enough for Charles, who was just off to Windsor with James. He told Tonge to take it to Danby.

Shortly afterwards a note was sent to Danby telling him to intercept letters which had been written to Father Bedingfield, who was James's confessor, but the note did not reach him at the time planned by the conspirators. Meanwhile, Bedingfield, passing the post office in Windsor just as the mail arrived, called to see if there were any letters for him and was given a thick packet. He saw at once that though apparently written and signed by Jesuit friends of his, the letters were in fact clumsy forgeries designed to incriminate him and them in the assassination plot. He took the letters straight to James, and James, well aware of the rising tide of anti-Catholic feeling and of the innocence of the people named, demanded an investigation by the King's Council.

Charles saw through the whole thing at once. 'And the King himself was so fully appris'd of the Vilany from the beginning, that he intended to have nipped it in the bud, and hindered it from being made publick, which he said would alarm the whole kingdom, and put thoughts of killing him into men's heads who had no such thoughts before, had he not been diverted from it by the Lord Treasurer, who foreseeing a storm gathering against himself, thought to cover his own head and elude the Parliament's displeasure by throwing this pretended conspiracy before the House of Commons as soon as they met, which otherwise, as the Duke had earnestly pressed, might have been fully sifted into, and the forgery detected by the Council itself, before the Sessions, had not that Lord [Danby] industriously delayed it.'

Once the Plot became 'publick', the hunt was up.

One of the people accused by Oates when he, Tonge and Kirby came before the inquiry, was Edward Coleman, a Catholic, a member of James's household and Mary Beatrice's secretary. But he was much more than her secretary for he had been acting as an agent for various French Ambassadors, keeping them informed on what was going on in the House of Commons and paying out their bribes. He was undoubtedly deeply implicated in the original Grand Design and had been corresponding with Jesuits in France, trying to promote the close alliance and the consequent 'reconciliation with Rome'.

James regarded him as a 'busy, meddlesome man' and warned him on several occasions that unless he was careful he would find himself in serious trouble. Learning that Oates had named him, he told Coleman to destroy all letters that might be incriminating, but Coleman, self-confident and extremely conceited, was unwilling to burn papers which proved what an important man he was. He was arrested, the papers were found and Oates and another of his confederates, Bedloe, gave evidence to the effect that Coleman was concerned in the assassination plot. This was quite false because no such plot existed, but Coleman had been scheming to subvert the religion of the country and therefore, under the existing law, he was guilty of treason.

Condemned to death on November 27 he went to the scaffold on December 3 confidently expecting, until the very last moment, that a horseman would gallop up, waving his reprieve. It was perhaps because he was so sure James could save him that he said nothing to incriminate him, but this was a time when suspicion was as good as proof. Coleman's connection with James's household vastly increased the pressures against James himself.

Neither Charles nor James ever had any illusions about the scoundrel Oates. On one occasion, when being examined by the Council, Oates referred to his acquaintance with Don Juan of Austria, who had commanded the Spanish Army at the Battle of the Dunes, and Charles told Oates to describe him. Oates said he was 'lean, tall and black', presumably his idea of a Spaniard, but, as James says, 'he was a little, fat well complexion'd man, thō he had browne hair'. Oates was emphatic in identifying Coleman at his trial although on a previous occasion he had said he had never seen him before.

The first fruit of the suspicion aroused by the link between James and Coleman was a motion by Shaftesbury in the Lords that James should be barred from all councils and public affairs, for to Shaftesbury's clique the Plot was just what was needed in the campaign against James, 'to work to his utter ruin'. Charles gave instructions to all members of the court party in the Commons to oppose every motion of that sort, but feeling was rising. Five days later the Commons voted an address to the King demanding that James 'withdraw from his Majesty's Person'. Charles went down to the Lords in his robes, called up the Commons and told them he would pass any Bills in favour of the Protestant religion 'both now and for future ages', provided they did not try to 'impeach the Succession or the right of the Crown in the true Line'.

This checked the attack on James, and when a Bill for preventing Catholics from sitting in Parliament came up to the Lords a proviso was inserted 'exempting the Duke from the penalty of that Act'. But there was 'a hot debate', and James noticed that Monmouth left the House before the end of it, to avoid having to vote. Seeing how events were flowing against James, Monmouth was becoming bolder in his private campaign for legitimacy: he was now graciously permitting his friends and sycophants to drink his health as 'Prince of Wales'. Monmouth had been persuaded to believe that James was now the only obstacle to his succession.

In the uproar against Catholics, none was safe from attack: the Catholic Lords Stafford, Arundel, Bellasis and Powis were impeached and sent to the Tower; Danby, generally believed to be the friend and ally of James when he was nothing of the sort, faced the same fate, and it was to give him an opportunity to prepare his defence that Charles, on January 24, 1679, dissolved the Cavalier Parliament. Seventeen years previously 'it had been assembled to heal those National wounds which had bled nearly twenty years before, and thō it had then concurred with inexpressible joy to reestablish injured Monarchy, it was broken for endeavouring with as much ardour and earnestness to pull it down again'.

James was now strongly advised, particularly by the Lords in the Tower, to go abroad—to anywhere except France—until things were quieter. He asked Charles for his opinion, but Charles, not prepared to take a decision which might be construed as an admission of his brother's implication in the Plot, felt that the whole problem might be solved if James could be persuaded to come back into the Church of England. He asked the Archbishop of Canterbury and the Bishop of Winchester to go and talk to James. James listened patiently to what they had to say and then regretted he was not capable of arguing such matters with theological experts. Later he wrote to the Archbishop saying that he had for years been a zealous son of the Church of England, 'educated and fully instructed by the learned Dr. Stewart' (who had really been far more of a courtier than a divine) and it was not until he was old enough to understand exactly what he was doing that he changed and accepted a religion 'he well foresaw would change his condition in this world from one of the happiest princes in Europe to that of the most unfortunate and abandoned man upon earth'.

This is a clear enough indication of how miserable James was feeling, but few people then, or since, seem to have realized that instead of being a bigoted, obstinate fool—a fairly general opinion—he had changed his faith for reasons of deep conviction, and it was therefore quite impossible for him to abandon it for purely political reasons.

Disappointed, but not really surprised, Charles wrote to James on February 28, 1679: 'I have already given you my reasons at large why I think fit that you should absent from me for some time beyond the seas, as I am truly sorry for the occasion, so you may be sure I shall never desire it longer than it will be absolutely necessary both for your good and my service; in the mean time I think it proper to give it you under my hand, that I expect this compliance from you and desire it may be as soon as conveniently you can . . .'

James and Mary Beatrice left England on March 4 and went first to The Hague where they spent a few days with Mary and her husband. They then travelled on to Brussels, where accommodation was found for them by the Governor, the Duke of Villa Hermosa, 'to await there the designs of Providence to which they always bore an entire submission'.

Any hopes Charles might have had of a more tractable Parliament were very rapidly dispelled. He had anticipated that all the agitation over the Plot might be allowed to die down, but he found the new Members eager to proceed against the Lords in the Tower and to impeach Danby. Danby, very sensibly, surrendered to Black Rod on April 15 and was sent to the Tower where he remained, out of sight and out of mind, for the next five years. A move to present a Bill of Attainder failed for lack of evidence and Charles granted him a pardon, but its validity was questioned in long debates which achieved nothing.

On May 15 the Commons brought in the first Exclusion Bill, designed to prevent James from 'inheriting the Crown'. The Bill passed the second reading on May 21 but Charles prorogued Parliament five days later and then dissolved it. James, learning that the majority vote against him had been seventy-nine, was greatly relieved by Charles's action. He wrote a long letter to him: '. . . let not therefore knaves and mean spirited people flatter you into an opinion that you may be safe by yielding and temporizing, for nothing less than the destruction of your family and the Monarchy itself will content them', and he was very forthright in his warning against Monmouth. 'I beg your Majesty will have a watchful eye upon his actions for your own security.' And again, James the soldier advised action: 'certainly the speediest way of breaking their measures is to break the Parliament itself, and proportion your way of living to your revenue, rather than to lie any longer at the mercy of these men'.

But Charles the politician knew what he was doing. This was no time for the sort of military action his father had taken, the results might well have been equally disastrous. He knew very well that what James wrote was true, and he also knew what that 'wayward youth' his son Monmouth was up to. On the very day when James and Mary Beatrice had begun James's 'second exile' Charles had declared formally in Council that he had never been married to any woman except Queen Catherine, but two months later, when a sect of fanatical Covenanters in Scotland rebelled, and murdered the Archbishop of St. Andrews, Charles gave Monmouth command of the force sent to restore order. This upset James considerably because he felt sure that if he had been in England, command would have been entrusted to him, and he felt it was dangerous to give Monmouth any opportunity to increase his standing in the country. He was not made any happier by Monmouth's competent handling of the little operation which culminated in the brief encounter at Bothwell Brigg. Monmouth returned in triumph leaving 'a mighty reputation in Scotland for the clemency and indulgence procured by his means'. Knowing how weak and easily influenced Monmouth was, and knowing too that he was in the hands of utterly unscrupulous men, James was uneasy about what might be happening behind Charles's back.

He asked if he could come home. Charles said no: the Catholics in the Tower had not yet been tried, and the Popish Plot still 'filled men's minds with apprehension'. 'I am sure,' he wrote, 'there is nothing troubles me more than to be deprived of your company, nor can I write anything more against my heart than this, but when I consider it is the last stake, I would not let my inclinations sway me so far as to give a Counsel so much to the prejudice of our interest, as matters stand at present.'

There was nothing James could do, and Charles was perfectly right about the Popish Plot: all over the country there was a systematic persecution of Catholics. Listed in James's Memoirs are the names of six Jesuits executed at Tyburn, two at York and one at Chester, during June and July. In the summer of 1679 James had every reason to fear that this second exile was likely to last for a very long time, but, on August 22, while at Windsor, Charles suddenly became ill.

Naturally those around him suspected poison, and when the doctors seemed to have made him worse with their 'Physic and Bleeding', there was a slight panic. James was out of the country, and Monmouth, head of the armed forces, was not. The danger was obvious to everyone. Lord Halifax and the Earl of Essex, who had avoided Monmouth's faction which Shaftesbury supported, sent post-haste to Brussels asking James to return. James himself says that Charles told the Earl of Sunderland* to send for his brother, who was to come with a small retinue, leave the Duchess behind and let it be known in Brussels and London that he was going back to London on his own initiative. Lord Feversham and the Duchess of Portsmouth also wrote urgently to James.

James, somewhat sketchily disguised in 'a black perruque and a plain stuff suit', left Brussels on September 8, telling Mary Beatrice where he

---

* Robert Spencer, second Earl of Sunderland (1640–1702), a Privy Councillor and Gentleman of the Bedchamber since 1674.

was going and leaving Sir Richard Bulstrode to make his apologies to the Spanish Governor for not saying goodbye. Accompanied only by Lord Peterborough, John Churchill and a barber, he rode hard, spending the first night of the journey at Armentières and the second at Calais. Crossing the Channel in a French shallop, the party arrived at Dover on the morning of September 10. Here he 'was recognized only by the Postmaster, an honest man who held his tongue'.

Lord Peterborough was left to follow more slowly while James rode post to London, arriving that evening. He spent the night at Sir Allen Apsley's house, and while there he sent for Laurence Hyde and Sidney Godolphin* to ask for news. They said Charles was better, and they also said that no one knew of James's arrival, 'not even the Duke of Monmouth nor any of his gang knew or suspected it'. On their advice James rose very early and reached Windsor by seven in the morning. Without being announced he walked straight into Charles's bedroom and found him shaving. They were both extremely pleased to see one another.

There must have been many occasions when Charles felt that life would be so much easier if his brother were more accommodating, but equally as many when he felt the need of James's uncompromising support. At this moment, confronted by what must have seemed to be almost insoluble problems, he was relieved and delighted to see again the only person he knew he could always trust.

Everyone—or nearly everyone—appeared to be pleased to see James: 'the courtiers flocked about him to make their compliments, his Enemies as well as his friends, for his presence always forced an awe and respect even from those who were the worst affected to him'. But it was all an unpleasant surprise to Monmouth; and Sunderland, who never seemed to be able to sort out which side he was on, went out of his way to disclaim any responsibility for James's return. It was no part of Monmouth's plans for James to be in England.

In this unexpectedly friendly atmosphere James was careful to thank Louise de Querouaille, Halifax, Essex and anyone else who had been involved in his return, and since Charles was so glad to see him he hoped he would be allowed to remain. But on this, Charles was quite adamant. He was afraid that James, who was incapable of hiding his feelings and

* When Danby went to the Tower, Charles divided the administration between Sunderland, Laurence Hyde and Sidney Godolphin. Laurence Hyde was the second son of Edward Hyde, first Lord Clarendon, and he later became Lord Rochester (not to be confused with John Wilmot, Earl of Rochester, whose title Hyde was given twelve months after Wilmot's death). Sidney Godolphin, during the reigns of Charles and James, was an excellent, unobtrusive civil servant concerned principally with Treasury affairs.

was apt to say what was in his mind, might create problems for him. Parliament was soon to meet and he wanted to keep that troublesome assembly in a good temper.

James, very disappointed, found some consolation in the fact that Monmouth was to be banished too, for Charles had come to several conclusions. What had seemed to be a triumph for diplomacy and clemency at Bothwell Brigg now appeared to have been appeasement, or worse, 'as if Monmouth had rather intended to put himself at the head of their forces than repel them, and as if he had more inclination to court their friendship than punish their rebellion'. In fact it looked very much as though Monmouth was already 'preparing for his succession in that kingdom'. Fond though he was of his son, Charles was becoming more and more annoyed by his 'foolish and ambitious fancies', and he knew all about his secret plotting with Shaftesbury, Montagu and other members of the faction, 'to the great prejudice of his Majesty's affairs'. But the primary reason for Monmouth's banishment was that Charles had no intention of letting him take advantage of James's absence should another sudden illness prove fatal.

Monmouth went off to The Hague where he received so friendly a welcome from William that James wrote a sharp letter about it to his nephew and son-in-law.

One concession that James did succeed in gaining during his two weeks' stay at home was the change of his place of exile from Brussels to Scotland. There had for some time been considerable agitation to dismiss the powerful Duke of Lauderdale who had been in charge of Scottish affairs for many years, but James opposed this on the grounds that it would damage the morale of any of Charles's ministers to see such a loyal servant of the Crown discarded without a good reason. There was also some feeling at court that it might not be wise to send James back across the Channel, 'and so put the heir of the Crowne into the power of a foreign Prince'. To send him as a viceroy to Edinburgh, where Lauderdale would be subordinate to him, would be an acceptable solution to both problems.

Charles agreed: from his point of view the important thing was to keep James out of London and away from his enemies until some way of dealing with the hostile elements in Parliament could be found. But he wanted James to return to Brussels first, collect Mary Beatrice and go direct to Edinburgh. This worried James because he was afraid his adversaries might persuade Charles to cancel the plan for Scotland as soon as he reached Brussels, but Halifax, Essex, Sunderland, Hyde and Godolphin all appeared to be on his side.

James left Whitehall on September 25, travelled to Brussels through Ostend, arrived there on September 27, 'thanked the Duke of Villa Hermosa for all his kindnesses' and packed up his small household. Five days later he went to The Hague with Mary Beatrice where he called on his daughter Mary and her husband William, to take his leave.

Not even William with his deep-laid plans could have foreseen that after this friendly parting he and Mary would never see James and his wife again.

James and his 'family' then went to Maassluis, the port where, thirty years ago, his sister Mary had come to meet him after his escape from St. James's Palace. He intended to make for the Downs, but a storm carried his ship northwards off the East Anglian coast. Here he sent John Churchill ashore with a letter for Charles, asking for permission to come to London and then travel to Scotland overland. Mary Beatrice was desperately seasick, so ill 'as to vomit blood', and she must have suffered dreadfully while she and James waited for Churchill to come back with a letter from Charles. They reached London on October 14 and set out again for Scotland on October 27.

The plan was that James should not remain in Scotland for more than about three months, and Charles pressed Mary Beatrice to stay at court and not make the long journey before she had really recovered from the recent voyage; but she insisted on going with James even though this meant leaving her own child, Isabella, born in January 1675, and her step-daughter Anne behind in St. James's Palace. Mary Beatrice, now twenty, was a loyal and loving wife who felt it was her duty to be with her husband, particularly while he was under constant attack by the anti-Catholics. It has been suggested that her real reason for always staying so close to James was that she did not trust him where other women were concerned. This may be true, but lack of trust does not necessarily imply lack of affection. She knew all about Arabella and she must have known that marriage had not interrupted James's association with her. She also knew that a short time ago Arabella had been supplanted by Catherine Sedley,* but she seems to have accepted her husband's infidelities and, to a certain extent, to have learned to put up with them.

* She was the only child of that notorious rake and *bon viveur* Sir Charles Sedley. In 1677 she was selected by the parents of John Churchill as a suitable match for their son, 'for though she squinted, she was rich'. This came to nothing and she joined James's household as one of Mary Beatrice's Ladies of the Bedchamber. She was constantly surprised by the strength of James's feelings for her: 'It cannot be my beauty for he must see I have none; and it cannot be my wit, for he has not enough to know I have any.' Oddly enough, Roman Catholics were the chief targets of her witty, caustic tongue.

This time the journey north was very different from the progress just after the battle of Lowestoft, at the height of James's popularity. There were no mayoral speeches followed by bags of gold at York. Everywhere James was made to feel that those of the local nobility and gentry who came to see him did so out of loyalty to the Crown and not because they wanted to pay any respects to a Catholic prince. But at Edinburgh the warmth of the welcome did much to restore his self-confidence: cannon roared from the Castle, bells were rung and bonfires blazed. To the Scots, James was the symbol of their ancient royal house, and he also offered relief from the long tyranny of Lauderdale. Despite all the Scots blood on his father's side, James never considered himself to be anything but English, but during the short time he was in Scotland he made himself very popular with the ordinary people.

He took his seat on the Council of Scotland and impressed everyone by his industry and his application to business. He was careful to take no sides and by being scrupulously equable to everyone acquired so much personal credit that Shaftesbury, far away in London, 'complained that the persecuting of him in England served only to make him reign as it were in Scotland'.

James had arrived in Edinburgh on December 4, and soon afterwards he heard that Monmouth had returned from Holland without Charles's permission. Charles was furious. He sent a message to Monmouth ordering him to leave the country at once; Monmouth ignored it and went straight to his lodgings in the Cockpit, opposite Whitehall Palace, where all his friends went to see him and welcome him back. Charles sent him another order to leave and on November 28 gave instructions for a commission to be drawn up giving his troop of guards to the Duke of Albemarle. Monmouth left the Cockpit and went to his house in Hedge Lane, whence he sent Lord Falconbridge, Lord Gerrard and finally his wife to beg Charles to see him; but Charles, now really angry at this deliberate flouting of the royal authority, replied by stripping him of 'all his posts and priviledges'. Monmouth appeared to be indifferent, saying that from now on he would have to live on his wealthy wife. He refused to leave London, despite his father's repeated orders, saying that 'he knew the King's life was in danger and he wished to be ready to avenge his death, if it happened, on the Papists'.

Short of arresting his son, and perhaps precipitating a crisis with Shaftesbury and his Green Ribbon Club, there was nothing Charles could do, so, as usual, he sat still and waited for the other side to make a mistake. James's friends in London told him what was going on and warned him not on any account to come back himself for this would place him in the same category as Monmouth. Nevertheless, in his letters to Charles, James was wont to say how much he was looking forward to receiving orders to return. Charles replied saying he would have to stay where he was until Parliament had been prorogued at the end of January 1680, and he added that while James's presence in Scotland was maintaining the peace there, his absence was achieving the same result in England.

Parliament was prorogued on January 26 and Charles recalled James, telling him that if Parliament continued to attack him when it met again on April 15 'he could make his own defence'. James bade the Council of Scotland a formal farewell, making a tactful speech in which he said all the right things. The Council acknowledged this in a most dutiful letter to Charles 'filled with gratitude for the Honour his Majesty had done them by sending the Duke thither, with huge commendations of his conduct and prudence'. Although it was midwinter, James and Mary Beatrice went back to London by sea and arrived at the Privy Stairs on February 24.

As soon as James returned to London, Shaftesbury redoubled his efforts to keep the Popish Plot alive and to establish Monmouth's legitimacy. He spread the now famous story of the 'Black Box', which allegedly contained the contract of marriage between Charles and Lucy Walters—no doubt the one the old Bishop of Durham had refused to sign. Rumour said that Sir Gilbert Gerrard had actually seen the document, and he was brought before the Council where he denied it flatly. So much publicity was given to the story of the Black Box that on June 3 Charles published a solemn Declaration, 'on the word of a King and Faith of a Christian', that he had never married any woman but the Queen, 'which together with the oath of all the Lords present was registered in Chancery'.

In no way abashed, on June 16 Shaftesbury, Russell, Titus Oates and a large body of their supporters went to Westminster Hall to indict James as a Popish Recusant* before the Grand Jury. At the same time Shaftesbury expressed the wish that 'the Duchess of Portsmouth might be presented also as a common nuisance'. These were the first mutterings of rebellion.

Chief Justice Scroggs, a fearless upholder of the law who had saved several Catholics from the scaffold, recorded the petitions and subsequently dismissed the Grand Jury before any action could be taken on them, but Louise de Querouaille was so frightened that she 'at once be-

---

* On the grounds that he had long refused to attend the services of the Established Church.

came a patron to her pretended persecutors'. For an agreed sum of money and the dropping of all proceedings against her she undertook to persuade Charles to agree to the exclusion of his brother and to accept any successor nominated by Shaftesbury. She was in fact considerably over-estimating her own powers, but James was afraid she would 'shake his Majesty's resolution' and persuade him to abandon the struggle to preserve the succession 'in the true line'.

When the King's mistress went over to the Opposition she took with her both Sunderland and Essex. Sunderland went because he had a habit of going over to any side which appeared to be winning, and Essex went because he was at heart a Whig.*

James's fear that Charles would be persuaded to turn against him was greatly increased by rumours that he was to be sent back to Scotland; both Sunderland and Godolphin said there was no truth in them, but there seemed to be no one he could trust. At length he went to Charles and asked several straight questions. Charles, as always, was charming and evasive, but James was in no mood for evasion, and during the conversation he was extremely alarmed to discover that Charles 'had begun to doubt whether he could stand by him or no'. James found that his brother's attitude had changed to such an extent 'that it gave him great reason now at last to apprehend what he had been oft told but never believed, that his Majesty would abandon him in the end'.

But Charles was playing a deep game. He was facing the worst political storm of a reign much troubled by his brother's conversion to Rome, because James's change of faith had given men like Shaftesbury and Essex an overt 'cause' with which to cloak their real designs. If he was to survive, Charles had to prove to the nation that James's enemies, the

---

* It was in this year, 1680, that the terms 'Whig' and 'Tory' were first used. The newly elected Parliament had met on October 7, 1679, but it was prorogued no less than nine times, successively, until it was at last allowed to function on October 21 in the following year. During this long interval, petition after petition was made to Charles, asking him to summon Parliament. The tenacity and methods of the 'Petitioners' was 'Abhorred' by the court party because in bringing pressure to bear on the King they were trying to interfere with his freedom of choice. Thus the party which hitherto had been called 'royalist', or 'court' or 'Cavalier', became known as the 'Abhorrers', while their opponents, the 'commonwealth', or 'republican' party, became the 'Petitioners'. These names were soon shortened into terms of abuse. 'Tory', a name given to Irish Catholic robbers 'prepared to act any daring or villainous enterprize', was used frequently by Titus Oates to anyone who dared question his evidence or the existence of the Plot. His supporters took it up and applied it to all those who supported the King. The Tories replied with 'Whig', which James says is synonymous with 'sour milk', and was a term used to describe the more fanatical Scottish Covenanters, particularly those who, in the rebellion put down by Monmouth at Bothwell Brigg, had murdered the Archbishop of St. Andrews.

Whigs, were revolutionaries seeking to overthrow the monarchy: in this he was helped by a great deal of loose talk among the Whigs about things now being much the same as they were just before the battle of Edgehill. Although they had little support and hardly any standing in the country,* the Whigs dominated Parliament which, as Trevelyan says, was the party's only medium. They knew Charles was desperate for money, and this simplified their policy: if he did not consent to the Exclusion Bill they would not vote him any supplies.

So far as James could see, Charles was in a hopeless position, but Charles was never without hope—particularly while his cousin Louis ruled France. Charles had much to contend with, and to have James beside him at this time, with James's military solutions to a problem which he regarded as a simple trial of strength, would have added to his difficulties. He had no intention of abandoning James, for this would have led to his own downfall, but if he let his brother know this, James might have tried to insist on staying with him to fight against the common enemy. In his battle with Shaftesbury and the forces of rebellion, whose primary target was James, Charles could not afford to give his brother any justifiable reason for remaining in London.

Full of apprehension, James and Mary Beatrice boarded a vessel at Woolwich on October 20—the day before what is known as the Second Whig Parliament was to meet—and six days later they landed at Kirkcaldy. Once again they had a splendid welcome from a loyal and enthusiastic people, but one small incident marred their reception at Edinburgh Castle. It had been decided 'as a testimony of Joy' to fire the huge gun 'Mons Meg' in a salute, and an English artilleryman supervised the loading. Unfortunately the gun 'in the shooting was riven', and it was at once assumed by the angry Scots that the Englishman had deliberately overcharged the gun, 'they in England having no cannon as big as she'.

The circumstances of his departure from London being much the same as at the time when he went to Brussels, James had no reason to believe his stay would be short. He therefore settled down and, as Charles's representative, once more took his place on the Council. There had been several changes in the administration since his last visit. The Earl of Moray had succeeded Lauderdale as Secretary for Scotland but since Lauderdale's dismissal had been only an empty gesture made by Charles to his enemies, he was still controlling affairs. To James's tidy mind this was an unworkable arrangement, as indeed it was; Lauderdale retired from public life, and he died two years later.

* A situation made possible by the 'rotten', 'pocket', etc., boroughs and the control that powerful landowners could exercise over voters and elections.

In Scotland at this time the Government's main problem was the perpetual state of rebellion among the fanatical Covenanters in the south-west. This had been going on ever since the Restoration—for no Covenanter could accept the rule of so 'ungodly' a man as Charles II—and at Bothwell Brigg, Monmouth had only succeeded in discouraging, and not destroying, the more militant members of a sect unable to acknowledge any government not sharing their views. The Scottish administration had tried to control these simple, narrow-minded, clean-living and sincere people by laws even more harsh than those which penalized the Catholics in England, but they would not be controlled, and they seemed to court persecution as an outward sign of their devotion to their cause.

James regarded them as rebels, for they refused to accept the rule of Charles II, and to so dedicated a monarchist there could be no purely 'religious' excuse for treason. Yet he held the opinion that people so misguided 'deserved a Bedlam rather than a gallows', and Burnet and Halifax, both of whom must be considered witnesses hostile to James, emphasize that he ruled Scotland with justice and clemency. But Burnet made one accusation which James's enemies and detractors, in their eagerness to do as much harm to his memory as possible, have seized upon. He writes of James's 'unrelenting severity' which 'appeared very indecently in Scotland', particularly in relation to the barbaric practice of torturing prisoners to obtain evidence. This was part of Scottish judicial procedure, and the method commonly used was known as 'the Boots', imported, like many forms of torture, from Russia. The leg of a prisoner was put into a form of clamp, into which wedges were driven in order first to squeeze and then crush the bones.

Burnet says: 'When any are to be struck in the boots, it is done in the presence of the council: and upon that occasion almost all offer to run away. The sight is so dreadful, that without an order restraining such a number to stay, the board would be forsaken. But the Duke, while he had been in Scotland, was so far from withdrawing, that he looked on all the while with an unmoved indifference, and with an attention, as if he had been to look on some curious experiment. This gave a terrible idea of him to all that observed it, as of a man that had no bowels nor humanity in him.'

Macaulay, naturally, not only accepted this but improved on it, ignoring a comment made by Lockhart of Carnwarth which is in a footnote to this passage in Burnet's *History*. Lockhart, in a letter written in 1724, when the *History* was first published, 'observes on the account, which the bishop gives of the cruel disposition of the duke of York, that it does not correspond with the character given by all other authors of the duke's natural temper; and is of the opinion, that if he had behaved as he is here represented to have done, it was impossible but others as well as Burnet must have heard of it and reported it. "Such an extraordinary instance of his cruelty and barbarity in so public and conspicuous a manner," wrote Lockhart, "could not have been unknown to all the world but the bishop; and it nevertheless was, I may safely aver, seeing that no part of this calumny was ever so much as suggested or laid to the duke's charge by any one of his many inveterate enemies before or since the revolution." '

There is a story that James was present on one occasion when the leg of a prisoner called Spreul was put in the boot, but Spreul was to be questioned about a conspiracy 'to blow up the abbey and the duke in it'. It is reasonable to assume that James wanted first-hand details of the threat to himself and his family, and was there for that purpose only. One must remember that this was an age when large crowds enjoyed watching the unspeakable horrors of protracted public executions, and James's presence at an interrogation so important to him personally—and which may well have been brief—can hardly be taken as evidence of his 'cruelty and barbarity'. Yet other historians have used the bishop's malice to portray James as some sort of sadistic inquisitor in the worst Spanish traditions. To him, with his military background and uncomplicated ideas about the proper conduct of a soldier, the spectacle of cold-blooded torture would have been revolting; but his dislike of such a scene does not mean that he did not accept this particular method of trying to extract the truth.* It was provided for in the legal code and therefore he did not question it. He was far more concerned with doing what he felt to be his duty than in debating moral issues.

Apart from the insoluble problem of the Covenanters, another matter of importance with which James was involved in Scotland was the arrest and trial of the Earl of Argyll. All the chief officers of State were required to take the Scottish Test Oath, and all did so; but Argyll—whose father had been executed soon after the Restoration for reasons hard to justify except on grounds of envy and revenge—had reservations about it: 'I think no man can explain it but for himself. Accordingly, I take it as far as it is consistent with itself, and the Protestant religion . . .'

He was allowed to make a formal statement of his feelings when he took the oath, on November 3, and many of his colleagues probably shared his views and wondered why he felt it necessary to make such a fuss about them if they did not prevent him from taking the oath. So very minor a point might soon have been forgotten if Argyll had not been a man of

---

* Only very recently have interrogators realized that since most men under torture will say anything to gain relief, such 'evidence' is totally unreliable.

great influence—whom Charles and James did not trust—and he had enemies in his own country whose antagonism had its roots in the early history of clan warfare. Some of these enemies suggested to James that Argyll's reservations constituted criticism of an Act of Parliament, and such criticism could well be treason. James could be relied upon to react sharply to the word 'treason'.

Argyll, as Commissioner of the Treasury, was asked to take the oath again. He made the same comment on it, but this time it was not accepted and he was dismissed from the Council. Next day he was arrested, charged with high treason and imprisoned in Edinburgh Castle. Charles was informed, and though he allowed the trial to proceed he made it quite clear that should there be a conviction, no sentence was to be pronounced without his approval. When it was mentioned to James that surely no man should be compelled to hazard his life and fortune on such a trivial issue, James was quite upset. He insisted there was no question of 'life or fortune' being involved. All he and Charles wanted to do was to convince Argyll that he was subject to the jurisdiction of the Crown and to reduce the power wielded by this arbitrary, unscrupulous owner of enormous estates.

The court found Argyll guilty, but before Charles could give any indication of his wishes the prisoner escaped from the Castle. Lady Sophia Lindsay, his stepdaughter, came to visit him, accompanied by a footman. The Earl changed clothes with the footman and walked out quietly behind Sophia. No disciplinary action was taken against the guards who cannot have been paying much attention, and it is possible that James intended him to escape. Argyll fled first to London and then to Holland.

At the next meeting of the Council it was suggested that Lady Sophia should be punished by being whipped through the streets of Edinburgh. James was horrified,* and said brusquely that 'in his country they were not used to dealing with Ladies in that way', thus in his indignation —or perhaps because of it—disclaiming his Scottish blood and ancestry. It was unfortunate that he had allowed himself to be influenced by the enemies of Argyll and by his own feelings of distrust, because, for all his power, Argyll was loyal. He had now become a rebel and a refugee, and when he returned to Scotland, in Monmouth's ill-fated cause, he was to meet the same fate as his father.

James was happy in Scotland. He was popular, successful and busy, and there were none of the political stresses which so harassed him in London. When the Scottish Parliament met, an Act was passed asserting

* This does not exactly support Burnet's opinion of his sadistic tendencies.

the rights of the succession, 'affirming that the Crown passed by direct lineal succession according to proximity of Bloud and this could not be altered by any difference of religion or Act of Parliament', and further, it was high treason to endeavour to alter, suspend or divert the right of succession. James, with a touch of irony, noted how surprised everyone was that 'this should emanate from the home of Presbyterianism asserting Royal Prerogative, where England flew against it'.

In these circumstances it was not out of character for Shaftesbury, in a speech which infuriated the House of Lords, to state that in Scotland James was raising an invasion force which, backed by French gold, was to conquer England.

The only blow to the comfort and happiness of James and Mary Beatrice was the sudden death in London of their little five-year-old daughter Isabella, in March 1681. James's real distress lay in not being there 'to see her and help her in her sickness'. Four months later, in July, his daughter Anne, now fourteen, was allowed to join him, and she and Mary Beatrice seem to have been very happy together. It was a peaceful life. As usual, James spent as much time as possible in the open air, and though disappointed that there was no good hunting round Edinburgh, he shot grouse and partridge, went coursing for hares and, whenever the weather was suitable, played 'goffe', to which he became addicted. In winter he enjoyed the Scottish pastime of curling, and he went skating,* a skill he had acquired many years before in Holland; according to Evelyn, who had much admired his 'sliding' on the ice in St. James's Park, he was very proficient.

Mary Beatrice and Anne rode a great deal, went to the theatre or organized their own private theatricals, and danced the country dances in which James joined them. All three played basset—the card game which originated in Venice and ruined so many courtiers in London—but James was not a gambler and played only for amusement. Yet despite the un-troubled atmosphere in which he now lived, so very different from the persecution and uncertainty in London, he longed to return there. He kept in close touch with what was going on by corresponding frequently with George Legge and Laurence Hyde, and on at least two occasions he used John Churchill as a courier to carry confidential mail.

It was noticed that he was present when prayers were read in the Scottish Parliament and since he was extremely co-operative in passing Bills relating to local religious matters, there was a rumour that he was contemplating a reversion to Protestantism. Charles had pointed out how difficult he was making everything for himself and for others: his own

* Using 'skates' made of carved bone, bound on to the sole of the boot.

dangers, many of Charles's problems, the sufferings of Catholics and the 'confusion the nation was in' could all in some measure be attributed to his Catholicism. James replied at some length. He described all his troubles and stressed that 'his Conversion was sincere and purely for the sake of Truth, since he had all the temporal discouragements immaginable, which by the Grace of God he was resolved to suffer with patience, let the malice and machinations of his enemies run to what excess it would'. He said he was 'reminded of the publick Odium Cardinal Mazarin lay under when he lived in France, what ever went amiss was laid at his door. If a horse did but stumble they would cry out, "Le Diable de Mazarin!" '

Laurence Hyde came up to Scotland to tell him quite flatly that his religion was still 'an invincible Obstacle to whatever good or favour his Majesty designed him', thus, when all seemed to be going so well, he was made to realize he was still an exile and likely to remain one; but his faith meant much more to him than Charles or his courtiers realized. He would not sacrifice it for 'temporal benefits'.

Hyde took back with him a report James had written about the government of Scotland: it contained extremely sensible advice which revealed much knowledge and understanding of administration at the highest level. Charles was greatly impressed but he showed no signs of allowing his brother to return. He had sent him away because he wanted to fight his great battle against Shaftesbury and the Whigs alone, and without the problems which the presence of James, their primary target, would add to a situation already difficult enough.

In the time between James's departure in October 1680 and December 1681 much had been achieved. Charles had conducted his political operations with unrivalled skill, but though battles had been fought and won, the campaign was not yet over.

TWENTY-ONE

ON the day after James left for Scotland, October 21, 1680, Charles opened the Second Whig Parliament with a Speech from the Throne in which he announced that he had made alliances with Spain and Holland, that Tangier had been costing a great deal recently and he needed money for it, and that 'he would not have them meddle with the Succession'. He said he was quite prepared to 'concur with anything else for the security of Religion', and suggested that the matters to be dealt with first were the Plot and the trials of the Catholic Lords in the Tower.

But the Commons ignored him and 'fastened upon the Succession', just as he knew they would. By November 11 they were ready with another Exclusion Bill which was hurried through its readings but delayed for four or five days 'until the Lords were prepared for it'. Then, with Lord Russell leading them and accompanied by the Lord Mayor and Aldermen, the Commons carried the Bill 'with a mighty shout' to the Upper Chamber.

In the carefully timed delay Shaftesbury and his well-organized mob had spread 'new tales of terrible treasons and plots', all connected with James and his supporters. Everything was now prepared, and Shaftesbury, Essex and Sunderland were confident of victory. Charles, tense with anxiety, for he knew what was really at stake, remained throughout the long debate. He heard his son Monmouth say that purely from pious motives he was compelled to speak against the Bill if only to put an end to the plots against his father's life. 'The kiss,' said Charles, 'of Judas!'

Then, at first to the surprise of the Whig Lords and later to their consternation, Halifax, who was known to have no liking for James or his religion, entered the lists on his behalf. He was determined, regardless of his personal feelings, to defend the succession against Shaftesbury's dictatorship behind the weak façade of James, Duke of Monmouth. The battle lasted until nine o'clock at night. In a series of the most brilliant debating speeches of his career, Halifax strengthened the supporters and rallied the waverers until, when the vote was taken, the Exclusion Bill was thrown out by a majority of thirty-three votes.

The Commons vented their impotent fury in a series of wild, violent and pointless resolutions, mostly directed against James. In November they impeached Viscount Stafford, oldest and most infirm of the Lords in the Tower, and in circumstances so similar that they may have reminded Charles of the trial of Lord Strafford years ago, when he was a child, Stafford stood his trial in Westminster Hall. It lasted for seven days, and in front of the crowded wooden galleries set up for the occasion, the infamous Oates and his crew strutted and grimaced and lied. On December 20, on Tower Hill, the executioner who had stood beside the prisoner during his trial held up the poor old man's head to the jeering crowd. Considered to be too old and ill to be capable of making a spirited defence, Stafford had surprised them all. His death is another disgraceful stain on the Stuart record but, in the face of the shouting mob of rebellious Whigs, Charles was powerless to save him.

Checked by the opposition of Halifax in the Lords, Shaftesbury now set out to consolidate his position in the City of London so that, like Pym, he could use the mob as an effective political weapon. He laid plans which, if all went well, would result in his becoming an Alderman and Lord Mayor at the next 'election', and give him control of the City he already regarded as his own.

Turning at last to the other matters which Charles had mentioned in his Speech from the Throne, the Commons discussed Tangier. It was typical of their state of mind that they refused to grant any money for the garrison on the grounds that 'it was a nursery not only for Popish soldiers but for Priests and Religions too of that Persuasion . . . thus to succour it was but to augment their present evils'.

On January 10, 1681, heartily sick of so intransigent an assembly, Charles prorogued Parliament until the 20th, but suddenly, on the 18th, dissolved it. Suspecting that this was going to happen, and just before being summoned by Black Rod, the Commons, as a Parthian shot, voted 'that whosoever advised the King against passing the Bill of Exclusion was a betrayer of his Majesty and the Protestant religion, a promoter of French interests and a pensioner of France'.

Knowing only too well of Shaftesbury's influence in the City, and of his plans for increasing it, Charles had no intention of allowing the London mob to do to him what it had done to his father. He therefore summoned the next Parliament to meet at Oxford, well away from its influence, on March 21.

Hoping to be able to support his brother in what promised to be the most turbulent Parliament since the days of Pym and Hampden, James sent John Churchill to ask if he might return. He was greatly distressed and disturbed by the efforts the Spanish and the Dutch were making to persuade Charles to become reconciled to his Parliament by agreeing to the Exclusion Act. William of Orange wrote to emphasize how important it was that 'King and Parliament reach agreement, otherwise all the States of Europe linked with England must be ruined'. James felt very bitter about his nephew's attitude towards the Exclusion.

Charles was polite, but firm. There could be no question of James coming home during the dangerous period just before and during an election.

Once again the electorate, such as it was, returned a Parliament with a strong Whig majority, and this time every member of it had assured his constituents that there would be no evasions and no compromises on the main issue of Exclusion: and they had every reason to be confident. The pay of the armed forces was so far in arrears that there was open talk of mutiny; the Crown was deeply in debt to every source from which it had managed to squeeze credit, and even in Whitehall Charles was hard pressed to keep up the appearances of a court.

To the Whigs, as they rode towards Oxford, it seemed clear that either the King must give in and exclude his brother from the succession, or the whole system of government must collapse into anarchy and civil war. They had no fear that Louis would come to his cousin's rescue, since it was known that only three weeks previously various politicians and other men of influence hostile to the Crown had received sums of money from Paul Barrillon, the French Ambassador.

Oxford, for so long a Royalist stronghold, lost all its academic calm when the Whig members rode in. They were accompanied by large parties of heavily-armed followers and retainers, decorated with blue streamers and slogans of 'No Popery No Slavery', who filled the narrow streets. Charles arrived in his coach on March 14, escorted by a strong force of his Life Guards. He had left behind a garrison to 'awe the City of London' and, unbeknown to the Whigs, 'Lord Oxford's regiment was quartered on the road to secure his return'. The church bells rang, bonfires were lit in the streets, and townsmen and undergraduates cheered the King. The Whigs found no local support but were unconcerned: in a day or two they would be the new power in the land.

Charles opened Parliament on March 21 by declaring that he would not depart from all he had said previously about the succession, but he was prepared to listen to any proposal to keep the administration of government in Protestant hands, 'by which the Religion might be preserved and the Monarchy not destroyed'. When James heard of this he began to despair; but Charles was carefully baiting his trap. Knowing his enemies were pledged to Exclusion he suggested an alternative which, not surprisingly, led James to abandon all hope, for he was to be banished and William of Orange or his wife Mary appointed regent to govern in his name.

One can imagine the tense, silent throng in the crowded Geometry School—rapidly converted into a House of Lords—while Charles with charm and good humour put forward this proposal which he would never in fact have conceded, and prayed would be rejected. Shaftesbury interrupted, demanding that the King should formally recognize Monmouth as his successor. The Commons rejected Charles's alternative and began to hurry through the initial stages of the third Exclusion Bill.

On the morning of Monday, March 28, the eighth day of the session, Charles was carried down to the temporary House of Lords in a sedan chair; behind him came another, with its curtains drawn. The Commons, sitting in Convocation House, were suddenly summoned to the Upper Chamber, and for them this was the moment of triumph. They surged across the quadrangle, jubilant and elated, to watch and listen to the King's surrender. Once again the hall was crowded. Charles appeared. But he wore the robes of State—brought with such secrecy in the other sedan chair—and it was only when wearing those robes that he could dissolve Parliament.

This must have been perhaps the supremely dramatic moment of his life. In a few formal words he broke the Third Whig Parliament and the Whig Party, which, as all the world could now see, had tried not only to humble the monarchy but set on the throne a bastard duke who, as some said,* was not even the son of the King. He had achieved complete surprise. He had taken the one course which the Whigs had believed to be impossible for they knew nothing of the secret treaty he had made with Barrillon before Parliament assembled. When he confronted them in the Geometry School he had Louis's promise of enough money to ensure his independence for at least three years, for though Louis delighted in meddling in the domestic affairs of his neighbours he was not prepared to support such politicians as Shaftesbury, Essex and Russell who would turn from him to his enemy William as soon as they came to power.

---

* There were strong rumours that Lucy Walters was already pregnant when she became Charles's mistress, and that Robert Sidney was Monmouth's father, but since Charles always acknowledged the child as his own this story is probably only malicious gossip.

When Charles left the House of Lords he got into his coach and, having previously arranged for relays of horses on the road, was driven at top speed direct to Windsor. He need not have hurried: the Commons were completely shattered. They saw now that 'they had no hope of a speedy Parliament in which they could force through their designs'. The Whigs had no plan, no aim and no future. Fearing that Charles would use his soldiers to arrest them they fled in panic across the face of the country, hurrying back to obscurity whence they had come. Shaftesbury made great efforts to keep them together while he planned his next move, but for the moment they had had enough of politics.

Charles wrote an express to James, telling him what had happened and saying, almost with a note of apology, 'he had to be quick with them for nothing but violence could be expected from such men'. James was delighted, and enormously relieved that 'the King had at last come to those methods of resolution and vigour he had so long pressed him to'. He asked again if he could come home, but Charles was well aware that although he had broken the power of the Whigs he still had to deal with Shaftesbury and his followers in the City of London.

On July 24 William came over from Holland to urge Charles to help Flanders and Holland in their struggle against the French. Well aware that Charles would have to summon a Parliament to vote supplies on the scale he was asking for, William also had good reason to believe that a Parliament elected so soon after the scenes at Oxford might be little different from the last one. The battle to exclude James would be continued. Charles asked him what he thought of the Exclusion Bill; William said he 'abhorred it'. He agreed that the Crown could not be tied by 'limitations' imposed by a rebellious Commons. 'And,' said Charles, 'they insist on having in authority only those they can trust, in the Militia, the Navy, Sea Ports and Judges.' William 'disclaimed it'. 'Very well,' said Charles, 'accommodate these contradictions', and he implied that when William had done so he would be prepared to discuss aid to Holland.

William went back to London from Windsor 'to consider these things' and also to attend a banquet in the City to which he had been invited by Lord Russell and the Whig faction, 'in direct opposition to his Majesty'. Both Halifax and Hyde told him he would be extremely unwise to accept such an invitation. William, unaccustomed to advice and coldly angry because of it, said he had already accepted and intended to go. A messenger rode fast to Windsor to tell Charles and he gave William a peremptory order to return at once to Windsor.

William went back to Holland having achieved nothing, but if a date can be given to mark the beginning of his plans—as opposed to his thoughts—to remove James from the throne, it is the summer of the year 1681.

One significant feature of Charles's victory over the Whigs at Oxford was the violent reaction of the Tories in support of the Crown. Almost overnight they became the champions of autocracy and the Royal Prerogative, and they declared that there must be no resistance to the King's will that James, Duke of York, the Catholic Heir, should succeed to the throne. Suddenly, from the depths of persecution and calumny, James was swung aloft on a great wave of popularity. 'Dismal Jimmy', as Nell Gwynn called him, had again become 'Our Jamie', and Tories all over the country drank to his health and succession. But Charles, who understood the English better than anyone, knew how ephemeral were these swift changes of feeling. The abrupt decline in Whig fortunes did not mean that 'Exclusionists' had ceased to exist. Given a little time to recover and rally their forces, Shaftesbury, Russell, Monmouth, Grey and all the other enemies of James would soon be back in the arena, and Charles felt that until what James would have described as 'the smoak of battell' had cleared, and he could see what his opponents' position was, it would be unwise to call James back to London.

Up in Scotland, James, Mary Beatrice and Anne all tried to be patient and make the best of things until Charles should change his mind, and it is ironical that they owed their return to England to the woman who, in going over to the Whigs, had done her best to have James banished for ever. Louise de Querouaille, Duchess of Portsmouth, had been greatly alarmed by Charles's sudden illness at Windsor for it made her realize that if Charles died unexpectedly it was most unlikely that James would feel under any obligation to provide for her. She would find herself out in the world on her own and, having always been extravagant, with nothing to live on. She explained all this to Charles and asked him for £100,000 which she could invest in a foreign country—she knew how much the people of England disliked her: from their point of view it was bad enough that she was a French whore and they also regarded her as a French spy. Charles could not find so large a sum from his resources and so she suggested James might be persuaded to settle an annual sum of £5,000 on her for fifty years out of his post office revenues, in exchange for an equivalent sum from the hereditary excise. On this security she could raise the lump sum she wanted.

James, who was no fool about money, saw how he could turn this to his own advantage, and he at once agreed to make over the sum to his brother's mistress. Saying 'the King's word is my law', he pointed out that he would have to come to London to make all the detailed arrangements and sign the necessary documents, but he was well aware that the post office revenues were so tied up by an Act of Parliament that he could not alienate any part of them. None of the lawyers trying to arrange the business seems to have known of this, and Louise de Querouaille now began a campaign to bring James back, at least temporarily. A plan was made for him to go to Newmarket, leaving Mary Beatrice and Anne be-behind in Edinburgh 'as a pledge for his return'.

James wasted no time. As soon as he received Charles's instructions he embarked on the yacht *Henrietta* at Leith on March 4, 1682, and after a stormy passage arrived at Yarmouth on March 10. The magistrates there gave him a splendid dinner and in the afternoon he went on to Norwich, to another magnificent reception by the Mayor and Aldermen of the city. Next morning he went to Newmarket, 'accompanied by many Gentry'. Everyone seemed delighted to see him, and there was 'much joy' on being once again with his brother. Announcing that 'London business' could not be done in Newmarket, Charles took James back to the capital on April 8 where he was greeted with enormous enthusiasm. All the animosity so carefully inspired and nourished by Shaftesbury and Oates and the Whig adherents to the Popish Plot had evaporated in the heat of Tory loyalty, and everywhere he went James was acclaimed and toasted with a fervour which he himself could not explain.

In London it was soon discovered that the plan for the post office revenues was not feasible. James said how very disappointed he was, and kept quiet about his knowledge of the entail, so he managed to keep his money and the goodwill of Charles's mistress, for all along he had shown nothing but willingness to help her.

From London he went with Charles to Windsor and then, on May 3, set off for Scotland to wind up his affairs and responsibilities and return with his wife and daughter. Charles now wanted him to bring Mary Beatrice back to London 'for he was resolved that the Duchess, who was big with child, should come there to lie in'. James travelled by sea in the frigate *Gloucester* 'with several small vessels to attend him', and the pilot, a Captain Ayres, when going up the Norfolk coast 'chose to take the collier route between the sandbanks and the coast, although the commanders of the other ships were against it and ordered him out to sea where they were'. Ayres stayed on course, thinking he had enough water, but the ship struck a sandbank known as the Lemon and Oare in Yarmouth roads.

Among the several accounts of the disaster are James's own—in a letter to his nephew William, Samuel Pepys's story, for he was in the yacht

Catherine and saw what happened, and the report by Sir John Berry, captain of the *Gloucester*. These are all eyewitness accounts. There are other versions: one written by Sarah Jennings, Duchess of Marlborough, sixty years after the event and based on what she says she was told by her husband who was in the *Gloucester*; another in the form of a letter written by the second Earl of Dartmouth forty-two years later and based on what his father, then Colonel Legge, also in the *Gloucester*, told him; and there is also Bishop Burnet's account.

The Bishop says: 'The Duke got into a boat: and took care of his dogs and some unknown persons who were taken, from that earnest care of his, to be his priests: the long boat went off with very few in her, though she might have carried off above eighty persons more than she did. One hundred and fifty persons perished, some of them men of great quality.'

Thus we are given a picture of James, eager only to save himself, his priests and his dogs, escaping in a virtually empty boat while his household and the sailors are left to drown. This version has appealed to several historians since Burnet; others have said that had it not been for James's inability to decide what to do, many more would have been saved, and the story has been twisted in various directions so that it reveals James in the worst possible light.

Taking the first-hand accounts written soon after the event, it seems that the *Gloucester* ran aground in daylight soon after five o'clock in the morning. A gale was blowing and the ship was badly damaged by being lifted on large waves and pounded on the sandbank. James dressed quickly and came on deck where he was told that there were nine feet of water in the hold 'and the sea fast coming in at the gun ports'. A small boat, variously described as a barge and a shallop, was launched and brought round astern below the window of the great cabin where James, John Churchill, the Earls of Perth and Middleton, and 'two of the bed-chamber men' got into it. There is no mention, except in Burnet, of any priests, and it is quite certain that fond though he was of the animal, James's dog Mumper had to 'fend for itself'. In any case there was no room for it in the little boat. Mumper was subsequently picked up, and so was the physician Sir Charles Scarborough; both were exhausted after a tremendous struggle with each other for possession of a floating plank.

When the sailors in the *Gloucester* saw that James had reached the yacht *Mary* safely they 'gave a great huzza', but soon after, the frigate slid off the bank into deep water and sank immediately, 'taking about a hundred men with her'. Colonel Legge, later Lord Dartmouth, was picked up by Pepys's little vessel *Catherine*, and Sir John Berry, last to leave the *Gloucester*, swam to the *Happy Return*. It is more than likely that high winds and waves hampered rescue, and the ships' boats which stood by to help the *Gloucester*'s crew did not go close enough in for fear of being sucked down when she sank. One can hardly accuse James of cowardice in taking advantage of the special efforts made to save the heir to the throne, yet his Whig denigrators imply that he played a discreditable part in the affair. One fact not so well known is that he gave eleven months' pay to the widow and a sum of money to each child of every drowned seaman. Captain Ayres, the pilot responsible for it all, was tried by court martial and 'condemned to perpetual imprisonment for his negligence'.

Continuing his voyage in the *Mary*, James arrived in Edinburgh on May 7 and left on May 15 with Mary Beatrice and Princess Anne. Reaching London on May 27 they were met by Charles and Queen Catherine and moved back into their old quarters in St. James's Palace. After so much oppression and unpopularity they must have been delighted by the bells and bonfires 'and other expressions of joy' which marked their return.

Back in London at last, James began to take more and more of the affairs of state into his hands, not only 'holding his Majesty firm against his enemies' but, to Charles's relief, doing much of his work. In June, after somewhat irregular manipulation of the electoral system, the City of London came into the hands of the Tories; Sunderland, helped considerably by the Duchess of Portsmouth, crept back into the royal favour, and in August James was approached by Lord Shaftesbury with an offer of reconciliation which must have surprised him. When Shaftesbury asked for pardon James said that since the greatest damage had been done to the King rather than himself, Shaftesbury should go first to Charles for forgiveness; but from Shaftesbury's point of view this would be going too far. Ever since the loss of London to the Tories, he and the leading members of the Green Ribbon Club—Monmouth, Essex, Russell, Algernon Sidney, John Hampden (the younger) and Lord Howard—had been discussing what they called 'the Insurrection', and at the same time two old and hardened Cromwellians, Colonel Rumsey and Rumbold, an ex-subaltern, were planning 'the Assassination'* of Charles and James.

Monmouth, who had made a 'progress' through the West Country two years previously, and had been highly gratified by demonstrations of affection in the areas he visited, made a similar tour in September. Nicknamed 'Prince Perkin' by Nell Gwynn, vain, spoilt and easily misled by outward appearances, he gained an impression of his own popularity which

* Also involved in 'the Assassination', later to take shape in the Rye House Plot, were West, a lawyer whose chambers were used as a meeting-place for the gang; Norton, Ayliffe and Tyley, also lawyers; Walcot, a republican officer; Goodenough, a Whig ex-sheriff of London; Ferguson, a Scottish clergyman and retainer and agent of Shaftesbury; and Rous, Hone and Kieling, described as 'men of inferior rank'.

was not only false but was to prove fatal to him. He travelled in state with a mounted escort of more than a hundred followers and retainers, and it was perfectly clear that he was still trying to establish himself as the rightful heir. This was too much even for so indulgent a parent as Charles. Arrested under a royal warrant in Chester, Monmouth was brought to London and not released until he had given sureties of future good behaviour.

On November 17, the anniversary of Queen Elizabeth's accession, the normal celebration with bonfires and burnings of effigies of the Pope was suddenly banned. Since the Whigs had intended to make use of the festivities to begin 'the Insurrection' it seemed that someone in government circles knew of their plans. Shaftesbury, accompanied by Walcot and Ferguson, fled to Holland where, six weeks later, in Amsterdam, he died. Walcot and Ferguson returned to England and the Insurrection and the Assassination were both postponed until the spring.

James now felt secure enough to call his enemies to account and when one considers what he had suffered at their hands—denial of his right to succeed to the throne, threats against his life and three periods of exile, one in Brussels and two in Scotland—he behaved with remarkable mildness. Of the few people against whom he took action under the ancient statute *De Scandalis Magnatum*,* only four came to trial. Of these, Sheriff Pilkington of the City of London had said, when James returned from Scotland, that 'he had fired the City and was now come to cut our throats'; John Dutton Colt, bailiff of Leominster and a Whig Member of Parliament, had slandered James and threatened his life, as had a man called Covert; and the fourth was Titus Oates. The cases all being proved, James was awarded damages of £100,000 against each, and this in effect meant that the defendants, being unable to pay such a huge sum, remained in prison.

In June 1683 the famous Rye House Plot came to light. The assassination of Charles and James—the actual killing was always referred to as 'lopping'—had long occupied the minds of the Whig plotters and various methods of lopping had been discussed. One idea was to shoot the brothers in their sedan chairs when they passed through the streets at night; another was 'to fire at once twenty pocket blunderbusses into the King's box when he and his brother should come to the theatre', but the final plan was an ambush on the road from Newmarket. Ex-Lieutenant Rumbold, whose occupation was that of maltster, had a farm called the

---

* 'Libel Against Great Persons.' Under this statute, any peer of the realm who could prove that he had been libelled or slandered by a Commoner could obtain damages by instituting criminal proceedings, and the Commoner could not plead justification.

Rye House on this road, at a place where it narrowed, and he, as the originator of the plan, suggested overturning a cart in the narrow part so that the royal coach, bringing Charles and James back to London from the racing at Newmarket, would have to stop. Its occupants could then 'be despatched with ease'. All was prepared and the date fixed, but the house in which Charles was staying in Newmarket caught fire and he and James drove past the Rye House a week earlier than expected.

Among 'the lesser order of conspirators' was a man called Kieling, a salter by trade. Apparently filled with remorse for the intended crime he went to Sir Leoline Jenkins, the Secretary of State, and told all he knew. Warrants were issued for the arrest of the plotters. Monmouth fled, but the Earl of Essex and Lords Russell, Grey and Howard of Esrick were caught. Howard was dragged from a hiding-place in a chimney of his own house and embarrassed everybody by trembling like a leaf, bursting into tears and then incriminating everyone he could think of: in particular, Lord Russell and Algernon Sidney as the instigators of 'the Insurrection'. Both Russell and Sidney were tried by packed juries and it seems that the law was stretched a little to provide for their convictions. Russell's head was hacked off by an incompetent executioner on a scaffold erected in Lincoln's Inn Fields. Algernon Sidney, at his trial, found himself facing the new Lord Chief Justice of the King's Bench, Sir George Jeffreys, lately Chief Justice of Chester. The violent pain he suffered from recurrent attacks of the 'stone' may well have been the cause of much of his unusual and sometimes passionate behaviour in Court, but there is little doubt that Jeffreys was a very able lawyer. Sidney, an avowed enemy to monarchy, was found guilty on slender evidence, and sentenced to be hanged, drawn and quartered. Charles remitted what was euphemistically described as 'the ignominious part' of the barbarous sentence and Sidney was beheaded on Tower Hill.

Essex cut his own throat with a razor while in the Tower, at a time, unfortunately, when Charles and James were in another part of the fortress, inspecting some new guns. They were, of course, accused of arranging the 'murder' despite incontestable evidence of suicide. Lord Grey escaped from his escort on the way to the Tower and Ferguson, the Scots preacher, also got away. Walcot, Rous and Hone the joiner were all tried at the Old Bailey and executed.

Monmouth wrote to Charles some three months after going into hiding, begging forgiveness, denying that he was ever involved in any assassination plot and blaming and accusing everyone else. Charles, who was always prone to believe 'his wayward son', pardoned him, whereupon Monmouth at once resumed his intrigues. Charles then demanded a full written confession, which Monmouth gave him. Apparently realizing how dangerous such a document could be, Monmouth persuaded his father to return it to him; he then denied everything he had previously confessed. Charles, now really angry, was prevented by the pardon he had given from taking any further action against his son, except to banish him. Accompanied by 'one Gentleman and a servant', Monmouth left Greenwich in a fishing boat at the end of December 1683 and landed in Zealand. William and Mary welcomed him warmly and put houses in the Hague and in Leyden at his disposal. James wrote angrily to his daughter Mary objecting to the reception and hospitality given to 'this criminal plotter' who was known to be 'his mortal enemy', but William had his own plans for 'Prince Perkin'.

In Holland, Monmouth was joined by Lord Grey and Ferguson, and they began making their arrangements for the last, and fatal, adventure.

The discovery of the Rye House Plot had been the final blow to the Whigs for they were now shown to be the party of revolution through assassination. Charles's personal authority and influence increased immensely for in the drifting smoke of the political battlefield the Crown stood revealed as the symbol of law and order. Now unchallenged, and with his enemies everywhere in disorderly retreat, Charles sought to quieten fears of 'Popery' by the marriage of James's daughter Anne to a Protestant prince. Her sister Mary's sterility had been a disappointment to all those who looked towards Holland for a continuation of the Protestant line, and hopes were raised by the prospect of Anne's wedding. On July 28, 1683, at Whitehall Palace, she was married to Prince George, brother of Christian V, King of Denmark. Prince George was not a man of outstanding character and he owed this match more to his religion than to any personal accomplishments or family influence. Evelyn says 'he had the Danish countenance, blonde, of few words, spake French but ill, seemed somewhat heavy, but reputed to be valiant, and indeed he had bravely rescued and brought off his brother in a battle against the Swedes, when both these Kings were engaged very sharply'.

Shaftesbury was dead, and so were most of the leaders of the Whig party. Monmouth was in exile, and the plots against the Crown had been turned to its own advantage. Charles had at last found the peace for which he had longed throughout his reign. On May 12, 1684, James was reinstated as Lord High Admiral, and sixteen days later he resumed his seat in the Privy Council; he thus returned officially to the affairs he had been controlling secretly ever since his return from Scotland. Made independent of Parliament by French gold, Charles relaxed, happy to leave matters of state to his brother 'whose indefatigableness in business took a great share of that burden off his shoulders'. James, wielding almost unlimited power but without the final responsibility, was secure and successful in the role for which he was best suited by training, temperament and experience: he was the ideal second-in-command.

Then, in February 1685, there occurred the event which James and Mary Beatrice must have talked about often enough but seldom seriously considered because the possibility seemed so remote.

Charles II died and his brother succeeded to the thrones of the Three Kingdoms.

TWENTY-TWO

JAMES ascended the throne at a time when, to all outward appearances, the Stuart monarchy had never been more firmly established. In the last few years of his life Charles had vanquished and overcome all his enemies —or so it seemed—and had handed over to his brother a crown apparently loyally supported by a population predominantly Tory in opinion, in conditions of absolute rule. Burnet refers to 'all the great advantages' and many historians would have us believe that they were all thrown away by James's tyrannical incompetence, religious bigotry and a general mismanagement as imbecile as it was incredible. James is made out to be a madman, on the grounds that no sane man could have behaved as he did, and thus he brought all his misfortunes upon himself.

Yet, looking closely at the opening of James's brief reign, the great advantages that Burnet writes about are not easy to discover. Charles, when he died, may have felt he had no enemies left, but James had. There were the obvious ones: his nephew William—whom he certainly did not realize was his enemy until it was too late; Monmouth, plotting to drive him from his throne, and Argyll, bent on revenge for what had happened in Edinburgh. And there were the ones who were not so obvious: the Whigs, for example, particularly those in exile, who had been humiliated and driven out of power by his brother; and the corporate body of the Anglican Church which, reasonably enough, had a deep-rooted prejudice against a Catholic King. There were all the 'Parliament men', still loyal in their hearts to the 'good old cause' of republicanism, who had no time at all for the Divine Right of Kings and the Royal Prerogative; and there was Sunderland, a Minister of the Crown who was in the pay of both William of Orange and Louis XIV. Behind and below Sunderland there were others, like John Churchill, who served no one but themselves and whose energies were devoted to remaining on—or rapidly changing to— whichever side offered the greatest benefits.

On the surface there were peace and loyalty and approval for autocratic rule, but under this surface the forces of resentment, ambition, religious bigotry and revolution lay barely concealed. Furthermore, a situation which had appeared to be calm enough while Charles was alive, and which had remained calm because of his personality and character, would not necessarily remain so under so different a temperament as that of James.

Charles, often enough, had chosen the path of least resistance, whereas James was apt to adopt the somewhat impatient attitude of the soldier or sailor who could not see why a lot of civilians made such a fuss about what appeared to him to be some perfectly straightforward issue. When he was younger his mind had been rather more elastic: he realized that sometimes there might be unforeseen complications. But as he grew older, and age combined with experience led him to think he had acquired wisdom, like so many retired officers he prided himself on being able to see the whole wood as well as each tree. All his life he had gone straight to the point. He had no 'feel' for the delicacies, the nuances, of a political problem in which time might be the most important factor in finding a solution. He took the soldier's view that if action had to be taken, and a particular course appeared feasible, the sooner the better. Professional naval and military men are seldom successful in political life simply because they usually possess such attributes as precipitance and determination which, while admirable in their original professions, can be disastrous to politicians.

Unfortunately, James was not, by character, ability or practice, suited for supreme command, for he was of the type that although possessing intelligence, initiative and skill within a particular sphere, operates best when given directions from a superior. In general, servicemen—and perhaps civilians too—tend to fall into three separate categories: the leader, the led, and the third sort, the second-in-command. The difference between the leader and the second-in-command is that although the second-in-command is usually able to exercise command perfectly adequately and perhaps for long periods in the absence of his superior, he lacks the 'flair' and the instinct to make the right decision from a crucial and confusing choice of options. He needs a guiding hand if he is to give of his best.

Throughout his soldiering days James had been guided by Turenne in the French army, and in the Spanish forces there had always been the experienced Condé. As Lord High Admiral, in action, James had been aware that though he was the commander-in-chief at sea, the direction of the war lay in the hands of his brother and the Council. He had never, at any time in his life, found himself faced with a decision of national importance which he could not refer to 'a higher authority'. Though there had been much talk in his youth of outshining his indolent brother by his industry and application, he had in fact grown up in Charles's shadow. Throughout all the persecution by his enemies he had never been really on his own, for there had always been Charles whose sometimes reluctant shoulders bore the full weight of royal responsibility.

While Charles lived, James was in the position of being able to advise and recommend and suggest without having to take the final blame if things went wrong. This gave him confidence and the comfortable feeling of power without responsibility. Then Charles died; and for the first time James was on his own. No doubt among his early reactions was a measure of relief that at last he was the leader, for very few natural seconds-in-command are aware of their own limitations. But James, without Charles's gentle, friendly hand to steer him, was lost.

Charles's death came as a great shock to him for, according to his Memoirs, 'it had never entered into his heart or imagination that he should outlive the late King, for though he was three years and about four months younger, yet he always looked upon him as of a much stronger constitution, and subsequently had not the least fancy he should come to the crown'.

Charles was only fifty-three when he died on February 6, 1685. James was then fifty. Of the two brothers James was probably the more muscled and robust because of his devotion to hard physical exercise, but Charles's habit of rising extremely early, despite the most debilitating activities the previous night, and his long walks taken at great speed in the chilly dawn, gave everyone the impression of enormous vitality. Like James, he had survived smallpox, and the undiagnosed illness which had brought James back from Brussels in 1679, and, again like his brother, he was hardly ever even 'indisposed'. 'Thus died King Charles II,' wrote Evelyn, 'of a vigorous and robust constitution, and in all appearance promising a long life.'

Indeed there was every reason for James to assume that his brother would live for a good many years, and the shock of his death certainly had a profound effect on James's policies as king. He suddenly realized that if Charles could die so young, he too might only have a short while left, and since there was much to be done he felt he had to move quickly. This was one of his many mistakes. It is so easy, now, to say how different things might have been if he had not tried to rush his religious reforms, but he had to make his decisions on facts, and deductions from those facts, as they appeared to him at the time.

When he came to the throne he had no male heir, though he had been married to Mary Beatrice for twelve years, and he had every reason to believe that his Catholic influence in the country would die with him.

The succession would pass to his Protestant daughter Mary and her husband William, the 'Protestant Champion', and this was another reason why, if anything was to be done to improve conditions for the Catholics in England, it would have to be done quickly.

James had rigid ideas about the functions of a monarch and to him monarchy was synonymous with absolute rule. He sums up his point of view in his *Advice to My Son* (1692): 'Kings being accountable for none of their actions but to God and themselves, ought to be more cautious and circumspect than those who are in lower stations, and as tis the duty of Subjects to pay true allegiance to him, and to observe his laws, so a King is bound by his office to have a fatherly love and care of them.'

The Protestant succession, which he would never have attempted to change by any Act or law or declaration, and which he accepted as being inevitable 'in the true Line', is a strong and often ignored argument against the accusation that James tried to convert the country to Roman Catholicism. He knew perfectly well that any radical or universal changes he might attempt would be reversed by a Protestant successor, spurred on by the Anglican Church; and though he may have been a hopeless politician he could estimate, even on the lines of a military appreciation, what was, and what was not, feasible.

To suggest, as many do, that James's purpose in life was to establish the Roman Catholic Church, if necessary by force, is to assume that he was a fool, not only blinded by religious zeal, but determined to ignore the true situation in a nation excessively biased against the tiny minority of Catholics in its midst. So far as the use of force was concerned, James himself makes the point that it would have been difficult to do this with the English Protestant army, the only 'force' available. Fiercely independent, militarily, he even turned down his cousin Louis's offer of foreign troops at the time of the Dutch Invasion.

All James's problems, all his troubles and his eventual downfall stem from his conversion to Rome. Had he been born a Catholic it is conceivable that he could have become a Protestant for political reasons, for he might not have given much analytical thought to the faith in which he had grown up. But he was a convert to Catholicism and had given it a great deal of thought before taking a decision which he knew must create every sort of difficulty in the religious climate of the times. Like every sincere convert, he had convinced himself that his choice was the right one, and thereafter nothing would make him change his mind. It is a pity that his steadfast adherence to what he knew to be right should have been condemned as mere obstinate bigotry.

All he ever tried to do, in the few years before the Whigs overthrew him, was to make life more tolerable for the persecuted Catholics, to give all creeds equal opportunity to live and worship as they felt inclined and, above all, to allow all men what he so often described as 'Liberty of Conscience'. He failed largely because, as he said himself, religious toleration would take from the hand of the Anglican Church its weapon of persecution, and without that weapon the Church could not feel secure.

But in fact, as he himself slowly came to realize, all the dust and smoke raised by the so-called religious controversy was really only a cloak for revolution. It was his misfortune that whereas his more astute brother had realized that behind the uproar of the Popish Plot lay the plans of Shaftesbury to destroy the monarchy, James tended to see things as they appeared to be, without looking to see what they might conceal. When Charles died and James the Catholic came to the throne, William of Orange saw that with a little care he could succeed where Shaftesbury had failed. By fomenting Anglican bigotry the real design could be shielded: James could be brought down and he could take his place. That he was able to succeed was due very largely to James's political innocence, his enthusiasm for religious reform, his determination to govern firmly and his straightforward approach to his problems which made it so easy for his enemies to deceive and out-manœuvre him.

Perhaps one can say that so far from taking over the throne 'with great advantages' James, as king, never really had a chance. William wanted his throne, the Whigs wanted William and the Church wanted no part of toleration. James, who as a soldier and a sailor had developed dangerous habits of loyalty and trust, was launched upon a sea of troubles with no hand but his own on the tiller of a leaky boat which, in the end, was sunk 'by the knavery of false and treacherous servants'.*

*

At first all seemed to be well. Burnet says that when orders were given to proclaim the new King 'it was a heavy solemnity: few tears were shed for the former, nor were there any shouts of joy for the present King. A dead silence, but without any disorder or tumult, followed it through the streets.' Burnet was in self-imposed exile in Holland at the time and he wrote of things as he hoped they were. One comment by a witness hostile to James, in a footnote to Burnet's *History*, says 'all the former animosities seemed to be forgotten amidst the loud acclamations of his people on his accession to the throne'. Evelyn listened to the proclamation at Whitehall Gate where the sound of the trumpets and kettle-drums 'ended with the people's acclamations', and again, at Bromley, 'after many shouts of the

* Cole's MS annotation to Vol. III of Burnet's *History*.

people His Majesty's health was drunk in a flint glass of a yard long by the Sheriff, Commander, Officers and chief Gentlemen'.

The Privy Councillors assembled immediately after Charles's death and James, who had been kneeling in tears beside his brother's bed, went to the meeting and after 'passionately declaring his sorrow' made a brief speech which caused considerable excitement and relief. 'I have been reported,' he said, 'to be a man for arbitrary power, though that is not the only story which has been made of me. I shall make it my endeavour to preserve the government in Church and State as it is by law established. I know the principles of the Church of England are for Monarchy, and that the members of it have shown themselves good and loyal subjects, and therefore I shall always take care to defend and support it. I know likewise that the laws of England are sufficient to make the King as great a monarch as I can wish, and therefore as I will never depart from the just rights and prerogatives of the Crown, so I will never invade any man's property. I have often ventured my life in defence of the nation and will go as far as any man to preserve it in its just rights and priviledges.'

From the Council he took Mary Beatrice to hear Mass in the little chapel in St. James's Palace, leaving the door open to show 'as he was resolved not to invade other men's religion, so neither would he conceal his own'.

His brother's funeral presented an awkward problem, for since Father Huddlestone had received him into the Church of Rome on his deathbed, he could not now be buried according to Anglican rites. There had been the usual clumsy post-mortem—which gave Burnet scope for highly imaginative accusations of poisoning—and his body had lain in state in the Painted Hall 'with all the proper illuminations and mourning', but the form of service had to be a compromise. Finally, as Evelyn says, on February 14 'the King was this night very obscurely buried in a vault under Henry VII's chapel at Westminster, without any manner of pomp'. There was in fact a very stately procession from Whitehall and, as was customary, all the great officers broke their white staves over the grave.

Inevitably, James made some changes in these appointments. Halifax, to whom he was always grateful for his great defence during the second Exclusion Bill but whom he never trusted, was moved from Lord Privy Seal to Lord President of the Council, in place of James's brother-in-law Lord Rochester who became Lord Treasurer. His other brother-in-law Henry, second Earl of Clarendon, became Lord Privy Seal, and Sidney Godolphin was made Chamberlain to the Queen. The ageing Lord Arlington remained as Lord Chamberlain because James, though he had disliked him for years, said it would only be an unkindness to move him; Lord Guildford stayed as Lord Keeper, and Sunderland continued to be the Principal Secretary of State.

James had promised the country that he would call a Parliament and on March 5 the writs were issued—for the first time since the débâcle at Oxford. Evelyn commented that 'great industry was used to obtain elections which might promote the Court interest', and in May, just before Parliament assembled, he said the elections 'were thought to be very indirectly carried on in most places'. This was an understatement, but James had no wish to confront the sort of 'turbulent assembly' that his brother had had to deal with, and he achieved the results he had hoped for. Barrillon, the French Ambassador, reckoned that the opposition element did not amount to more than six members; James thought it was about forty.

But a month before this Parliament came together the coronation of James and Mary Beatrice took place amid scenes of great splendour in Westminster Abbey. On St. George's Day, April 23, James received his crown, which unfortunately did not fit properly, from the Archbishop of Canterbury, and the Bishop of Ely preached. 'But,' says Evelyn, 'to the sorrow of the people, no Sacrament, as it ought to have been.' As a religious ceremony the coronation was much criticized by both Protestants and Catholics: the Protestants were distressed about the Sacrament and the Catholics regarded the whole thing as heretical anyway.

The new Parliament assembled on May 22 and elected Sir John Trevor as Speaker. In a brief speech James repeated what he had said to the Council about preserving rights and liberties; he then, with fine dramatic timing, announced the arrival of the Earl of Argyll in the Western Highlands who had brought with him 'men from Holland' and declarations charging the King with usurpation and tyranny.

Scotland was very loyal to James and his feelings towards the country were much affected by the constant support given to him at the time when he was so persecuted in England. The Scottish Parliament had already affirmed their loyalty, passed a bill ratifying all Acts in favour of the established religion and continued to ban conventicles. James had a good reason for urging this prohibition for he saw in the 'field conventicles' a perfect opportunity for rabble rousers to 'summon the people and disturb the peace'. He was also sure that Argyll would one day return, and he had no wish to present him with so effective a system for raising a rebel force.

Argyll, when he landed, let it be known that his only reason for delaying his invasion until James was king was that Charles had signed the Covenant just before the battle of Dunbar and he would not rebel against a Covenanter. He was an angry man, embittered by what he felt were the hardships of his trial and condemnation for equivocating over the Test oath. Since he was now an outlaw and an exile 'any hazard was to be preferred to his present state' and he was confident that the accession of a Papist King would rally the clans to him. His sad little invasion* was doomed to failure by a delay of three days in the Orkneys, where he arrived on May 6. He sent his secretary and physician ashore to collect intelligence but they were collected instead, and retained by Bishop Mackenzie. Unable to arrange their release he went on to Kintyre, but by this time news of his plans was out and his supporters dispersed. His 'rising' was stamped on almost before it had begun, but the implications of it made Parliament in London extremely co-operative. Full of loyalty they granted James new import duties on such things as wine and sugar, vinegar, tobacco and French and East India linen, and also revoked the Act preventing the import of these commodities from France. This, with the annual income of £260,000 for life voted by the Scottish Parliament, and the revenue from his carefully invested capital when he was Duke of York, brought his annual income to well over two million pounds. 'Enough,' as he says in his Memoirs, to ensure that 'with careful husbandry' what he describes as 'peace', but meaning independence from Parliament, could have continued almost indefinitely 'had it not been for those who for their own ends persuaded the people that their laws, religion and lives were in danger, and thus beguiled them into real slavery under William of Orange'.

*

The English, with their admiration and sympathy for lost causes, find much that is romantic and pathetic in the attempt by James, Duke of Monmouth, to push his uncle off his throne, but there is little to admire

* He brought with him Rumbold of the Rye House and Ayliffe, the lawyer, who had also been involved in the Plot. Unable to make any headway against the Royal troops under the Marquis of Atholl and the Earl of Dumbarton, and after a disastrous night march in which most of his few troops lost their way and fell into a bog, it was every man for himself and Argyll rode off alone to seek safety after his force had broken up. While riding along the bank of the Clyde two servants of Sir John Shaw, envying his horse, tried to rob him of it. He fought back, thinking they were trying to capture him, whereupon a drunken weaver, living nearby, heard the noise, joined in the fight and Argyll was chased into the water. He tried to fire his pistol at the weaver but being wet it failed to go off and the weaver hit him on the head with a rusty sword. The Earl fell into the water crying, 'Ah, unfortunate Argyll!'—as indeed he was. He was beheaded. Rumbold, captured in a skirmish by Hamilton the Younger of Raploch, was mortally wounded but was kept alive just long enough to be executed. Ayliffe was taken to London because it was thought he might have valuable information to impart, but he had no illusions left and was very rude to everyone. He was 'hanged before the Gate of the Temple'.

in the character of Charles's bastard and any sympathy should perhaps be given to the misguided peasants of Dorset, Somerset and Devon who let the rabid preacher Ferguson persuade them to fight—and die or be transported—for 'King Monmouth'. Perhaps at the time it all sounded very exciting and offered a stimulating break in the monotony of their lives.

Monmouth, Lord Grey of Werk and Ferguson landed at Lyme in Dorset with a hundred men in a frigate and two small tenders on June 11, and although the local Militia offered no opposition and seemed anxious to avoid embarrassing anybody, no one of any importance joined the rebels, and having marched about the West Country for several weeks in the pouring rain, Monmouth decided to risk everything in a night attack on the Royal camp on Sedgemoor. James's forces were commanded by Lord Feversham who had not inherited any military skill from his uncle Turenne, and in his small army he had the promising young soldier John Churchill at the head of Trelawney's Tangier Regiment of five companies, and Piercy Kirke who, in the previous year, had brought his regiment, The Queen's, back from the evacuation of Tangier.

Monmouth's local guide to Feversham's camp, Benjamin Newton, confused by the darkness and the thick mist rising from the sodden ground, lost his way and instead of leading the rebel army to their sleeping enemy, ended up on the wrong side of a deep, unfordable ditch called the Bussex Rhine, within comfortable musket range of the experienced regular troops. There was a great deal of shooting, but hardly a battle* at all. In the early dawn, as soon as the cavalry could see where they were going, the rebels were winkled out of the hedges and ditches and herded together to await trial for high treason.

Lord Grey was captured in the New Forest and on the following day Monmouth was found hiding in a ditch near Ringwood. 'King' Monmouth was taken to London for execution: a Bill of Attainder had been passed

---

* *An account of the ffight that was in Langmore the sixth of July 1685 between the King's Army and the Duke of Monmouth.*

The Ingagement began between one and two of the clock in the morning. It continued nearly one hour and a halfe. There was killed upon the spott of the King's souldiers sixteen; ffive of them buried in the Church, the rest in the churchyard, and had all a Christian buriall. One hundred or more of the King's souldiers wounded; of which wounds many died, of which we have no certaine account. There was killed of the rebels upon the Spott aboute 300; hanged with us 22 of which 4 were hanged in gemmasses. About 500 prisoners brought into our church, of which there was 79 wounded and 5 of them died of their wounds in our church. (This is the contemporary account by the Rev. Andrew Paschall, Rector of Chedzoy, and it hangs today on the wall in Westonzoyland Church in Somerset. If one sits alone in this church on a bright July morning it is not difficult to imagine the scene, as the Rector saw it.)

on him so there was no need for a trial. Much under the influence of soothsayers and seers, he had been told, and firmly believed, that if he survived St. Swithin's Day he would live to be a great man. His last letter* to James was an appeal for time. Ironically enough he was executed with almost unbelievable inefficiency on St. Swithin's Day, July 15, and rather like an incompetent matador, the executioner had to be protected by the soldiers round the scaffold on Tower Hill from a crowd infuriated by the standard of his performance: 'The wretch,' says Evelyn, 'made five chops before he had his head off, which so incensed the people that had he not been guarded and got away, they would have torn him to pieces.'

Monmouth was only thirty-six when he died. Lord Grey, having told all he knew about the Rye House Plot, was pardoned, and Ferguson was 'dismissed without punishment'. At the time there was no doubt in anyone's mind, including Monmouth's, about the justice of the sentence. He was a rebel, taken in armed revolt against the King, obviously guilty of high treason, and the penalty for that was death. James had always had a powerful prejudice against rebels and he had not forgotten what had happened to his father. It would never have occurred to him to commute the death sentence, yet, in sending Monmouth to the scaffold, he made perhaps the worst mistake of his life.

Monmouth was James's only overt rival, the 'Protestant Prince', tool and pawn as well as the nominal leader of the Whigs, and the only pretender to the throne. If James had spared his life and kept him closely guarded in some secure fortress he would have remained the nominal

---

*   Tuesday.
  I have received your Majesty's order this day, that I am to die tomorrow. I was hoping sir by what you said to me yesterday of taking care of my soul, that I should have had some little more time, for truly Sir this is very short. I do beg of your Majesty if it be possible to let me have one day more that I may go out of the world as a Christian ought.
  I had desired several times to speak with My Lord Arundel of Ward, which I do desire still. I hope your Majesty will grant it me, and I do beg of your Majesty to let me know by him if there is nothing in this world that can recall your sentence or at least reprieve me for some time. I was in hope I should have lived to serve you, which I think I could have done to a great degree but your Majesty does not think it fitt. Therefore I shall end my days with being satisfied that I had all the good intentions immaginable for it, and should have done it, being that I am your Majesty's most dutiful
                                                                         Monmouth
I hope your Majesty will give Doctor Ferguson
leave to come to me—or any other that your
Majesty will be pleased to grant me.
  (The original of this letter is in the Bower Collection at Chiddingstone Castle, Kent.)

leader of the Whigs and they would not have been able to transfer their allegiance to a Dutchman. While Monmouth remained alive William had no chance of winning political support in England: Monmouth's death paved the way for William's invasion.

Both expeditions, Argyll's and Monmouth's, were mounted in Amsterdam, and it is impossible to believe that William, with his excellent intelligence service, did not know about them; but he was certainly not prepared to give them any active support. Nor was he willing to stop them. Able to see much further ahead than his father-in-law, because the aggressor always has the initiative, he was glad to let them go, hopelessly ill-equipped and entirely dependent on local support which he knew from his agents would probably not be forthcoming. It was as good a way as any to clear the scene for his own plans.

The battle of Sedgemoor was followed in due course by the so-called 'Bloody Assizes', a name given to Judge Jeffreys's work on the western circuit long after the event, and with the object of underlining the horrors of life in the reign of James II. Much time and trouble have been devoted by James's Whig detractors to showing that the appalling cruelty and vindictiveness in the western counties turned the country against him, but there is nothing to support this, and the evidence is all on the other side. Anyone who took part in armed rebellion knew very well what the penalty would be if he was caught, and bearing in mind the number of rebels at Sedgemoor—about 5,000, of which 1,200 were killed and 600 taken prisoner—the number of executions for high treason is comparatively small. In Exeter the lists giving the names of all the people sentenced to death by Jeffreys in the West of England in the year 1685 contain 249 names. Of these a large number were reprieved, and the figure of actual executions is between 160 and 170.

In the late summer of the following year James toured the West Country and 'was received with great testimonies of duty and respect', and two years after that, when the usurper William arrived and sat his army down outside Exeter, the response from the local people was so disappointing that he very nearly returned to Holland. Even thirty years later, James's son received much support for the Jacobite cause from the people of the West of England.

Since there have been errors and deliberate perversions of facts, it is not unreasonable to assume that other aspects, not only of Monmouth's Rebellion but of events in James's reign, have been deliberately misrepresented. Sir Charles Petrie, in his book *The Stuarts*, has written what must be regarded as the final word on the twisting of Jacobean history: 'That the faults of James have had more attention from historians cannot be denied, and the reason is not far to seek. His cause received so much support that more than half a century after he had lost the throne his grandson came within an ace of recovering it, and thus it was a matter of life and death for the Whig oligarchs to denigrate his memory. He was depicted as a veritable ogre, and the adherents of the Hanoverian regime never tired of denouncing the terrible state of affairs which was supposed to have existed, as may be seen in *Tom Jones*. The last monarch of a fallen dynasty is always treated in this manner, and writers under the Tudors so blackened the character of Richard III that to this very day we do not know what manner of man he really was.'

TWENTY-THREE

THE reign of James II began on February 6, 1685, and ended on December 23, 1688, just under four years later. In that time, apart from the abortive rebellions of Monmouth and Argyll, and the final invasion by his nephew and son-in-law, there are few really striking events. In order to find material with which to denigrate his memory, the Whigs and their fellow-travellers have had to pick on comparatively trivial matters and exploit them as best they can. A typical example is the horror expressed at the 'carnage' of the Bloody Assizes and the allegations that James was so delighted with Jeffreys's 'murderous work' that on his return to London Jeffreys was elevated to the peerage and made Lord Chancellor.

He was created a peer before Monmouth even landed, and his promotion was decided before the Assizes, when Guildford the Lord Keeper died: so he did not in fact receive any rewards for his services. James is blamed for failing to intervene and 'stop the slaughter', and he is also accused of failing to show any disapproval for what Jeffreys was doing. But James would only have shown disapproval if he had been capable of judging by the standards of a penal reformer of today—events under extremist regimes debar any comparison with 'twentieth-century standards'.

It was a cruel age. On May 16, a few weeks before Monmouth landed, Titus Oates was taken from his debtor's prison, tried for perjury and sentenced to be pilloried and then whipped at the cart's tail, twice, from Newgate to Tyburn,* a punishment obviously intended to be fatal. But Oates, roaring like a bull, survived it all, receiving some 3,000 strokes and lived to enjoy a pension granted to him for his services to the Whig party when William came to the throne. This was a far worse punishment than hanging, but Evelyn, who 'chanced to pass just as execution was doing on him', says that though 'some thought it to be severe and extraordinary, his punishment was but he deserved'. This was the general opinion, *at the time*, of the verdicts in the Bloody Assizes. Undoubtedly

* In other words, from just opposite the Old Bailey to Marble Arch.

the beheading of Alice Lisle* who harboured fugitives, and the burning of Elizabeth Gaunt† for trying to save one of the Rye House Plotters, were black injustice, but the cases were no worse than the judicial butchery of Jesuit priests known to be innocent at the time of the Popish Plot, and to blame James for them is straining prejudice a little far.

A great deal of Whig indignation had centred round James's army, in which he took so much pride. He had always held strong views about the need for a standing army, but the nation as a whole, after Cromwell's rule, wanted no soldiers except the local militia. This was hardly even a police force, called up when the need arose and therefore usually too late to be effective. Venner's Insurrection had shown the need for a small permanent force, which had gradually increased during Charles's reign,‡ and James did not hesitate to make use of Argyll's and Monmouth's rebellions as justification for increasing his army. He concentrated it in a large camp on Hounslow Heath—some 13–14,000 men, which he described as the best paid, the best equipped and best disciplined troops in Europe, and so they were. Though resented at home they raised his credit considerably abroad, and William, always in need of well-trained land forces in his endless struggle against His Catholic Majesty Louis XIV, included them in his plans.

The Whigs claimed that the presence of the army at Hounslow was intended 'to awe the people of London', but in reality they refused to be awed. The camp became extremely popular: all Society went there to be seen in so fashionable a spot, to watch the parades and enjoy the company of the soldiers. James was often there, reviewing his troops, dining in the messes and probably re-living some of the happiest days in his life when he had served in Turenne's army. To regard this force as a menacing mailed fist uplifted to crush the London mob is ridiculous. James loved soldiering and really enjoyed the society of soldiers: he spoke their language. And the camp was at Hounslow not to threaten London but because it was conveniently almost midway between Whitehall and Windsor.

It is not surprising that the principle of a standing army should have

---

* She was the widow of one of the regicides and that cannot have helped her. Apparently no appeal for a pardon was made to James and he knew nothing about the case until after the execution. It was Jeffreys, not James, who changed the sentence from hanging to beheading.

† Tried before Sir Edward Herbert, who succeeded Jeffreys as Chief Justice, on October 19 for aiding and concealing a man called Burton, she was condemned on his evidence.

‡ The two Tangier regiments of Foot (2nd and 4th by the old numbering) had not been disbanded when Tangier was evacuated in 1684, and others had been raised.

caused concern in a people determined to defend their religion and liberty against a Popish King, but their concern rings a little hollow when facts and not emotions are considered. James in his lifetime had seen a great deal of civil strife, and in his brother's reign there had been a republican faction, supported in Parliament, trying to 'convince the nation with fears' not only of the Popish religion but of Popish violence. He had seen two rebellious armies, those of Cromwell and Monmouth, take the field allegedly in the cause of religion but really in the cause of destroying the monarchy, and he was beginning to suspect that there might soon be a third. He needed the army to keep the peace, and it was unrealistic to imagine, or fear, that he could establish Popery with a Protestant army— for the number of Catholics he tried to introduce into it was infinitesimal.

James had seen enough of war and wanted only peace, prosperity and the rule of law, but he knew there could be none of these things without the power to enforce the law and quell disturbances. A small standing army gave him this power. He had his suspicions that William wanted the resources of England to use against his great enemy Louis XIV, who showed every sign of becoming the master of Europe. While James and Lord Dartmouth were being driven back from Monmouth's execution Dartmouth had told him that although he had disposed of one enemy, the really dangerous one was still alive; and James now had an idea of William's intentions although his nephew's open friendliness raised many doubts in his mind. He had been dismayed to find that the troops he had recalled from Holland during the rebellions 'were poisoned against him' —in that they were strongly anti-Catholic—and he knew that even if William had given little help to Monmouth and Argyll he had done nothing to discourage them. William was moving very carefully. He sent his friend and minister Bentinck to James with smooth messages and offers of help against Monmouth, but James says he saw himself how worried Bentinck was when he agreed to see Monmouth before he was executed. Bentinck had been afraid that Monmouth would implicate William, or perhaps betray William's financial arrangement with Sunderland, and though his fears had been groundless he was not at all happy until Monmouth could no longer talk.

*

In strengthening the army, James behaved unwisely over Ireland where he knew he could count on Catholic support. He sent Henry, Earl of Clarendon, there as his 'Deputy', apparently forgetting that he was just as stern a Protestant as his father had been, and soon discovered he was not the man to improve conditions for the oppressed Irish nor to carry out his plans to allow Catholics to serve in the army. He then gave a Lieutenant General's commission to an old friend of his youth, Dick Talbot (later the Earl of Tyrconnel), a Catholic, and told him to open the way for recruiting Catholics. He also told him that if necessary he could get rid of 'the Protestants who were of the Cromwellian stamp'. Talbot interpreted his instructions in his own way, dismissing without any compensation all those, and the sons of those, now loyal soldiers who had served in the Parliamentary or Cromwellian armies, particularly any who were in any way associated with the massacres at Drogheda and Wexford. James says that the majority of them were paid off, and the arms in their possession stored in magazines, but the evidence does not support him. There seems to have been a great deal of hardship and brutality, men being stripped of the uniforms they had bought by stoppages of pay, and turned half-naked into the streets. James himself was probably never told what was really happening, and those who served him did not always observe his principle of reform without violence.

Clarendon, a loyal, conscientious and humane man, took exception to Talbot's methods, and James, unable to reconcile the two men, elevated Talbot to the peerage and announced his intention of recalling Clarendon and replacing him by Talbot. Even his Catholic advisers objected to the promotion of so extreme a man who was unlikely to serve James's best interests, but Talbot, trading on his life-long friendship with James, went into close alliance with Sunderland and between them they eventually persuaded James to bring his brother-in-law back to England.

＊

The Parliament interrupted by the rebellions met again on November 9, and James caused some alarm by his proposals to augment the regular forces and to bring Catholic officers into the English army. After some debate on his speech the Commons presented an address against 'employing Papists', and on November 17 James replied to it: 'I did not expect such an address from the House of Commons, for having recommended so lately to your consideration the great advantages a good understanding between us had produced, in a very short time, and given you warnings of fears and jealousies amongst ourselves, I had reason to hope that the reputation God has blessed me with in the world would have sealed and confirmed a good confidence in you of me, and of all that I say to you; but however you proceed on your part, I will be steady in all the promises I have made to you, and be just to my word in this and all my other speeches.'

These few words to a House full of his loyal supporters are perhaps a good example to illustrate James's unfitness for supreme command. No leader can have any lasting influence over those he tries to lead if he takes that sort of attitude. He withdrew from the chamber and there was a profound silence. Then someone suggested that a day be chosen on which to consider the King's remarks, whereupon a certain Captain John Coke, the royalist Member for Derby, stood up and made the famous remark: 'I hope we are all English men and not to be frighted out of our duty with a few hard words.'

The odd thing about this incident is that although practically every individual present must have felt exactly as Coke did, the corporate feeling was so royalist that the unfortunate man who voiced everyone's secret opinion was, by vote of the Members, sent to the Tower for his impertinence.

James's announcement about Catholic officers in the army could not in fact have been made at a more unfortunate moment, because in the previous month (October 1685) Louis XIV had made one of his gravest political errors. With the approval of all the great churchmen in France he had revoked the Edict of Nantes, by which his grandfather Henry IV had granted 'Liberty of Conscience' to the Protestant minority in France. Amongst the people the French Protestants were extremely unpopular because they were hard-working, successful and, above all, rich. To Louis they were an obstruction in his progress towards a state united in religion and everything else. He sent the Marquis de Louvois to superintend the 'conversions' as they were called, and his troops enjoyed a long season of atrocities. Nearly half a million refugees, valuable citizens who took their skills with them, managed to escape from their tormentors and settle in Holland, Germany and England. They also brought with them the stories of the 'conversions', and they spread horrifying, and no doubt largely true, anti-Catholic propaganda in which France appeared as a dangerous and permanent threat to all Protestant countries.

It was all extremely awkward for James, torn between what he knew to be the true faith and his cousin's obviously unacceptable temporal interpretation of it. His problems were made more complicated by the fact that he had continued to accept the 'pension' Charles received from France. He had to avoid so offending Louis by his care for the Huguenot refugees that diplomatic relations might be cut off, and at the same time, by his treatment of them, prove to his own people that their fears of Popery were unjustified; and all the time the French Ambassador Barrillon was reporting almost everything he said and did.

Refugees had been coming into England in fairly large numbers ever since Louis had started his campaign against them in 1681, and so the arrival of even larger numbers after the Revocation created no sudden crisis. James achieved a rather wobbly compromise. The Huguenots settled in, James gave £500 of his own money to start a fund for their relief, and they were absorbed into the population—but they were no help to James's plans for religious toleration. There was much talk in the Commons during November on James's proposals for 'Popish officers', and finally, on November 20, James prorogued Parliament until February 10 in the following year.

Having not been very successful in his handling of Parliament, James, soon after the prorogation, created considerable dissension in his own household by his behaviour with his mistress, Catherine Sedley. Much had changed at court when Charles died: Pepys and Evelyn both comment on the sharp upward trend in moral standards and the absence of 'buffoonery'. James told Catherine Sedley that now he was King she would have to go, and he sent her away from her lodgings in Whitehall but bought her No. 21 St. James's Square, which had formerly belonged to Arabella Churchill. As well as giving her the house he increased her allowance from £2,000 to £4,000 a year, and said goodbye. Several months later they met, perhaps by accident, perhaps not, under the roof of William Chiffinch, the 'confidential person' who had worked for Charles and was now working for James. They went on seeing each other secretly, and on January 19, 1686, James suddenly created her Baroness Darlington, Countess of Dorchester.

Mary Beatrice, of whom Barrillon says 'she loves her husband sincerely and is very proud', was so upset that for two days she refused to eat anything and would not speak to James. He tried hard to persuade her that all was now over between him and Catherine,* and the title was only his way of making the parting easier for her. It is most unlikely that she believed a word of it. After much distress—and intrigue—on all sides, Catherine was persuaded to go to Ireland where her friend Clarendon was viceroy. She arrived in Dublin on March 2 but he, obviously reluctant to become involved in her sort of intrigues, saw very little of her. Five months later she returned to London and, despite all his promises to his wife, James continued to see her, right up until the Revolution. Poor James could never overcome his passion for variety. 'I must own,' he wrote to his son years later, 'with shame and confusion, I let myself go too much to the love of Women which but for too long gott the better of me: I have paid dear for it.'

*

* She had several children by James—in February 1686 two of his sons were being educated in Paris, but all except Lady Catherine Darnley died young.

In the year 1686 Sunderland achieved one of his primary objectives, complete control over all access to the King; and of all Sunderland's activities this was probably the one which had the most disastrous effect on James. When Halifax was dismissed in the previous year Sunderland took his place as Lord President of the Council and yet retained his post as Principal Secretary of State. He was thus in charge of all the sources of information and James, who trusted him absolutely, received all his intelligence, news and any other reports through him. This explains much that would be difficult to understand when considering some of James's actions. He knew only what Sunderland wanted him to know—and Sunderland was taking money from both William and Louis.

James was very well aware that Sunderland had been his enemy, siding with Shaftesbury and Louise de Querouaille at the time of the Exclusion campaign, and the reason he gives for not dismissing him as soon as he came to the throne is his reluctance to get rid of a man his brother had trusted: for he respected Charles's judgement of people. But he had made up his mind to send him off to some foreign embassy, and Sunderland managed to avoid this by winning over James's brothers-in-law, Clarendon and Rochester, and persuading them to intercede on his behalf 'so that he could keep the Seal'. He repaid them for their help by a cautious and entirely successful campaign to remove them from James's favour.

Another significant event in that year was the emergence, in the summer, of the Jesuit Father Petre as the dominant influence over James's mind. His influence had been increasing rapidly over the previous three years and he now reached the position where James consulted him on most things and usually took his advice—particularly on matters connected with religion. Unfortunately Petre was a man who, as James says in his Memoirs written much later and with the advantages of hindsight, was 'a plausible but weak man, and had only the art by an abundance of words to put a gloss upon a weak and shallow judgement'.

James, lacking the flair for leadership and quite unable to cope with the ambitions and intrigues of the men around him, was beginning to get out of his depth.

His efforts to improve conditions for Catholics in Scotland were not well received, and he realized that the English Parliament would not lighten their burden either, if it could be helped, and was extremely resistant to any move to increase the army or navy or employ Catholics in them. By careful management—and because of the initial Parliamentary enthusiasm after his accession—he was financially independent and did not need a Parliament for voting 'supplies', and so he felt that if they were going to be unco-operative over his religious measures, there was really no point in calling them again. But resistance outside Parliament was beginning to spread, and James took swift action against a clergyman, Samuel Johnson, who published what James considered to be a seditious libel addressed to all soldiers and sailors telling them not to associate with 'idolators and bloody Papists who fight for the Mass book and to burn the Bible'. He was unfrocked, pilloried and fined.

Sunderland, forever plotting against James's brothers-in-law, prevailed upon James to set up a secret Council, deliberately excluding Rochester and others 'who might be dangerous to him', consisting entirely of Catholics. He then set out to form an alliance with Father Petre, and arrange for him to be accepted into the secret Council. This was one of his craftier moves because he knew his friendship with Petre would increase his own credit with James and at the same time Petre would be given the blame for all 'unpleasing Councells' and thus be 'an instrument and a cloake to all his dark designs'.

Even Mary Beatrice, who seldom interfered or was allowed to interfere in such matters, saw the dangers of this arrangement and opposed it, but James 'was so bewitched by My Lord Sunderland and Father Petre as to let himself be prevailed upon to do so undiscreet a thing'.

Roger Palmer, Lord Castlemaine, was sent off on an embassy to Rome to ask for a cardinal's hat for Petre, but he had singularly little success. Though he was a good choice for such a task—he was intelligent, possessed a quick, analytical mind, spoke Italian and had travelled in Italy—the only generally known facts about him were that he was the husband of Charles's mistress, Barbara, whose special skills had earned him his title, and that as a Catholic he had been tried for his life at the time of the Popish Plot.

James's relationship with Pope Innocent XI was not a happy one, largely because James had always allowed the Jesuits to guide him in spiritual matters, and the Pope, who remained in a permanent and bitter state of discord with Louis XIV, did not approve at all of the French and English Jesuits. He was a wise man, possessing great diplomatic skill, and he considered that their activities were likely to do great harm to the Catholic Church in England.

So Lord Castlemaine had no chance of succeeding. There is a story that whenever he obtained an audience and tried to raise the subject of his mission the Pope would suffer from an attack of coughing which compelled everyone to retire. It seems very unlikely that a man of the Pope's calibre would find it necessary to resort to such measures; on the other hand the story sounds as if it was the sort of excuse for failure that Petre, no doubt aware of the Pope's disapproval, might understand.

James had very little luck with his plans for Catholics: everything he did was misconstrued and gave offence, despite his care in trying to avoid interference with 'the possessions, priviledges and immunities' of the Church of England. He took the chapel at St. James's Palace—the house he really knew and seems to have loved—for himself, and he and Mary Beatrice revealed much knowledge and artistic appreciation in collecting pictures for it. Another Catholic chapel was built in Whitehall, and the Jesuits were told they could build one in the Savoy and establish a school there for children. The school was a great success, according to James, who says that in a very short time it contained 200 Catholic and 200 Protestant children, and the Protestants were not required to play any part in 'the Catholic ritual'. Other chapels were set up elsewhere, but always on ground specially bought for the purpose, and the trouble was that there were too many: more than could be filled or for which officiating priests were available. This caused a certain amount of ridicule but illustrated James's point about the small number of Catholics in the kingdom.

James realized that the main obstacle to obtaining toleration for Catholics was the Test Act—which had forced him to resign all his offices in 1673. He knew he could never persuade any Parliament to repeal the Act and he therefore tried to find a way round it. He argued that since the Kings of England had to give final assent to the laws of the Kingdom, the laws were thus in effect the King's laws, and since the Kings could not renounce the prerogatives annexed to the Crown they could, legally, dispense with 'all laws that regarded penalties and punishment as oft as necessity required'. In short, since the King instituted penalties he could abolish them when they were no longer needed. He felt that the time had come to abolish the penalties attached to the Test Act, and he arranged for a test case.

Sir Edward Hales, a 'gentleman of fortune and family in Kent', an open and professed Catholic, accepted command of a regiment and began to exercise the functions of a commanding officer without taking the Test. His coachman, Godden, informed against him and claimed the £500 reward provided for in the Act. Sir Edward was indicted, and the case came up for trial at Rochester Assizes on March 29, 1686. He was duly convicted but pleaded 'he had a dispensation under the broad Seal to act *non obstante* the Statute' and produced the King's dispensation with his non-conformity remitting all penalties and disabilities he had incurred. The plaintiff, the coachman, then brought his suit into the King's Bench as an action for debt, and it came before the Lord Chief Justice, Sir Edward Herbert, who declared 'there was nothing whatever with which the King, as supreme lawgiver, could not dispense'.

The matter was then laid before twelve judges—who were not selected at random—and on June 21 the Lord Chief Justice announced in Westminster Hall that eleven of the twelve judges upheld his decision 'on various grounds'. But, 'finding general alarm', he then published his reasons for making his judgement which, according to James, 'put the matter so far beyond dispute that all the erudition of his adversaries or malice of his detractors could not furnish them with the least colour of a reply'.

This was all very well, but brilliant legal arguments seldom impress anyone except lawyers who can appreciate them. To the general public this judgement 'laid the law in ruins at the foot of the throne'. There were legal precedents for what James had done, and it is probable that had the case not been connected with 'Popery' no one would have been upset by this use of the 'dispensing power'. As it was, they saw a Catholic King making way for the establishment of his faith and, bearing in mind what had happened in France, they were extremely uneasy. This use of the dispensing power* and the timing of it did James serious harm for it provided his enemies with effective ammunition.

Assured by his advisers that his actions were perfectly legal, and no doubt insulated from public opinion, James then went a little further down the path to his own destruction, for he set up what he called the Ecclesiastical Commission. This, in effect, was a revival of what had been the Court of Star Chamber in the reign of Elizabeth and the High Commission in his father's reign. Perhaps he had forgotten that Archbishop Laud, who had christened him, had gone to the block largely because of his use of this weapon of Church authority.

As so often, James had the best of motives for doing something vastly unpopular. Because he was a Catholic he felt he neither could nor should exercise over the Church of England the jurisdiction which the law gives to the sovereign. Discussing the problem with his judges he was assured, once again, that it would be perfectly legal to confer this jurisdiction upon a Commission and that there were precedents dating from before the time of Queen Elizabeth. The High Commission in his father's reign had not been very successful because Laud had exercised its powers somewhat freely, but that need not happen again. Genuinely feeling he was doing what was best for the Anglican Church, James issued the instructions which brought the Ecclesiastical Commission into being on August 3, 1686.

It was regarded with the deepest suspicion, and there was a general fear that its powers would be applied solely for the benefit of the King.

* It was removed by the Bill of Rights in 1688.

Almost at once this fear appeared to be justified. The Rector of St. Giles-in-the-Fields, Dr. Sharp, made a number of 'reflections' against the King and his government, and James told Compton, the Bishop of London, to suspend him. Compton wrote to the all-powerful Sunderland saying he was always prepared to 'obey his Majesty in anything he could with a safe conscience', but this did not extend to condemning a man unheard and untried. The matter was brought before the Commission and after some argument the conclusion was reached that Compton should have reprimanded Sharp and that by creating difficulties was in fact disputing, or perhaps failing to acknowledge, the King's authority. The Bishop was found to be at fault and the Commission moved he be suspended 'from function and execution of episcopal office though not from benefice or revenue'. James, reluctant to make an issue of something that appeared to be getting out of hand, soon restored him, hoping he had made the point that as the King he was not prepared to do nothing while 'he was censured and traduced from the Pulpit'.

This was reasonable enough, but to his people, on the watch for any sign of an invasion of their religious 'liberty', this attack on Compton was an ugly warning.

TWENTY-FOUR

ENTERING the third year of his reign, James appeared to be in an extremely strong position. He was free from any obligation to summon Parliament and his judges had established that he possessed a 'dispensing power'. Thus, in so short a while, he had achieved his ambition to rule as an absolute monarch.

Even if he could not make laws he could at least make adjustments in the existing statutes which affected his plans for religious toleration, and these now seemed to be progressing. His aims were clear enough in his own mind: peace, prosperity and the rule of law; and religious toleration was an essential step towards peace and prosperity for everyone. If he had been a natural leader he might, had he gone slowly and carefully, have carried the country with him as he moved towards 'Liberty of Conscience', but his years as the 'second-in-command', and lack of the special 'sense' which makes a leader, combined to defeat him. A natural leader does not require advisers except in the form of specialists in particular subjects which, for various reasons, he cannot master for himself. He does not need men to tell him what to do. He may, and should, listen to criticism of his plans and intentions and make changes where change is needed, but he does not allow anyone else to make his major decisions.

James did. He did not have that final polish of self-confidence which distinguishes the leader from the second-in-command, and, in leaning upon his advisers, he made the mistake of relying on men like Sunderland and Petre. He made many mistakes: over Monmouth and the dispensing power and the Ecclesiastical Commission, over Tyrconnel in Ireland, and the speed at which he tried to do things, and over Sunderland. Sunderland effectively separated him from such men as Clarendon and Rochester whose actions 'were balanced by zeal for the Church of England and the King's true interests'. Sunderland was apt to applaud, where he had not inspired, all James's measures, while Rochester fully appreciated the difficulties likely to arise from straining complex points of law, and opposed everything likely to cause trouble on that score. James had already alienated men like Halifax who could see which way things were going and might, had James been more reasonable, have slowed the tempo of events and steadied James on his course. It was everyone's loss that in succeeding to the throne he had taken over a task that was beyond his capabilities.

While outwardly in England all was calm under the King the seeds of discontent and dismay over two main issues, autocracy and Catholicism, had germinated, and across the waters where James the sailor had so often led his fleet, the dark silent man in Holland watched and listened and waited for his opportunity.

In his long campaign for toleration James made what was generally regarded as a strange friendship with a man from whom he differed radically in almost all respects, but with whom he had one fast link. To William Penn, the Quaker, liberty of conscience was as dear as life itself.

That valiant old sailor Sir William Penn, Captain of James's flagship *Royal Charles* at the battle of Lowestoft, had on his deathbed spoken of his son to James, and from this there had grown no mere acquaintance but a solid friendship which nothing was ever to disrupt. Even after the Revolution, when any communication with James in exile was treated as high treason, William Penn continued to write long letters to the King for whom he seems to have had sympathy and compassion as well as real affection. He also seems to have seen in James a true spirit of toleration and a real desire to grant to all men freedom to worship in their own way. If James had not been genuine, there could have been no such relationship.

The Quakers benefited considerably from Penn's friendship with James; one cannot describe it as influence because Penn himself would have scorned the word. In 1685 they became no longer subject to penalties for refusing to attend the services of the Church of England, and hundreds were released from prison. No doubt Penn had a hand in James's first Declaration of Indulgence—he himself called it a Declaration of Liberty of Conscience—published in Scotland on February 18, 1687. James always considered Scotland to be more loyal to the Crown than England. The Declaration contained sweeping changes in support of James's 'settled opinion that men's consciences ought not to be forced'. He did not consult Parliament before publishing it because his advisers assured him it was not necessary, and since its reception in Scotland appeared to be favourable—the discontent under the surface did not appear for some time—James declared in Council his intention to publish it in England, and he did so on April 4.

The main points made in the Declaration were that four of James's predecessors had tried to establish uniformity in religious worship, but without success. The restraint upon Dissenters' consciences had been extremely prejudicial to the nation—for example, the civil war which had led to the death of his father. The penal laws against Dissenters had in fact increased rather than reduced their numbers. The King felt sure nothing could be better for the peace, quietness, progress and trade of his kingdom than a complete Liberty of Conscience, which accorded with true Christian principles, 'that no man should be persecuted for conscience' sake'.

This really amounted to leaving the Church of England exactly as it was, but repealed the laws against non-conformists, abolished the oaths of Allegiance and Supremacy and the Test, and pardoned all alleged crimes of non-conformity. There had been no objection by the Council to proposals which seemed both sensible and fair, but the Established Church at once regarded them as an attack on its position, rights and privileges. The Anglicans, who had lived with the penal laws for so long and successfully kept all other beliefs well trodden down, were not prepared to accept any measures which appeared to lower their status. In addition many of the old fears of 'Popery' as a political and military threat were revived, and the Church felt that existing measures must be retained for its own preservation.

To the Anglican objections James tried to make the point that a Church which does not pretend to be infallible should not compel people, under threat of horrible punishments and even death, to conform to its own beliefs. To him this did not make sense and he was convinced that the Church of England 'enjoyed its dominion over the others'.

The effect of his Declaration was to release thousands from prison all over the country, and congregations were free to hold their own services, in public, in their own way. For all that may be said about and against James, his sad mistakes and his misguided zeal, there can be no doubt that he was the originator of religious freedom in England, and this freedom dates from the year 1687.

Unfortunately he went about it in the wrong way and tried to do everything too quickly. He could not accept that where men's consciences and sincere beliefs, and the fears which may be linked with those beliefs, are concerned, there can be no immediate, arbitrary and enforced changes. Years may be needed, for guidance, persuasion and example; but James was haunted by time and the Protestant succession.

He made what were regarded as direct attacks upon the two great Universities—long acknowledged as the recruiting areas and training

James's daughter Anne
with her son the
Duke of Gloucester

Photos: Charles Cole

William of Orange and James's daughter Mary

James FitzJames,
Duke of Berwick

Photo : Charles Cole

Prince James Francis Edward
and his sister Louisa Maria,
by Largillière

James II in exile

The Château of Saint-Germain-en-Laye

grounds of the Anglican clergy. The first was unspectacular. Dr. Obadiah Walker, the Master of University College, Oxford, became a convert to the Roman faith and, by royal dispensation, remained in his post. He set up an oratory in his college, and though constantly opposed, and even persecuted, by undergraduates, he maintained a small Roman Catholic element in the University.

The second began on March 24, 1687, with the death of Dr. Henry Clarke, the President of Magdalen. On April 2 the Bishop of Winchester, visitor of the college, advised the Fellows to proceed with the election of a successor and suggested a suitable candidate. But on April 5 Sunderland signed a royal mandate instructing the Fellows to elect a certain Anthony Farmer to be their President. Farmer, apart from being a drunkard fond of consorting with private soldiers 'and other undesirable persons', occasionally enjoying a little vandalism,* and being involved in 'things not fit to be heard or spoken', was not and never had been a Fellow of Magdalen. Thus, discounting his character and record, under the Statutes of the Founder, he could not be elected. Though he was not a professed Catholic he was certainly not a good Protestant—another essential qualification for the post.

The Fellows ignored the mandate. They elected a Dr. John Hough to the Presidentship, and the appointment was confirmed by the Bishop of Winchester. James regarded this as wilful disobedience and an attempt to deny the overriding authority of the King. He refused to accept Dr. Hough's election and demanded an explanation. In very loyal terms the Vice-President and Fellows explained about their Statutes, the oaths they had taken when they became Fellows, and how impossible it was for them, legally, to have acted otherwise. Nothing happened for two months and then they were summoned to meet James when he was visiting Oxford. Nothing was achieved and they were ordered to appear before the Ecclesiastical Commission.

Even Jeffreys, prepared to strain most things in James's favour, admitted that on the evidence Farmer was totally unfit to hold such a position as the Presidentship of Magdalen. In the end the Fellows all resigned or were dismissed—there seems to be some doubt—but in December twelve new Fellows were admitted, six of whom were Catholics.

The third 'attack' came to nothing. A Catholic missioner for the county of Cambridge, a Benedictine monk called Alban Francis, was given a royal mandate for an honorary degree as Master of Arts of Cambridge

* As when at Abingdon he helped to uproot the town stocks and throw them in a pond.

University which exempted him from taking the oaths of Allegiance and Supremacy. The mandate was rejected by the University and on May 7 the Ecclesiastical Commission dismissed the Vice-Chancellor. His successor, in a bold speech, said he would not tolerate any interference with the rights of the University, and the matter was dropped. No doubt James, preoccupied with all the trouble at Oxford, felt the issue was not worth pursuing.

His clashes with the Universities, which seem to have originated with Petre and to have been supported by Sunderland for his own ends, had the unfortunate result of alienating the Anglican Church which, with its policy of supporting the monarchy, had not hitherto shown any noticeable inclinations towards disloyalty. James's championing of Farmer shows that he cannot have made any inquiries about the man, and in taking someone else's word for his character, and then supporting Farmer with the full weight of his authority, he brought great discredit upon himself and upon the Crown. He was gradually succeeding in doing what even his father had never done, unite the anti-court, or Whig, party with the Established Church in opposition to the Crown.

The atmosphere of discontent was thickening. People were beginning to feel that the attitude and activities of the Ecclesiastical Commission nullified James's promise to protect the Church of England, and few believed that its object was to correct disobedient members of the Church and not to destroy it. There was real alarm at James's arbitrary power, not held in check by any Parliament, for the country would accept laws and amendments to laws from Parliament but not from a Popish King.

On July 2 James finally dissolved Parliament, but in making the proclamation he had every intention of summoning another when he felt confident he would get one that would do what he wanted. The opportunity never arose, and could never have arisen because all James's authority was based on an autocracy which would have been the first target of any elected Parliament.

In the middle of August James and Mary Beatrice set off on a royal progress in the West of England, on a larger scale than James's tour in the previous year. He had intended to start in July, but had to postpone his journey because of the death of Mary Beatrice's mother. Plans for the progress included a visit to the waters at Bath and to Holywell, on the south side of the estuary of the River Dee in Flintshire, North Wales.

For four years there had been no prospect of an heir, and James, finding so much opposition to his 'Liberty of Conscience', and constantly aware of the Protestant succession, felt that his wife might benefit from the waters at Bath; and, perhaps offering even more hope for pregnancy and a son, there was the famous holy well, at what James calls Holliwel, in Wales. The well marked the place of the martyrdom of St. Winefride in the seventh century, and provided a large supply of water of unvarying temperature. The plan was that Mary Beatrice, and James, should pray for the blessing of a son at the shrine of St. Winefride, 'a place much frequented out of devotion', and said to have been built by the mother of Henry VII. Thereafter, according to superstition, Mary Beatrice might await results with confidence.

From James's point of view the progress was very nearly a complete success: not quite, because on his way back, when he passed through Oxford on September 4, he summoned the Fellows of Magdalen, 'hoping by his presence to mollify their stubborn spirits'. He went away sadly, having lost his temper with them and come to the conclusion that they were 'deliberately creating a cause for complaint' and might have the ulterior motive of forcing the Ecclesiastical Commission to take action against them so that they could try and discredit it. Confronted by what he regarded as disobedience, James usually found difficulty in seeing the other side's point of view.

Except for this discordant note in Oxford, everything went extremely well. All along their route* the King and Queen were received by cheering crowds, with loyalty and lavish hospitality. At Chester, where they stayed for three days, James had a meeting with Tyrconnel, who had come over from Ireland to meet him, and was given a long, one-sided and very inaccurate report of conditions there. Tyrconnel had by this time replaced Clarendon as 'Deputy', and Clarendon, in England, was finding life extremely difficult. Sunderland had so far succeeded in destroying Clarendon's credit with James that he was not allowed to return to his post as Lord Privy Seal—filled temporarily by a Commission while he was in Ireland—and he had practically nothing to live on. It seems likely that this apparent royal ingratitude had much more effect on his son, Lord Cornbury, than on him, for he remained extremely loyal to James.

Returning to Windsor, James had good reason to feel pleased with the results of his progress, for his popularity in the country seemed assured, and the effect of his reforms appeared to be far less adverse than he had feared. Then, later, there was the best result of all: St. Winefride—and presumably James too—had done what had been hoped for, and Mary Beatrice became pregnant again.

* To Portsmouth, where he was well known as a sailor, and Governor of the Port, then to Salisbury, Bath, Bristol, Gloucester, Newport, Worcester, Ludlow, Shrewsbury, Whitchurch in Denbighshire, Chester, and back through Coventry, Banbury, Oxford, Winchester to Windsor. He and Mary Beatrice went to Holywell from Whitchurch.

James's happiness was matched only by the dismay of the majority of his subjects. They were prepared for things to continue as they were for the rest of James's life, but the possibility of a male heir and 'continuation of Papist rule' was totally unacceptable. James really had no idea just how unacceptable they thought it was, and he commissioned Henry Purcell to write an anthem to mark the Queen's pregnancy.

Rochester had now left James's Council, out-manœuvred by Sunderland who wanted his job at the Treasury, but not in effect dismissed. He had been put into a position in which he had to choose between changing his religion or remaining a Protestant and resigning his post. To Sunderland's surprise and disappointment James did not give him the Treasury. Where money was concerned James usually kept his wits about him: he well understood that 'that Lord's cunning lay in intrigue, not in management, for he scarce knew how to form a figure, and the King was too prudent in what concerned his revenue to trust a man with his purse who could never keep a penny in his own'. It seems probable that James's refusal led Sunderland to reconsider his position and to come to the conclusion that with a change of government he might do better for himself.

*

The year 1688 is marked by three major events: the issue of the second Declaration of Indulgence which led to the trial of the seven Bishops and James's final rift with the Anglican Church; the birth of his son, which made William decide to wait no longer, and the so-called Glorious Revolution which was so singularly devoid of glory.

James prepared his second Declaration in May. It was a repetition of the first one, with the explanation that attempts were being made to convince the people he was no longer so determined to repeal the penal laws against Dissenters, and this was not true. By an Order in Council dated May 4 he gave instructions for the Declaration to be read on May 20 and 27 in the pulpits of all churches and chapels in and within ten miles of the City of London, and on June 3 and 10 everywhere else. The Bishops were told to distribute copies of the document throughout their dioceses.

There was nothing new about this method of broadcasting information but the clergy, taken completely by surprise, regarded the edict as a renewal and intensification of the attack on the Established Church. After much time had been wasted, largely because James had achieved such surprise, a meeting at Lambeth decided that the order was illegal and since the King could not commit an illegal act, 'for the Law says the King can do no wrong', it could not therefore be the King's order, and so 'by consequence they were not obliged to obey it'. An Address to His Majesty was prepared on these lines and signed by Sancroft, the Archbishop of Canterbury, and six Bishops.* Sancroft had incurred James's displeasure and was forbidden to go near the court, so his six colleagues presented the address to James on May 18, two days before the Declaration was to be read in London.

James adopted a perfectly straightforward attitude. To him this was rebellion. Once again, he lost his temper. He seldom did, for on the whole, in his later years, he was a patient man, and he was formidable when he was really angry. The Bishops, told that their address was 'a standard [i.e. flag] of rebellion', were completely taken aback. If they had foreseen that this might happen, few of them would have signed the address. They assured James of their loyalty, but he, not surprisingly, found it difficult to believe them.

Matters were then made infinitely worse by the appearance of their extremely confidential address that same evening, in printed form and widely distributed throughout London. No one knows who 'leaked' it, but it could easily have been Bishop Compton of London, who may have felt he had a debt to pay over the incident involving Dr. Sharp.

Two days later the Declaration was read in some churches and not in others. One unwilling incumbent achieved an excellent compromise by telling his congregation that he was compelled to read it but they were not compelled to listen. He then dutifully read it aloud in an empty church. Against the advice of Jeffreys but with the approval, and possibly the urging, of Sunderland who could now see he was on the wrong side, the seven Bishops were prosecuted for seditious libel.

Perhaps in circumstances less fraught with tension James would have abandoned the prosecution† when he heard that enormous crowds in London, the centre of Whigs and Dissenters, had roared their encouragement and support to the seven men on their way to the Tower. Again he had acted too precipitately, but he was resolved not to show 'that yielding temper which had proved so dangerous to the King his brother and so fatal to the King his father'. He was now convinced the Almighty was behind him. At last, having almost given up hope, Mary Beatrice

* Ken of Bath and Wells, Lloyd of St. Asaph, White of Peterborough, Turner of Ely, Lake of Chichester and Trelawney of Bristol.
† Henry, Earl of Clarendon, in his Diary wrote that Jeffreys was on the side of the Bishops and said 'the King was once resolved to let the business fall and not to have proceeded thus against them, that he [Jeffreys] was grieved to find the King had changed his mind, that he knew not how it came to pass but said there was no remedy; some men would hurry the King to his destruction'.

had given birth to a son on June 10, Trinity Sunday. With such an obvious manifestation of divine encouragement there could be no going back.

The case against the Bishops hinged on the 'dispensing power' of the King. If the dispensing power was a legal instrument, the King's command to the Bishops was just, and their disobedience was punishable. At the trial on June 29 the Lord Chief Justice Wright and Justice Allibone were for the King and Justices Powell and Holloway for the Bishops. The jury sat up all night.

James was at Hounslow on the morning of June 30, dining with Lord Feversham in his tent, and he was startled by a sudden outburst of cheering in the camp. He was told 'it was nothing but the joy of the soldiers at the acquittal of the Bishops'.

'And call you that nothing?' asked James. He rode back to London in a silence no one cared to break.

The sands of his brief reign were beginning to run out.

*

Prince James, only son of James II and Queen Mary Beatrice, was born soon after ten o'clock on the morning of Sunday, June 10, some two or three weeks prematurely. Clarendon, who hurried to congratulate James when he heard of the birth, was taken into the Queen's private bedchamber a few hours afterwards where the governess, Lady Powis, 'showed me the Prince. He was asleep in his cradle and was a very fine child to look upon.'

The birth was entirely uncomplicated but few babies can have been the subject of so much rumour, misrepresentation, slander and sheer malice. Even the behaviour of James's beloved daughter Anne was very peculiar. She and Mary Beatrice had been close friends for years, even before they lived in such intimacy during the second exile in Scotland, yet, pleading poor health, she went off to Bath to avoid being present when the baby arrived. James had particularly asked her to stay because she would be such 'a comfort to the Queen in advice and assistance', and it was only because he was concerned for her health that he let her go. Behind this desertion can be seen the hand of Sarah Jennings, wife of John Churchill, who exerted so powerful an influence over James's younger daughter; and her departure at so critical a time indicates that someone had been thinking ahead and making plans. The Churchills had now made up their minds which side they were on.

The actual birth was witnessed by Catherine the Queen-dowager, Lord Jeffreys, Lord and Lady Sunderland, the Duchesses of Portsmouth,

Bouillon and Mazarin, and a number of Privy Councillors and 'ladies of Quality'; many of the ladies stood round the great ornate bed.

William of Orange sent his congratulations.

It is very difficult to discover when the rumours first began and who began them, but the totally untrue story of the introduction of a male baby into the bed, in a warming-pan, under the eyes of all the people standing round it, grew into a belief as firmly and widely held as that attached to the Popish Plot ten years before. Apparently even Anne, prompted by Sarah Churchill, subscribed to it.

The reason for all the efforts to prove that the baby was not the child of James and Mary Beatrice is obvious—it stood in the way of the Protestant succession—but it seems extraordinary that so ridiculous a story should have found so much support. There had been rumours of a miscarriage in the sixth month of pregnancy, but everyone at court knew they were unfounded: they were now quoted as fact. It was true that Mary Beatrice had had two miscarriages in the past, and her five children had all died either almost at birth or soon after, and in view of this case-history it is even more strange that no one seemed to have any doubt that this baby would live. Nor did it occur to anyone that James might die while the child was still young and it could then be brought up in the Anglican faith, thus solving the problem. Everyone seems to have assumed at once that this was a durable Catholic heir and consequently large numbers of otherwise intelligent and sensible people went out of their way to support the 'warming-pan myth'.

It may have been that James's priests unwittingly helped to propagate it, because for some time, ever since Mary Beatrice's pregnancy was confirmed in January, they had been confidently predicting a male child who would be virtually the direct result of their constant applications for divine intervention. When the child arrived they clearly regarded it as a miracle—an inconsistency which was enough to arouse anyone's suspicions.

With the birth of the Prince the path of James's destiny plunged down an even steeper slope and events began to move with an accelerating beat.

Considerably shaken by the reaction of his troops to the trial of the Bishops, James disbanded the camp at Hounslow early in August and ordered Tyrconnel to bring over troops from Ireland. It was a perfectly natural and sensible thing for a military commander to do: if he was not sure of the loyalty of his local forces, it was logical to bring in others to redress the balance. It was the direct, but the most unfortunate, thing to do. About 3,500 Irish troops came over. They were undisciplined and untrained, and none of them, in view of Cromwell's activities and the treatment of Irish Catholics since then, felt that they were under any obligation or owed any loyalty to the King of England. The English opinion of them had not changed and they were still regarded as savages. They were hated as enemies and despised as barbarians, and, in their turn, resorted to robbery and rape. It was not a happy situation, and in Portsmouth, where James, Duke of Berwick, James's natural son by Arabella Churchill, was commanding the garrison, things were particularly bad. He may perhaps have thought that by distributing Irish troops among English units they could be kept under better control, but a crisis developed when in September he gave orders for a draft of some forty Irish recruits, surplus to the establishment of their own unit, to be posted in small detachments to local English regiments.

A Colonel Beaumont, supported by five of his officers, refused to accept them, saying they could only bring dishonour to his regiment and things had reached a sorry state if 'the army must have recourse to foreigners to fill the gaps in their Companies'. His attitude was perfectly respectful and he offered to resign rather than comply with the order.

James, unwisely, having apparently learned little of the general state of opinion from the trial of the Bishops, decided to make this a test case for the army. Colonel Beaumont and the other officers involved were court martialled. The court took a harsh line. It is said that Churchill, ranting about loyalty and discipline, wanted them shot—a measure which would have greatly increased the feeling against the King his former patron—but this may well be a biased embellishment by James's biographer. As it was, the officers were all dismissed the service, and the immediate effects of that were bad enough. A great many officers resigned their commissions, soldiers deserted, and James himself had to go to Portsmouth to try and redeem the situation.

Despite his close contact with military affairs at Hounslow, he seemed to be getting out of touch. There was almost as much trouble in the navy when the Catholic Sir Roger Strickland was appointed to command the fleet. The sailors so resented the presence of Catholic priests that some of the ships in the Thames estuary were almost in a state of mutiny. James had to go down and reassure the men: all the priests were withdrawn. Neither the navy nor the army was ready yet for any form of Liberty of Conscience.

It was not until the middle of September that James at last began to realize that what had hitherto been vague fears about his nephew William's intentions, were taking concrete form on the other side of the Channel. Lord Dartmouth had been warning him ever since Monmouth's rebellion that William was his enemy, but James was strangely reluctant to believe what so many other people knew. Suddenly he seemed to wake up and see for the first time in a clear light the effect on his people of all his hopes and plans and enthusiasm. It was as if he now drew back the curtain of his illusions and saw what was really happening. He perceived, perhaps for the first time, the real natures of the men around him: the fawning, garrulous, conceited Petre; Sunderland, as stable in his loyalties as dandelion seed; Jeffreys, who tried to say only what he knew his master wanted to hear; and all the others who were edging away now because they knew his star was setting. Perhaps he also saw more clearly the virtues of some of the men he had lost—Halifax, Rochester and Godolphin—yet even now there were men like Clarendon, Dartmouth, Middleton, and that gallant Scot, Lord Dundee, whose loyalty was unshaken.

Frantically James tried to restore what he had allowed to crumble away. He dissolved the Ecclesiastical Commission—for which there had never been any legal justification—he received a deputation of bishops under Sancroft and met all their requests, he tried to remedy all that had been accomplished at the Universities, he restored the charters taken from the cities and 'he left nothing undone which he thought might set the people right in their notions and obviate the groundless apprehensions they were prepossessed with'.

But it was all too late.

TWENTY-FIVE

To most of his subjects James was now the Catholic King who was doing what they had always feared he would do. All Evelyn's misgivings at the beginning of his reign, about 'Romanists swarming at Court with greater confidence than had ever been seen in England since the Reformation', had been more than justified.

The country was not ready for religious toleration. Few believed in Liberty of Conscience. The majority of the population feared that not only the Anglican Church but their own personal freedom were in danger while so autocratic and independent a monarch sat on the throne. Something drastic had to be done, and the only course of action, short of civil war, was to compel the King to summon a Parliament which must then persuade him that, politically, the country had passed beyond the stage of being able to submit without complaint to mediaeval despotism. But it was easy enough to say this: they were faced with the same problem as the mice when trying to cope with the cat.

It is probable that very few people ever thought seriously of removing James from his throne to make way for his Protestant nephew. So insular a nation did not contemplate replacing the descendant of a long line of their own kings with a foreigner, even a foreigner married to a member of the English royal house. But William of Orange, ruthless, ambitious and determined, seized the fine threads of opportunity and wove them into the rope with which the people of England, albeit with considerable reluctance, hoisted him to power.

Even while all James's hopes were tumbling into the dust and his enemies were making their final preparations, he took special pains over the ceremony of christening his son and declaring him Prince of Wales. In a solemn service held in the Chapel in St. James's Palace, at which the Pope, represented by Conte Fernando d'Adda, was godfather, and Catherine of Braganza the godmother, the four-month-old baby was named James Francis Edward.

Ever since the child's birth the fable of the warming-pan had been gaining more and more believers, and James was advised to 'prove' the birth of his son. Poor Mary Beatrice, to whom even the announcement of her pregnancy had been an embarrassment and who had undoubtedly been considerably distressed by the indignity of giving birth before so many witnesses, could not believe that such 'proof' was really necessary. She spoke, a little diffidently, to her stepdaughter Anne about it, and to her astonishment Anne said coldly that she was not at all surprised since many of the people who ought to have been present were not. Mary Beatrice was extremely upset. Anne knew very well that there could not possibly have been any 'arrangement', she also knew that rumours of a miscarriage in the spring were quite untrue for she had been with her stepmother at the time when there had been fear of it. It had been in the seventh month of her pregnancy, while James was away at Chatham. Mary Beatrice reminded her that she had seen her and often helped her to dress, all through her pregnancy, and once even 'felt the movement of the child'. It was a great shock to her to discover that the Churchills had succeeded in stealing the loyalty of the girl she had been so fond of.

James, too, at first thought a formal announcement was unwise; because denials often lend weight to rumours, and it was unnecessary in view of the roomful of witnesses. But at length, accompanied by Queen Catherine, he made a statement in the presence of the Members of the Privy Council, all the Lords Spiritual and Temporal who happened to be in London, the Lord Mayor, Aldermen, Judges and King's Counsels. He wanted Anne to be there too and make a statement of her personal knowledge of the pregnancy, but at the last moment she pleaded, falsely, that she herself was pregnant and all the emotional strain might make her miscarry. James, again putting her health before his own interests, excused her. His declaration 'was enrolled in Chancery' on October 23.

He had at last become convinced that Sunderland was a man in whom it was dangerous to place any further trust, and on the way back to St. James's Palace after making his formal statement about his son he told Lord Middleton to 'fetch the seals from him'. Sunderland made out that he was dismissed only because of his recent conversion to Catholicism, and that he was a sacrifice to the present wave of anti-Catholic feeling. It is doubtful whether his conversion had been for any motives other than political.

Through his Ambassador, his agents and his many contacts among both Whigs and Tories, William of Orange had been keeping in close touch with events and opinions in England ever since his visit to Newmarket and Windsor seven years before. In April 1688 he let it be known that he was prepared to lead an armed expedition, but before making any moves at all he demanded a written invitation from 'persons of quality' in England. Compiled by the members of an association formed to promote the 'Revolution' and join William when he arrived, the invitation was signed on June 30—the day on which the seven Bishops were acquitted—by a little group described by Dalrymple as the 'Immortal Seven, whose memories Britain can never sufficiently revere'. They were the Lords Devonshire, Danby, Shrewsbury and Lumley, Compton, the Bishop of London, and Henry Sidney. All these men knew that if anything went wrong they would lose their heads for having put their signatures on such a document. So did William.

He also knew that he was likely to meet considerable opposition if the fleet* and the army remained loyal to James, and so throughout the summer and autumn a great deal of quiet effort had been made to make sure they did not. After all the trouble there had been over the priests on the ships in the Thames, James was not entirely sure of the fleet, though he had complete confidence in Lord Dartmouth, 'trusting him more than anyone else in the Kingdom'. He felt that if his navy sighted a Dutch invasion fleet at sea there was still enough natural enmity between the English and the Dutch for his captains to attack it.

He was much happier about the army, now grown into a redoubtable force of 2,085 Officers, 4,172 Non-Commissioned Officers and 33,860 men.† The driving spirit and by far the most important man in his army was the officer he had taken into his own household as a boy, and with whom he had never had an angry word: John Churchill. James had no idea of the extent to which his officers had, in the jargon of subversion, been penetrated.

William had learned from Monmouth's descent on the West Country that he must take with him enough of his own troops to protect himself against a similar fate, and he mounted an expeditionary force of 10,692 Foot and 3,660 Horse and Dragoons, carried in a fleet consisting of 65 warships, 500 fly boats—to be used as assault landing craft—60 pinks and 10 fireships. When all was ready he set sail, with the British Admiral Herbert commanding his fleet, from the Brille and Helvoetsluys on October 19. Within a matter of hours a severe storm had dispersed his fleet and his damaged ships had to return to port; 900 horses had been

---

* In the Dartmouth MSS there is a complete list of the ships under Dartmouth's command at the time of the invasion. There were forty warships and twelve fireships in three Divisions of equal size. Dartmouth, the Admiral, had one; Sir Roger Strickland, Vice-Admiral, had another, and the third was commanded by stout Sir John Berry who had commanded the frigate *Gloucester* in 1682.

† From 'An Abstract of All His Majesty's Forces in England', October 26, 1688, Dartmouth MSS.

pushed overboard, an expedient apparently accepted without comment. Greatly exaggerated reports of losses and damage were published in order to persuade James that the whole project would have to be abandoned, but he, knowing William, did not believe them. 'I make no doubt,' he wrote to Dartmouth, now in a state of alert at the Gunfleet, 'but that God will protect me, and prosper my arms both by land and sea.'

William set out again on November 3.

It is very difficult to discover exactly what went wrong with the English fleet: there is no doubt that Dartmouth did his best but subversion and the strong east wind prevented him from offering any resistance at all. When his scouts, the 'eyes' of his fleet, reported that the Dutch were at sea he started out from the Nore and in a message to James said he was under sail and intending to anchor east of what he called the 'Galoper' (perhaps the Calliper bank near the Goodwins) so as to keep the weather and be on the flank of the enemy as they went westwards down the Channel. Apparently he did not go far enough out but anchored abreast of Long Sands Head and found himself held there by the east wind. William's fleet, unmolested, and borne along by what was called 'the Protestant wind', went away to the west.

Burnet says that William's original intention was to head due north, 'but the wind was so strong and full in the east that we could not move that way'. Danby was up in the north, busily subverting the local militia, and William wanted to land as far as possible from James's army, but he was not given to discussing his plans—he hardly spoke at all to Burnet who was on his ship. For the first twelve hours of the voyage he did in fact steer north and then, in darkness, swung away south-westwards. It may well have been this move which confused and fooled Dartmouth, but James refused to blame him until he had heard his story personally. They corresponded but they never met again, and some while later, when James had left the country, Dartmouth offered his services to William. It seems unlikely that Dartmouth had been negligent or disloyal to James because William's answer to his offer was to send him to the Tower where he died soon afterwards.

At dawn on November 5 the great invasion fleet, which had taken seven hours to pass one watcher on the Kent coast, found it was west of Torbay, where William proposed to land. Strangely enough, at just the right moment the wind which had been so favourable to him veered into the south 'and a soft and happy gale carried in the whole fleet in four hours time into Torbay'. Meanwhile Dartmouth, vainly pursuing and now off the Isle of Wight, ran into a storm which forced him to shelter in Portsmouth. This dispelled any hope of naval action against the invaders.

As soon as James learned that the enemy fleet had passed Dover and was running west he assumed William was making for the coast of Dorset or Devon. He therefore ordered three battalions of the Guards, the Royal Dragoons—commanded by Clarendon's eldest son Lord Cornbury—and a hundred mounted grenadiers to move at once to Portsmouth to increase the garrison, in case William attacked, and to move on to Salisbury if the enemy went on to the west. The rest of the army was to concentrate at Salisbury.

His twenty squadrons of cavalry and ten of dragoons he divided into three parties: Sir John Lanier was to take one to Salisbury, Sir John Fenwick was to take another to Marlborough, and the third was to move to Warminster, where Lanier and his troops were to join it as soon as Feversham, the Army Commander, reached Salisbury. James's intention was that as soon as these detachments reached their objectives they were to move on westwards, locate the invasion force, prevent it from advancing, and at the same time intercept any 'disaffected persons' who might be tempted to join it, thus containing it until the whole army with its artillery and baggage, now moving towards Salisbury, could come up. These were very sound tactical moves: Turenne had been a great advocate of the containing cavalry screen; and while they were going on a certain Captain Langham was captured and found to be carrying copies of William's 'Declaration'. The point in it which caused James most concern was a statement that William's coming 'was at the earnest invitation of divers Lords both spiritual and temporal'.

Langham was imprisoned, and James resolved to find out how true this statement was. He called together 'such Lords as were then about Town' and these included Lord Halifax, the Earls of Clarendon and Nottingham, Lord Burlington, the ageing Lord Arlington and others. When James questioned them 'they disclaimed any share of that invitation, adding all immagineable protestations of loyalty'. James says rather bitterly that 'the King thought when Honour, Conscience and Religion was in everybody's mouth it should have been in some people's hearts too, which made him credit what they said'; but a few days later he saw how wrong he was. He sent for Sancroft, the Bishops of London, Winchester and one or two others, and put the same question to them. He saw 'they were a little puzzled what to answer, not being quite so artful dissemblers as the others', and he realized he could not trust them any more than the Lords temporal.

Down in the West Country William had landed at Brixham on November 5 and was bringing his army ashore. The horses were in very bad condition after the voyage, and the men, seasick and miserable in the cramped conditions of the transports, were not much better. But William wasted no time in marching to Exeter. He had been led to believe that the whole country would fall over itself in rushing to join him and it was an unpleasant surprise when the Mayor of the city—which had no local garrison and could not defend itself—not only closed the gates against him but arrested and put in prison a man called Hicks, sent on ahead by William to raise recruits. Bishop Burnet tried to reason with the Mayor and 'pressed him to meet the Prince', but he refused.

Forced by the state of his army and the lack of any support from the people of Devon to remain outside Exeter for the time being, William occupied himself in assembling his troops, artillery and stores ready for a move eastwards. He also wrote another Proclamation in which he took pains 'to purge himself from the imputation of having any design to conquer the nation'. He assured his readers, and listeners, that his only intentions were to procure a free Parliament, 'vindicate their religion and the liberties of England from Popery and the Arbitrary and Dispensing Power', to assert the succession of the Crown and to 'examine into the birth of the pretended Prince of Wales'. In fact, as he said, to redress all irregularities, civil and military, and settle peace and plenty in the nation.

Like most promises in political manifestoes, very few were mentioned again.

What really upset William was that despite all the promises and assurances made to him before he sailed from Holland, for the next week no one came to join him and he found himself facing exactly the same problems as Monmouth. He knew that James's army, the best in Europe for its size, was marching towards him and he also knew that Dartmouth and the English fleet blocked the way back to Holland. The forces opposing him were not yet in position and could not prevent his supporters from reaching him: it appeared that there were simply no supporters. He began to feel he had been persuaded into an extremely dangerous and unpleasant situation. If there was a battle, in which it was highly probable he would be outnumbered and defeated, he, like Monmouth, would be regarded as the leader of an armed revolt, and his position as the virtual ruler of Holland would not prevent James from treating him in the way he would treat any other rebel. William had no intention of climbing the scaffold on Tower Hill, a prospect daily becoming more possible, and he told his staff that since he had clearly been betrayed, the only thing to do was to return to Holland. This view was shared by the British supporters who had come over with him, for they were becoming understandably nervous and filled with vivid and uncomfortable memories of what had happened to Monmouth. They agreed that William should re-embark his army and be gone, an opinion strengthened by the discovery that William's Proclamation, instead of being distributed as planned, had been sent to James. Angry and frustrated, William decided that before he left he would publish the names of all those who had invited him or promised to join him, 'as a just return for their treachery, folly and cowardice'. Then, in this atmosphere of dejection and spite, one man suddenly lit the fuze which fired the explosion of treachery.

As Lord Shrewsbury said, the real problem among William's supporters was 'who should run the hazard of being the first, but if the ice were once broke they would be as much afraid of being the last; which proved true'.

Lord Cornbury, sent forward as part of the cavalry screen to hold William down in the Exeter area, arrived at Salisbury at the head of the Royal Dragoons on November 13, and found there 'the regiments of the King, St. Albans and Fenwick'. Since all the Colonels of these regiments were absent, Cornbury, as the senior officer present, assumed command and next day gave orders for all four regiments to get on the move. Sir Francis Compton, Lieutenant Colonel of the King's, and Lieutenant Colonel Langston—who apparently knew what Cornbury's intention was—obeyed, but Lieutenant Colonel Southerland of Fenwick's did not.

The three regiments marched by Blandford to Dorchester, halted there for an hour or two to rest the horses, and then went on towards Honiton. This seemed odd to all the officers, particularly to Major Clifford of the Royal Dragoons who asked to see the orders 'which required so long a march directly towards the enemy'. Cornbury made some vague reply about attacking an enemy encampment, and when he arrived at Axminster he gave orders for a troop of sixty dragoons to assault an imaginary outpost. By this time the officers were highly suspicious and began asking a lot of awkward questions. Unable to conceal his intentions any longer, Cornbury departed with the troop of dragoons taking his Lieutenant Colonel, Hayford, Captain Russell and all the other captains with him, but without telling the troopers where he was going.

Lieutenant Colonel Langston followed with St. Albans regiment, saying nothing to anyone until they reached Honiton, where two regiments of enemy infantry were awaiting them. Langston then announced that he had brought them there to join the Prince of Orange, and when Major Norton and some of the subalterns said they had no intention of doing any such thing they were immediately disarmed, dismounted and plundered, and had great difficulty in returning to the remainder of the still loyal army. The other two regiments, the Royal Dragoons and the King's, 'finding that they had been betrayed', marched back in great disorder, and only Cornet Compton, a few subalterns and about ten

276

troopers went over to the enemy, 'though it was believed that Lieutenant Colonel Sir Francis Compton would have gone too had not he been stunned and afraid that his major would arrest him'. So he went back to the King, and Major Clifford brought back the main part of the Royal Dragoons. Subsequently most of the men of St. Albans regiment, who 'had not been consulted about their alliegance', began to filter back as the opportunity arose.

James observed bitterly that 'the common men showed a greater honour and fidelity than in the generality of officers who usually value themselves so much for those qualifications'.

In terms of numbers this loss from James's army was negligible, but the effect was enormous. Apart from the fact that by his forced march Cornbury had put the horses of three cavalry regiments out of action for at least a fortnight, his defection was a blow at the morale of the whole army. If he had gone, who would be next? Who could be trusted? The sparks of suspicion and disloyalty fanned, as James rightly says, by the officers, grew into flames which burnt up all hopes James had of resisting the invader; and at the heart of it all was Churchill, who owed everything to James's patronage.

Split and torn by conflicting loyalties, the army became virtually ineffective. The propaganda disseminated so insidiously by James's enemies had ripened, and the harvest had begun. There was nothing now to prevent the country squires, the hard core of the resistance to James's religious reforms, from joining the man who, so they had brought themselves to believe, had come to 'protect them from Popery'.

William must have been vastly relieved to see Cornbury and his companions in treachery, but he did not say so. He said only 'that he had come upon their invitation and expected them sooner'. It was hardly the way to inspire affection among men whose consciences may perhaps have been nagging a little.

*

Hearing what Cornbury had done, James, in London, called together all the available General Officers and Colonels and said in so many words that if there were any amongst them who were not free and willing to serve him 'he gave them leave to surrender their commissions and go wherever they pleased'. But he said 'he looked upon them as men of too much honour to follow My Lord Cornbury's example, and was therefore willing to spare them, if they so desired it, the discredit of so base a desertion'. In his Memoirs he says that 'they all seemed moved by this discourse and vowed they would serve him to the last drop of their blood.

Lord Churchill and the Duke of Grafton were the first that made this attestation, and the first who, to their infamy, broke it afterwards; as well as Kirke, Trelawney and the others who were no less lavish of their promises on this occasion, though as false and treacherous as the rest at the end.'

On November 16 James decided to go down to Salisbury and be with his army in the field and, on the night before he left, a deputation of Bishops presented him with further proposals about assembling a Parliament and coming to terms with William of Orange. All he could say was that they were too late. It was now ten o'clock at night and he was leaving for Salisbury very early in the morning; this was hardly the time to call a Parliament, when the army was on active service, nor was it tactful to suggest that he 'should treat with the invader who had come without provocation, against all the laws of God and man, and against the duty he owed as nephew and son-in-law'. He went on to say—and one can imagine the acid seeping into his tone—that it might perhaps be more becoming if those who were Bishops of the Church of England spent more of their time instructing the people in their duty to God and the King instead of presenting petitions in the middle of the night, and telling him how to govern and 'fomenting the rebellious temper they had already begot in the nation'. 'Religion,' he added coldly, 'the common cloak for rebellions, scarce proves a security against one.'

He had managed to find time to write and issue a declaration to counter the Proclamation William had sent out from Exeter, but it seems most unlikely that anyone, in the high excitement of the moment, bothered to read it.

James arrived at Salisbury on November 19, and his officers came to him in a body to express their 'abhorrence' of Cornbury's defection. He regained some of his confidence in his troops and decided that next day he would go and visit the forward elements at Warminster, where Kirke's Brigade, of two battalions of the Royal Scots, The Queen's, the Tangier Horse and a troop of Life Guards, was located. He was prevented from doing this by a haemorrhage which began early next day, and he bled copiously from the nose all that day and for most of the next. Most historians relate this 'nose-bleeding' to a plot by Churchill and Kirke to kidnap James when he went to Warminster and hand him over as a prisoner to William, saying it was lucky for James that because of it he did not go to Warminster. But there is rather more to it than that. The existence of such a plot is very doubtful. The one thing William seems to have wanted to avoid was a confrontation with his uncle and father-in-law. To have had James dumped in his camp as a prisoner would have been extremely embarrassing and could very easily have suddenly turned the tide against him. Quite probably, public opinion being what it is, James might immediately have become the under-dog, victim of a Dutch attack against the sovereignty of England. Everything might have swung in line behind him and he would have been saved; William would have known this and could hardly have countenanced such a plan. The only authority for the story seems to be the Duke of Berwick in his Memoirs, but he only says '*it is said* that a schiem was laid, and the measures taken, by Churchill and Kirk to deliver up the King to the Prince of Orange'.

The far more important effect of the nose-bleed was its physical and mental effect on James. In those days there was no means of stopping a severe nasal haemorrhage, and during November 20 and 21 James must have lost a great deal of blood. The Duke of Berwick, who was there, says it was 'a prodigious bleeding'. This would have made James extremely lethargic, slowed down all his reactions and made it very difficult for him to concentrate, or even think straight at all. The picture James's detractors try to conjure up—of James wandering about with a handkerchief to his nose, getting in everyone's way—is all part of the campaign against him.

A council of war was held on November 22, and James, who at any other time would have argued against a withdrawal, for he knew from experience what an adverse effect it always had on soldiers' morale, agreed to Feversham's proposal to retire to London. The withdrawal began, and like most similar operations it was hurried and untidy—although the enemy's leading troops were still sixty miles away, at Axminster, and William did not reach Salisbury until December 4. One peculiar aspect of the whole campaign—if one can call it that—was that James's army appears to have had no intelligence organization at all. Churchill, unquestionably one of the greatest military commanders who ever lived, had a highly developed sense of curiosity about what the enemy was doing; it was he who, years later, wrote 'no war can be conducted without early and good intelligence', but no one seems to have known what was happening away to the west. Perhaps Churchill did, but he did not say. But it was not just his curiosity which led him to ride off from Salisbury during the night of November 23, and join William at Axminster. The Duke of Grafton went with him, and Churchill left behind a letter explaining his defection. In it he 'protested that his desertion from his Majesty proceeded from no other reason than the inviolable duty of conscience, and a high and necessary concern for his religion with which nothing could come in competition'. He was not a particularly religious man but no doubt at such a time it was as good an excuse as any. The fact that he left a letter at all shows that he must have had some twinges of conscience, and he must have felt even more uncomfortable when he arrived in William's headquarters and met that grand old warrior Marshal Schomberg. Schomberg had fought side by side with James in the old days in France and knew him for the man he was. His only comment when James's protégé Lord Churchill rode into what was an enemy camp was that 'he was the first Lieutenant General he had ever heard of who had deserted from his Colours'.

Soon afterwards James's son-in-law Prince George of Denmark disappeared too. He had been in the habit of remarking on every fresh desertion in the mounting stream with an incredulous '*Est-il possible?*' and, told of his flight, all James said was, 'So! Est-il-possible gone too!'

James returned to London on November 26, leaving behind him an army in which the whole structure of command was sliding away, and was given the news which hurt him far more deeply than any other defections. His daughter Anne had abandoned him. James did not love many people but Anne was one of them; he cried out, 'God help me! My own children have foresaken me!' and wept. When she went, escorted by Compton, the Bishop of London, Sarah Churchill and Mrs. Berkeley, a Lady-in-Waiting, her father never recovered from the shattering blow to his morale. He began to think now only of the safety of his wife and infant son.

On November 29 he sent the baby, in the charge of Lord and Lady Powis, down to Lord Dartmouth, who was still with the fleet at Portsmouth, and where his lifelong friend Henry Jermyn, now Lord Dover, was Governor. In a letter to Dartmouth he wrote: ''Tis my son they aim at, and tis my son I must endeavour to preserve, whatsoever becomes of me. Therefore I conjure you to assist Lord Dover in getting him sent away in the yachts, as soon as wind and weather will permit, for the first port they can get to in France.'

Dartmouth replied in a long letter written from Spithead that he could not do it: 'I beg of you to apply yourself to other counsels for the doing this looks like nothing less than despair.' But he also had reason to fear that there was a plot to seize the child and he was not prepared to take any risks.

James then told Lord and Lady Powis to bring the baby back to London. Lord Dover instructed the loyal Major Clifford of the Royal Dragoons, now promoted to Lieutenant Colonel, to provide an escort for the coach and to be ready to leave at six in the morning. Then for some reason he changed his mind and said they would start an hour earlier, and he would come too. No doubt he felt that close friendship placed a special responsibility on him. The coach, with one or two outriders, set off at five o'clock, in the darkness. Three miles out of the town they were crossing the great barrier of Ports Down and it was getting light; there was still no sign of any escort which they had hoped would join them outside the gates. Since no one knew quite where William's forward troops were, Lord Dover felt it would be better to push on and hope that the escort caught them up rather than remain as a sitting target on the open hillside. They went on until they reached the Forest of Bere, just south of the village of Horndean, and there they paused, feeling it was far too risky to go on alone through country so well-suited for ambuscades. An Irish officer called Macartney who was with them was told to ride back and chase up the escort. On the way Macartney met a countryman and asked him if he had seen any horsemen. The man said that there was very little happening in his part of the world, but he did know that a party of horsemen had spent the previous night in the nearby house of a Colonel Norton and had gone off into the forest a short while ago. Macartney, quick to realize who they might be, asked if there was any coach road round the forest. The countryman said there was, and it was better than the main road because it was less used. He explained how to get to it, Macartney galloped back to the coach and in due course they arrived safely at Petersfield, where the escort caught them up. It subsequently transpired that the party of horsemen consisted of two captains, two lieutenants and two cornets with 200 men, which had been sent forward to lay an ambush, for William had been told by his far more efficient intelligence service what James's plans were. Yet it is difficult to see why William wanted the child and what he would have done if it had been kidnapped.

James sent a squadron of the Life Guards to meet the coach on the outskirts of London and to escort it to Whitehall.

Shortly after his return from Salisbury James called a meeting of the Council to discuss the petition presented to him by the Bishops on the night before his departure, and the outcome of this was that writs would be issued for a Parliament to meet on January 15, and a deputation consisting of Halifax, Godolphin and Nottingham would open negotiations with William. This mission set off on November 30 to meet William on his way up from Axminster.

It seems that James spent most of the following week in trying to make up his mind what to do. He has been much criticized for his apparent inability to take a decision; it has been alleged that he was now in a pitiable state of mortal terror; and it has been said that by some form of mental disease he was incapable of coherent thought. He was not mad, nor was he anything more than alarmed and perhaps apprehensive, and in his position almost anyone would have needed time to decide what to do next.

Throughout his reign, and before it, he had lived among courtiers whose own future was, to them, infinitely more important than his. Most of them, Sunderland* in particular, for their own ends had insulated him from what was really going on and from what the rest of the country thought and felt. They went out of their way to counteract the influence of men like Rochester who really tried to serve the best interests of the King. James's contact with soldiers and sailors had become that of a monarch with his subjects; in the old days it had been that of a commander with the men he led in battle. From the ordinary people he had gained an impression of loyalty and affection, demonstrated on his 'progresses', and the two attempts at rebellion had been put down so easily because there was so little support for them. He had been told, largely, only what his advisers thought it would be good for him to hear, and trusting with the misguided loyalty of a soldier the men who served him he had come to the conclusion that although there were certainly some dissidents—in the Universities and the Church in particular—everything was going rather well, and he was moving steadily towards his cherished objective of Liberty of Conscience.

He had been a little alarmed recently by signs of trouble in the navy and the army, but then, as an experienced commander, he knew that all soldiers and sailors occasionally have their bad patches, and when he had gone to see them himself he thought the stories were somewhat exaggerated. He had found it difficult to believe that William, always so carefully polite, had really decided to make trouble, and the first real shock had been to discover how much he had been misled about William's ambitions.

Cornbury's defection had been distressing, but not unduly so, and he had been reassured by the declarations of loyalty made to him by his officers in London and again in Salisbury.

Then, quite suddenly and with no warning that he heard or saw, all that he had built up so carefully, cracked, crumbled and crashed into the torrent of treachery of which he had been completely unaware.

'If only my enemies had cursed me,' he said miserably when he saw the ruin of his hopes, 'then I could have borne it.'

* On March 13, 1687, Princess Anne wrote to her sister Mary in Holland: 'I have once before ventured to tell you that I thought Lord Sunderland a very ill man and I am more confirmed everyday in that opinion. Everybody knows how often this man turned backwards and forwards in the last King's time . . . He stirs up the King to do things faster than I believe he would of himself—his wife is just as extraordinary in her kind, for she is a flattering, dissembling false woman, but with such a fawning and endearing manner that she will deceive anybody. Yet she will cheat though it be for a little: and she has her gallants. Sure there never was a couple so well matched as her and her good husband: for she is the greatest jade that ever lived, so he is the subtellest, workinest villain on the face of the earth.' (Anne was twenty-three when she wrote this classic example of rancour. She was not entirely lovable herself.)

He had been abandoned, overnight, by everyone in whom he had faith —even his own daughter. He felt that there was now no one in the whole kingdom he could really trust; for when deceived on so vast a scale he could not believe there was anyone still on his side. From whom could he obtain honest advice? To whom could he turn for help? Some advised him to stay and face the new Parliament—and in all probability see all he had striven for over the past four years disrupted and discarded by the Acts of what to him would be a 'turbulent Assembly'. Some advised him to go—to a temporary, voluntary exile until the dust of this Dutch Invasion had settled; and, when his people realized what manner of man William of Orange really was, to return on his own terms.

One gets the impression of an honest, earnest, not over-intelligent man, full of good intentions, totally bewildered by this universal and incomprehensible rejection of his simple and genuine motives; lost now, and quite out of his depth in the dark waters of despair. In these circumstances perhaps he may be forgiven for his indecision.

Of course William wanted him to go, for that would be the solution to what was otherwise, for him, an insoluble problem. While James remained in England William would never be able to shoulder him aside and sit down in his place. And so, covert threats were made, mainly through Halifax: there could be no guarantee of his safety. James gave his own reaction to these threats, with perhaps a clearer indication of what had been said to him, in a letter he wrote to his old friend Lord Middleton just before he left Rochester for the last time: 'How can I hope to be safe so long as I was in the power of one who had not only done this to me and invaded my kingdoms without any just occasion given him for it, but that did by his first declaration lay the greatest aspersion upon me that malice could invent, in that clause of it which concerns my son. . . . What had I then to expect from one who by all arts had taken such pains to make me appear as black as Hell to my own people as well as to all the world besides—what effect that hath had at home, all mankind hath seen, by so general a defection in my army as well as in the Nation amongst all sorts of the people?'

After much deliberation he decided that he must send the wife he loved and the child in whom rested all his hopes for the future of the Catholics in the three kingdoms, away to safety in France. As soon as they were safe, he would follow.

It is clear that in making this decision his real concern was for Mary Beatrice and the baby. She, whom Evelyn describes as 'universally beloved', was now terrified for the safety of her husband and her son. It had been bad enough for her when she was left behind—one of the very rare occasions that this happened—and James went off to the army at Salisbury, leaving her 'in the midst of a mutinous and discontented city'. It was even worse when Lady Powis carried her child off to Portsmouth, and she had been afraid she would never see him again. Now, with William and his Dutch troops and English deserters marching towards the city, James felt he had no alternative. But there must have been other thoughts in his mind.

Intensely patriotic and with a great love for the country which did not love him, he genuinely hated the prospect of another civil war: and if he stayed, there might be war. If he went, now, he might be able to return. If he stayed, and if what Halifax had hinted was true, he faced imprisonment—which, to a man with his passion for the open air, would be intolerable—and there may have been another thought. Perhaps he carried in his mind some idea of the scene in Whitehall, outside the great Banqueting Hall, on that cold January afternoon when the executioner lifted up his father's head and the crowd groaned in horror at what had been done. He had seen Monmouth's horrible death. He had never shown the slightest fear of death in battle either on land or on the water, but death by the axe was quite different. It was planned and premeditated. In war one was in the hands of God and one took the risks in the hot blood of battle. To climb a scaffold, slowly, to look out upon a silent sea of faces, tense, waiting; and then, when it was over, to be nothing but a sprawling, headless corpse, killed in cold blood. This was not the death for a king: it had about it such a dire indignity. James was not afraid of death, he never had been, but he was supremely conscious of the dignity of kings.

He had a genuine and very understandable dread of captivity: he said so, in that last letter from Rochester: 'I was born free and desire to continue so, and though I have ventured my life very freely on several occasions for the good and honour of my country, and am as free to do it again (and which I hope I shall yet do, as old as I am, to redeem it from the slavery it is like to fall under) yet I think it not convenient to expose myself to be secured, so as not to be at liberty to effect it, and do for that reason withdraw; but so as to be within call when the nation's eyes are opened so as to see how they have been abused and imposed upon by the specious pretences of Religion and property.'

As soon as he had made the decision he put into the hand of the Envoy of the Duke of Tuscany a very heavy box, to be got away in secrecy to France. The Envoy, assuming it contained jewels and treasure, took great care of it and gave it to a merchant, to be consigned to Leghorn. The merchant made the same assumption and, being dishonest, 'proposed to embezzle it'. The Envoy had his misgivings, took the box back and 'sent it safe to Leghorn'. When it arrived there the Grand Duke sent it over to France with an escort of two war galleys and, heavily guarded on the long journey up through France, it was finally delivered to James at the Palace of Saint-Germain. No one except him knew—because he had forgotten to tell anyone—that it contained only his papers and his Memoirs, 'thrust all confusedly into it'.

Knowing how dreadfully his wife suffered from seasickness, James proposed to send her and the baby by coach to Dover and then across to Calais, but, when all was ready for them to leave, there came news of demonstrations at Dover which made it unsafe for them to go that way. The narrow escape on the Prince's journey back from Portsmouth only a few days before, coupled with this news, made James decide that all must be done in secrecy and at night. And so, in the very early hours of the morning of December 10, he and Mary Beatrice said goodbye to one another, and, in disguise, with her baby, escorted by the French comte de Lauzun and an Italian servant called Riva, and with two nurses, she went out to the waiting coach. It was a filthy night, with a howling wind and driving rain, bitterly cold. The coach took them to Horseferry where they got into an open boat and crossed the river to Lambeth in a storm of rain. A 'common' coach had been ordered to wait for them on the far side and when they reached it they found that the horses had not been put into it; and during the hour it took to collect horses from a nearby inn and harness them, Mary Beatrice tried to shelter with her child in the lee of the church wall. There was one small incident with a curious passer-by, dealt with by Riva, who pushed him into the muddy gutter with enough force to persuade him to lose interest, and when the horses arrived the coach was driven down the river to Gravesend. Here a yacht was waiting to take them to Calais, and there were other Catholic refugees already on board: Lord and Lady Powis and the wife of the naval officer Sir Roger Strickland.

Two frigates were lying in the estuary, waiting to intercept any attempt to smuggle the baby Prince out of the country. The yacht evaded them and reached Calais safely. Poor Mary Beatrice had a wretched voyage: in her own account she wrote that it was very sad and that she did not know how she survived it; 'I left the King not knowing what would become of him, and I feared to fall into the hands of our enemies.'

James had promised to follow her within twenty-four hours and so she decided to wait for him at Calais. When he failed to arrive she went on to Boulogne where she heard that he had been seized by the rabble near the coast where, treated with 'great rudeness and barbarity', he was now their prisoner. Such was her loyalty and courage that she determined to send the Prince on with his nurses to Paris and return herself to England. Both the duc d'Aumontin, with whom she was staying, and the comte de Lauzun told her she could achieve nothing and would only make things worse for James.

As soon as Louis XIV heard that she had arrived in France he sent off 'officers and coaches and everything for her journey'. The roads were in a shocking state and the country covered in snow, so, with a typically splendid gesture, he gave orders for a direct route to be marked out across country over the frozen ground, and a gang of pioneers 'levelled the difficult places and removed obstacles'. In due course she set off southwards, but with a heavy heart and wondering if she would ever see James again.

Saint-Victor, one of the comte de Lauzun's attendants, rode back from Gravesend to tell James that his wife and baby had set sail. It was an open secret that he would now follow them. Of his advisers, Petre had long since slipped away: he went while James was in Salisbury. Sunderland fled on December 7, making for Holland disguised as a woman. Apparently he was not very convincing because he was at once arrested. William ordered his release and he then published an account of his political activities. He subsequently informed the Dutch General Ginkel, who had distinguished himself in William's Irish campaign, that though he conceded to Ginkel the honour of subduing Ireland he would not yield to him in merit since 'he had the glory of contriving the provocations to the Revolution and of laying the first foundations of the Prince of Orange's grandeur'.

On December 10 James wrote to Feversham telling him that he had sent Mary Beatrice and his son away 'that they might not fall into my enemy's hands' and that he was obliged to 'do the same thing'. He went on to say that if he could have relied upon all his troops, 'I might not have been put to this extremity I am in, and would at least have had one blow for it: but, though I know there are many loyal and brave men among you, yet you know you yourself and several of the general officers told me it was no ways advisable to venture myself at their head. There remains nothing more for me to do but to thank you and all those officers and soldiers who have stuck to me and been truly loyal . . .'

This was not the letter of a man in terror for his life, nor of a man whose mind had given way under misfortune. It has a sad dignity: he had made up his mind and he knew exactly what he was going to do. Unfortunately, like so many of the decisions in his short reign, he had again made the wrong one.

TWENTY-SIX

THERE were three courses of action open to James: gather what was left of his army and give battle; come to some arrangement with William, Parliament and the people; or leave the country. No one was in the mood for war; William, despite his Proclamations, had no intention of reaching any sort of arrangement which did not put him on the throne of England. This was what he had come for. James saw this perhaps more clearly than most. He left because he really thought there was no acceptable alternative.

Reading about it now, with all the knowledge of what happened and possessing facts which could not have been known to James, it is easy to say that he ought to have stayed. If he had, William would have had to negotiate, and he would have had to deal with a King *de facto* and an insular people who wanted a change in the trend of government but not necessarily a change in the government itself. They preferred a Stuart to a Dutchman, no matter how much Stuart blood the Dutchman had in his veins. Looking back, it seems most unlikely that William could have imprisoned James, and virtually impossible that there could have been any high drama on Tower Hill. One can speculate endlessly—and pointlessly—on what might have happened if James had stayed; all one can finally say is that on balance, from his point of view, it might have been better if he had remained to confront William instead of going off to join his wife and son.

Just before he left he received a message from his 'negotiators' Halifax, Godolphin and Nottingham, which outlined William's 'demands' for a Parliament, for the dismissal of Catholic advisers, for powers to limit the sovereign's right to prorogue and dissolve Parliament, and for the abolition of the 'dispensing power'. James, with his plans made, paid very little attention to it.

He had promised Mary Beatrice he would follow her within twenty-four hours, and he did. Soon after midnight, on the morning of December 11, he left Whitehall accompanied by Sir Edward Hales—the Hales of the test case of Hales *vs* Godden which established James's 'dispensing

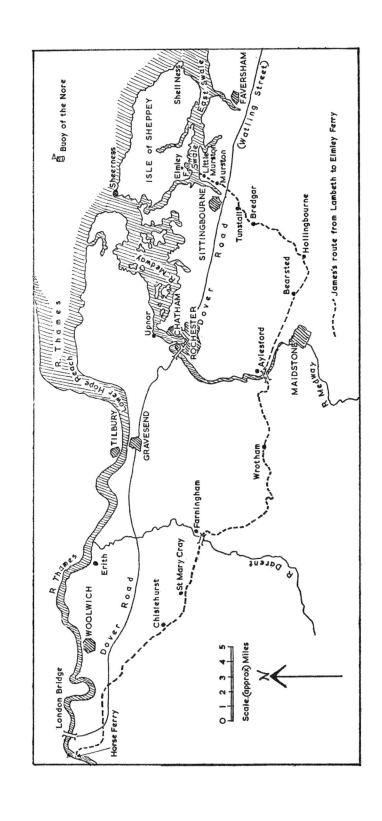

Buoy of the Nore

ISLE of SHEPPEY

Shell Ness

Sheerness

Elmley
F.
Swale
Little Murston
Murston

East Swale

FAVERSHAM

SITTINGBOURNE

(Watling Street)

Bredgar

Tunstall

Hollingbourne

Bearsted

R. Medway

Upnor

CHATHAM

ROCHESTER

Dover Road

Aylesford

MAIDSTONE

R. Medway

R. Thames

Lower Hope Reach

TILBURY

GRAVESEND

Wrotham

Farningham

R. Darent

R. Thames

Erith

Dover Road

WOOLWICH

St Mary Cray

Chislehurst

London Bridge

Horse Ferry

James's route from Lambeth to Elmley Ferry

0 1 2 3 4 5 Miles

Scale (approx) Miles

power'—a page called Labadie and a guide. Like Mary Beatrice, they crossed the river at Horseferry, and when they were out in the middle of the stream James dropped the Great Seal overboard. Just before leaving Whitehall he had burned all the writs for the Parliament to be called in January: perhaps this jettison of the Great Seal and the burning of the writs were the last defiant gestures of an absolute ruler; perhaps the Great Seal was too heavy to carry in his pocket.

Horses were waiting at Lambeth, and at two a.m. James mounted his bay Ailesbury and the little party rode away. The wind had dropped and there was no rain, but the roads were waterlogged. To avoid the risk of being stopped James had decided to travel by the lanes—hence the guide; and from the outskirts of London they went to Chislehurst, down into the valley of the river Darent at Farningham and then along the old Pilgrims' Way through Wrotham to the bridge over the Medway at Aylesford. Here Ralph Sheldon was waiting with fresh horses. It was seven o'clock when they arrived, and they breakfasted at the Woolpack Inn. From Aylesford they went on in the growing light, skirting Maidstone on the northern side and then going eastwards along the valley of the Len, through Bearsted to Hollingbourne, and then, turning north, crossed the high spine of the hills through Bredgar to Tunstall. In the low ground between the Downs and the Swale they crossed the main Dover road east of Sittingbourne and, going through Murston and the hamlet of Little Murston a mile further on, they reached Elmley Ferry on the Swale. It was now ten o'clock. In eight hours, mostly in darkness, they had covered fifty-six miles with only one change of horses. James, who was now fifty-five, must have recovered completely from the haemorrhage at Salisbury.

A friend of Hales had hired a Customs House hoy—a small coasting vessel—to take the party to France. It appeared soon after they arrived, and James, Hales and Sheldon went on board; they did not tell the Master who they were. The wind 'was fair and strong' but James, hoping to get away at once, was told by the Master that he had no ballast and could not go to sea without it. James, as a sailor, took his point. They fell down the Swale, eastwards to Shell Ness on the Isle of Sheppey, ran the vessel ashore at half ebb and took in ballast, intending to sail at half flood to the nearest point on the French coast.

It was most unfortunate that James had put his escape in the hands of Sir Edward Hales, now notorious because of the test case and thoroughly disliked in his own county of Kent. He had made things worse for himself by being a convert to Catholicism. From James's point of view Hales had local knowledge and contacts which would be invaluable, but being well known in the area of Faversham and Sittingbourne there was always the chance that he might be recognized, and there were parties out everywhere looking for escaping recusants. Someone had seen him with his small party, crossing the Dover road and obviously making for the coast, and a posse of forty men led by a Captain Ames was collected and sent out to find him. The pursuers must have spent a great deal of time searching the Swale and all its creeks, but finally, at eleven o'clock in the evening, only a few moments after the flooding tide had floated the hoy, the three boatloads of men came alongside. With a sword and a pistol in his hands Ames burst into the little cabin, seized James and his two companions and told them they must go with him to the Mayor of Faversham to be questioned.

Coming across the hoy in the darkness must have been entirely a matter of luck, but for James, within an ace of escape, it was supremely frustrating. Unrecognized, he was now to be taken back, accused of being an escaping Papist—which of course he was—and he would have to start all over again.

Sir Edward Hales, picking his moment, gave Ames fifty guineas and said there would be another hundred if he let them go. Ames took the money and said he would arrange matters. The hoy was taken to the mouth of Faversham creek to wait for the high tide which would carry her in, and Ames went off after telling James and Hales that he was going to find means to get them away. He had previously warned them that his men were a rough lot, and on his advice they handed over all their valuables to him—to be restored if they were 'innocent men' and divided equally as prizes if they were not. He gave each of them a receipt.

But James did not hand over everything. He kept 'the great diamond bodkin' which belonged to Mary Beatrice, and the Coronation Ring which 'he put within his drawers'. It was daylight by the time Ames went off, and as soon as he had gone several men came into the cabin saying they were going to search their prisoners because they were sure they had not given all their money to the Captain. James and the other two told them to proceed with the search, they would not find anything; but the intruders 'searched poskets and opening their breeches felt about in a very rude manner, the more because they found nothing'. One of them, feeling around James's knees, got hold of the bodkin and cried out that he had found a prize. James, who appears to have remained remarkably cool throughout the whole affair, told him he was talking nonsense. He had several things in his pockets, a pair of scissors, a toothpick case and some keys: it was one of those things he had felt, and the man, suddenly thrusting his hand into James's pocket, lost his hold on the bodkin and finding all the other things James had mentioned, seemed satisfied. 'And so the bodkin and the Ring were preserved.' It was clear that the men knew nothing about jewels because in one of James's pockets they found a pair of diamond buckles wrapped up in a piece of paper, and assuming they were only glass, handed them back to him.

Some while later Ames returned. He had done nothing about getting them away—perhaps the local feeling against Sir Edward Hales was too strong for him to risk the anger of his posse—but he had brought a coach in which to take the party to the Mayor. They got into the hoy's small boat, went ashore and on the way back to the town were under the guard of a man called Edwards and what James describes as the 'Rabble'. Taken to an inn, the Arms of England, James went upstairs and, although disguised and wearing a black periwig, he realized several people knew who he was. Thereafter he made no attempt to conceal his identity, 'upon which the Rabble dispersed'.

Napleton, a local lawyer, was one of the first to recognize James and he agreed to ride to Canterbury with a letter James wrote to the Lord Lieutenant of the county, Lord Winchelsea, who was presiding over a meeting of the local gentry there. Apart from the excitement of 'escaping Papists' there seems to have been a very general fear of the Irish troops, many of whom had been disbanded and released from any form of control, and were now believed to be on the rampage and a genuine menace. In reality, the comparatively small number of Irishmen, disarmed and dispersed, were in great distress. Not only were they homeless and starving but likely to be knocked on the head wherever they went.

In his letter, James asked Lord Winchelsea to come and see him, and thereby placed him in a quandary. No one could guess what William's intentions were or what plans he had for James, and since there was no information nobody knew what to do. Most people decided that the best way of avoiding trouble was to do nothing. Winchelsea and the other gentlemen at his meeting discussed the problem for over two hours and then the Lord Lieutenant and a small party started out to ride to Faversham.

In the meantime James sent Ralph Sheldon off to see the Master of the hoy, who he reckoned was 'an honest man', and tell him to get his boat ready for sea, moor it a little way away from the town and arrange for horses to be available to fetch him from the inn. Some word of this must have got out, because Edwards suspected what was going on, 'raised the rabble' again and made it impossible for James to leave the Arms of England. That evening Winchelsea arrived, bringing with him only two gentlemen instead of the guard of militia for which James had been hoping, and it was decided that James should move into the house of the

Mayor, 'he being a loyal man'. Edwards, the 'factious fellow', and his rabble were still outside the inn, and as James went down the stairs and outside 'the rabble were very rude to him', and it was all he could do to force a way through them even though Winchelsea and several others went in front of him. Most of the trouble was because of Sir Edward Hales, against whom the crowd had 'a mighty spleen' for having changed his religion, and at that moment another angry mob was looting his country house and slaughtering his deer. Hales very wisely remained in the inn and no doubt most people in the crowd thought he was James.

Outside the inn James suddenly found himself in the middle of an escort of seamen who roared at the rabble that 'not a hair of his head was to be touched', and 'keeping very close to him' they all marched off to the Mayor's house where they upset that worthy somewhat by turning his drawing-room into a guard room.

It was now the evening of Tuesday, December 12, and having established James in the house of the Mayor, the sailors showed no signs of letting him go. There were no instructions from William, who was on the move towards London, and for the time, James had to stay where he was. He was guarded for most of the time by 'a crude fellow' called Hunt, who at other times was the master of a small fishing vessel. James, with no success at all, tried to persuade and bribe him to let him go, but Hunt took his duties as a guard very seriously and took away the swords of James's visitors, 'nor would restore them until they departed'. James thought he was very rude.

News of James's capture reached London and 'several loyal officers called on him bringing messages from Lord Feversham that he was on his way with a detachment of Horse Guards and Grenadiers to secure him from the rabble and bring him to London'. Feversham reached Faversham early on the morning of Saturday, December 16. To avoid possible conflict with James's 'rabble' he had left the escort at Sittingbourne. James bade the rabble a very friendly farewell and 'dismissed them'. Escorted by two troops of the local militia as far as Sittingbourne, he then travelled with his Horse Guards to Rochester and sent Lord Feversham on from there with a letter to William arranging a meeting in London on Monday, 'to settle the distracted Nation'.

Feversham took the letter to William who immediately ordered his arrest and confinement in Windsor Castle. The trouble was that in his last letter to Feversham, written just before he left London, James had omitted to include any instructions about the disposal of the army. All he had said was, 'I hope you will still have the same fidelity to me and, though I do not expect you should expose yourselves by resisting a foreign army and poisoned nation, yet I hope your former principles are so rooted in you that you will keep yourselves free from associations and such pernicious things.' Either Feversham interpreted this as an order, or he deliberately wished to spite William, but he assembled at Uxbridge all the troops he could find, read the letter to them and then dismissed them on the spot. William, who had been counting on James's excellent troops as reinforcements for his struggle with Louis, was very angry indeed. On December 13 he put out an order to all 'Colonels and Commanders-in-Chief' telling them 'to call together by beat of drum, or otherwise, the officers and soldiers who had been disbanded by Lord Feversham and to keep them in good order and discipline'. But whatever his feelings, he had absolutely no right to arrest James's Army Commander, though as a calculated and gross affront to his uncle it was typical of his unpleasant nature.

In going off without any warning and leaving no instructions about anything James had been somewhat irresponsible. Perhaps he felt that if his people rejected him, he would reject them and go away without bothering, but he left behind him a potentially dangerous situation, particularly for his Catholic subjects. There was a great deal of trouble in London: the volatile mob stormed through the streets destroying and burning all Catholic property they could find, including the Spanish and Florentine Embassies; those of the French and Venetians were protected by their own guards.

Lord Jeffreys realized that the time had come for him to get away for he had never been popular with the London mob. He was caught at Wapping, dressed as an ordinary sailor, and taken before the Lord Mayor still in his blue jacket and with his hat down over his face. The story is that when standing in front of the Lord Mayor someone pulled the hat off his head and the Lord Mayor, looking up, 'beheld the face which had previously inspired so much fear'. Apparently it still did, because the Lord Mayor fainted, and died next day. It could perhaps have been a coincidental coronary thrombosis.

On the way back to London from Rochester James was met on the road by several officers who told him that his Grenadier Guards had declared for William, and the Horse Guards had done the same. Therefore it was not safe for him to return to Whitehall: James did not agree. He intended to go back to his palace, crossing the river by the way he had come, at Horseferry. At Dartford, where he dined on Sunday, December 16, he got into his coach—he had ridden up from Faversham—and went on towards London.

It is impossible to guess what was in his mind as he was taken towards the city from which he had tried to slip away almost a week before. His enemies were marching up on the other side and it was in London that he had first realized the scale of his unpopularity. He had heard of all the destruction that had been going on in his absence, and the best he could hope for was to be ignored. He must have been shattered by what happened.

The crowds had come right out from the City and the suburbs: when he reached Blackheath it was a sea of horsemen, and they were cheering and waving, and many were weeping with the strange hysteria imparted by a sentimental crowd. In the chilly dusk of a December evening it was as if the sun of the Restoration had returned. Perhaps he was suddenly transported back in time to that glorious May morning when he and Charles and Henry had ridden across this same heath with all the world before them and, as they had thought, all their troubles over. Was he, now, like Charles, coming into his own again?

He was told that the City was waiting for him. He turned aside long before Horseferry and drove from St. George's, Southwark, across London Bridge and through the City all the way to Whitehall. The streets were packed—his coach could hardly get through, the balconies and windows were thronged, bonfires blazed in the open spaces, every church bell was ringing, and he was deafened by the uproar of his welcome. All around him were 'all imaginable markes of love and esteem as made it look liker a day of triumph than humiliation'.

At first he was completely at a loss to account for his reception by the people who, so he had believed, hated him as a Papist. Then he thought that perhaps he had never really lost his personal popularity and that 'the anger was not at his person but at his religion'. It is very difficult to decide why the people welcomed him as they did and any surmise could fall below or overstep the truth.

Although when he returned to Whitehall James behaved as if he had never been away, it seems now that he had no intention of remaining in London. He was not afraid; he was perfectly clear in his own mind, and he was determined not to let William capture him.

When William heard that his uncle had left London he abandoned all the rather ridiculous pretence that he had only come over, with his army, to persuade James to call a Parliament and relax his efforts to emancipate the Catholics. He did not bother to reply to James's invitation to a meeting in London. He sent his Dutch Guards to take over guard duties at Whitehall, and when the gallant old Lord Craven told James that he would rather be cut in pieces than resign his post to a lot of foreigners, James had to sort out a difficult little situation 'with a great deal of care and kindness'.

Then William sent a deputation to James, consisting of Halifax—who now seemed to be entirely on William's side—Shrewsbury and Delamere. It arrived at midnight on December 17–18, while James was in a deep sleep, ordered his servants to wake him, and Halifax told him William had demanded, 'for the quiet of the city and the safety of his person', that within ten hours he must go to the Duchess of Lauderdale's house at Ham. James had the politeness of a man resigned to the inevitable. He said he would not go to Ham, the house was very cold in the winter, and damp, and in any case there was hardly any furniture in it. He was quite prepared to return to Rochester. William, now no further away than the Duke of Northumberland's Syon House, agreed.

Halifax informed James, in case he might be reluctant to leave London again, that according to what he had heard, the notice was short because William's Council had decided to seize James and imprison him. But James needed no spur. On December 18 he began his journey by barge to Rochester, guarded but not under any restraint. To the many spectators who watched him embark at the Privy Stairs it was clear that to all intents and purposes he was a prisoner. Many wept to see him go.

He spent the night at Gravesend and on December 19 arrived at the house of his choice. It belonged to Sir Richard Head, and he had slept there on the way back from Faversham only a few days previously. Its garden went right down to the bank of the Medway. There were no guards at the back of the house. The Captain in charge of the guard was a Catholic and half his small command came to hear Mass with him every morning. It was all rather obvious, but James, perhaps in tune with some long-buried spirit of adventure, maintained the fiction of escape.

He made arrangements with Captain Trevannion and Captain Macdonnel for the pinnace of the yacht *Henrietta* to be moored to the bank at the bottom of the garden just before midnight on December 23. He went off to bed at the usual hour and when the house was quiet and everybody had gone to bed he got up, dressed, and went silently down the back stairs and let himself out into the garden.

Captain Macdonnel was waiting, and he took him to the boat where Trevannion was. They were joined by the Duke of Berwick, and Mr. Biddulph, Groom of the Bedchamber. In silence they embarked. In the teeth of a bitter east wind and with the tide against them they were rowed down the Medway and it was nearly six o'clock in the morning before they reached the mouth of the West Swale River, near Queenborough, where the *Henrietta* was lying. But they could not find her in the darkness. Fortunately they were able to find refuge on board the *Eagle* fireship, commanded by Captain Wilford, known to James as an honest and loyal officer whose crew would obey him. At daybreak they saw the *Henrietta* at anchor within the Swale, not far away. She had been carried away from the agreed rendezvous by the gale. James, Berwick and Biddulph went aboard her immediately, despite the gale, and took the pinnace in tow after Captain Trevannion and his boat's crew had also embarked. The men had small arms and hand grenades.

The strong east wind, that 'Protestant' wind, was dead ahead but they beat up almost due north to the Buoy of the Nore, and with the wind still strong at east-north-east they had to bear upriver and anchor near the Essex shore, in smooth water under the lee of the Sands, until the ebb. It blew very hard all that Sunday but at dusk the wind dropped a little and when the tide turned they made sail, beat down as far as Red Sand and anchored a mile short of the buoy. Next morning, Christmas Eve, the weather had improved enough for them to set off before sunrise. Reaching the Buoy of the Nartow they turned through it and so on to the North Foreland, their intention being 'to have got about the North Sands Head and on the back of the Goodwins, and so escape the Downs', but being caught in the southward-running tide which ran ebb they could not weather it and so bore up through the Downs, choosing to run the risk of being intercepted by shipping there than to anchor in such weather. Strangely enough, all that day they saw no vessel under sail and there were only seven ships at anchor in the Downs.

Darkness was falling as they cleared South Sands Head and the wind had lessened. At six in the evening snow began falling, borne on the easterly wind, but at about eleven o'clock it cleared and they could see the cliffs of France about two leagues away and dead ahead. 'Standing in, all was blackness' as they 'bore up to Balloin Bay, not being able to fetch Calais, and so came to anchor before Ambleteuse'. Here they found a French frigate in the road, stationed to keep a look-out for them.

It had not been a pleasant voyage: the cabin of the *Henrietta* was tiny: James and his son almost filled it, and there were practically no feeding arrangements. James, who may well have been feeling that after so many years the burden of worry and responsibility had suddenly been lifted, was considerably amused by Captain Trevannion's efforts to provide him with a meal. After many hours on the ship he was extremely hungry and thirsty and Captain Trevannion said he would fry him some bacon, but the only frying-pan had a hole in it and had to be plugged with, of all things, a 'pitched rag'. The only drinking vessel was 'an old furred can which had to be bound with cord before it would hold any liquid'. Nevertheless, James said he had 'never ate nor drank more heartily in his life'.

'Coming to anchor before Ambleteuse,* they went on shore to that village at about three o'clock on Tuesday morning.' It was Christmas Day.

*

Mary Beatrice, travelling with her infant son as comfortably as could be arranged, felt a growing anxiety for James's safety. Although she found that each night 'the preparations of food and lodging were equivalent to a palace' she had much to occupy her mind. But at Beaumont, on the Oise about thirty-eight miles north-east of Saint-Germain, she was overtaken by a courier carrying a message which told her James had landed safely in France. She went on towards Paris in a much happier state of mind.

About three miles outside Saint-Germain she was met by Louis himself and an impressive gathering from the French court. He at once picked up the six-month-old Prince of Wales and 'made him a short speech promising both succour and protection'. He then did his best to reassure and welcome Mary Beatrice. There must have been a considerable amount of genuine kindness and sympathy behind the more obvious reasons for providing a sanctuary for James and his family—he knew that backed by French men, arms and money James could be very useful in making all manner of trouble for William, the enemy of all Catholic Frenchmen—for there had been no need to go to such lengths over her journey. Perhaps he had not forgotten that there had been many occasions in the past when James had risked his life in battle for the French throne.

Poor James, sailing through snowstorms in the Channel and then posting down the long undulating road to rejoin his wife and son at Saint-Germain, was once again on what his brother Charles had called 'his travels'. He left behind in England a dour, discourteous man who cared nothing for the country except as a source of revenue and manpower which would enable him to continue his fight against Louis XIV. James, who so loved England and longed for her peace and prosperity, was not a lovable man. Nor was William, and contemporary opinion of him is summed up in the brief verse:

> As I walked by myself
> And Talk'd to myself,
> Myself said unto Me,

* Today the fort at Ambleteuse bears little resemblance to the tower shown in the old print of the main events in James's life. Much of it is ruined and the emplacements for the German coast guns, when it formed part of the Atlantic Wall, have been blown up. But the foundations date back to before James's day, and the wall on the landward side, pierced for muskets, is very old, but it is difficult to decide what parts of the structure are original and which have been adapted.

Look to thy self,
Take care of Thyself,
For nobody cares for Thee.

The so-called Glorious Revolution was over. There was nothing in the least glorious about it and few events in history can rival it as a squalid tale of perfidy, but it had to be justified, and the traitorous Whigs had to prove they were not traitors at all but had acted from the highest motives. After the slaughter of Bosworth Field Henry Tudor did at least have the advantage that Richard III was dead and could not answer back: James was alive, and went on living for nearly thirteen more years. His court became a refuge for men hounded out of England; he had time to write, and did write declarations and letters to friends in England which William and his ministers took pains to suppress. The usurper and his sycophants were naturally anxious to ensure that they would not be condemned by posterity, and so the story was told their way: to communicate with James was high treason.

He ended that last letter he wrote at Rochester, just before going out to the *Henrietta*, with an appeal which in effect sums up the whole of his policy and his aims:

'I hope it will please God to touch their [his subjects'] hearts out of his infinite mercy and to make them sensible of the condition they are in and bring them to such a temper that a legal Parliament may be called, and that amongst other things which may be necessary to be done they will agree to a liberty of conscience for all Protestant dissenters, and that those of my own persuasion may be so far considered, and have such a share of it, as they may live peaceably and quietly, as Englishmen and Christians ought to do, and not to be obliged to transplant themselves, which would be very grievous especially to such as love their country; and I appeal to all who are considering men and women and have had experience, whether anything can make this Nation so great and flourishing as Liberty of Conscience—some of our neighbours dread it—I would add much more to confirm all I have said, but now is not a proper time.'

TWENTY-SEVEN

As soon as James had gone, and William had moved in, the people of England found themselves confronted with many problems. James was still the legal King, and William, in his proclamations and manifestoes which laid emphasis on his motives for coming over, had not included any suggestion of wearing the crown. These statements, in which most people had some confidence, made things very awkward for William at first and, as anyone in his position would have done, he tried to smooth over the more obvious differences between his words and his deeds with a veneer of legality. His anxiety over letting James escape shows he had foreseen the immediate difficulty, for he ran the risk of civil war if he simply pushed James off the throne, locked him up and took his place, particularly since he had announced all along that this had not been his intention. It always had been, but he could not say so now, and prove to all those who had taken his proclamations at face value that they had been deceived into a disloyalty they had never contemplated.

William had said he was coming to protect the Protestant religion; they believed and welcomed this, but they did not take it for granted that the protection of the Anglican Church automatically meant the removal of their hereditary King. Thus it was not surprising that during the period of the election for the 'Convention'—only a King could summon 'Parliament'—there was much uneasiness and division of opinion. Yet it availed James nothing. The arguments about whether or not his departure meant that he had abdicated, and if so, what the exact meaning of 'abdication' was, were no more than wasted words.

William was determined to be King and he had behind him a disciplined Dutch army and many Englishmen whose fortunes and futures were closely tied to his. The Convention met on January 22 and argued interminably about the abdication, but on February 13 the Prince and Princess of Orange were declared King and Queen of England. This must have been a considerable relief to Mary, who had inherited much of her mother's driving ambition, for she had never taken kindly to the title of Princess of Orange.

It is an interesting thought that of the seven Bishops who had been so 'persecuted' by James only one, St. Asaph, waited on the new King and Queen and took 'oaths to their government'. When Mary sent a message to Sancroft, Archbishop of Canterbury, to ask for his blessing, his reply was that it was her father's blessing she should ask, 'for his would not otherwise be heard in Heaven'.

On February 3 James at Saint-Germain had written a letter to the House of Lords and the members of his Privy Council, explaining in more detail why he had left the country and pointing out that 'we desire nothing more than to return and hold a free Parliament wherein we may have the best opportunity of undeceiving our people and showing the sincerity of these protestations we have often made of preserving the liberties and properties of our Subjects' . . . and so on, for quite a number of pages. Probably very few even saw the document and he does not seem to have had any answer to it, but his mind was full of plans for returning. On January 12, 1689 he wrote to Tyrconnel in Ireland and received an encouraging report on the loyalty of his Irish subjects and their willingness to fight in his cause.

Louis was all in favour of an Irish adventure, as it would take William's mind off Europe, but it seems very unlikely that he ever thought it was possible for James to be anything but a King of Ireland—a country fundamentally Catholic. Like Charles and his unfortunate excursion to Scotland, James felt that through Ireland lay the road back to London; so it all began with a misunderstanding.

In the middle of February James went to Brest where a flotilla of ten ships loaded with stores was awaiting him. There were weapons for 20,000 men, artillery, ammunition and money. No troops, but about a hundred French officers had been detailed or were willing to accompany him. From the beginning it was clear—except perhaps to James—that he was only a figurehead, a rallying point. He had not been actively involved in any of the preparations and he merely provided his presence and his name. It was a pity that the people of Ireland considered James to be 'too much of an Englishman to carry on their business'.

On March 12 James landed at Kinsale in southern Ireland. News of this came as a most unpleasant surprise to William and Mary—who had not expected quite such swift retaliation—and 'drums beat up mightily in and about London for volunteers for the Irish army, and they came in pretty well'. From Kinsale he went to Cork, and setting out from there on March 20 he arrived in Dublin four days later. He was to find, as many found before and since, that the problems of Ireland were beyond his power to solve. The troops available to him were potentially excellent material but there was no one able to turn it to advantage: the officers being 'miserable fellows' the men were useless. Yet, to outward appearances, the enterprise promised well. Except for Londonderry and Enniskillen—both were being besieged by Tyrconnel's forces—the whole country acknowledged his authority.

On May 1 there was a small naval engagement in Bantry Bay where French warships drove off several English ones. This was reported to James as a defeat of the English fleet by the French, and he revealed his true loyalty by saying coldly: '*C'est donc le premier fois.*' The Irish Catholics persuaded him to summon a Parliament on May 7—rather against his natural inclinations—and though illegal, because no Parliament could assemble in Ireland without the consent of the English Parliament, it served to underline Ireland's independence from England. But it was not a success. A number of Acts were hurried through—in particular the iniquitous Irish Attainder Bill which passed sentence of death, without trial, on some 2,000 Protestants, 'rebels', landlords and political enemies —but James soon realized that the Irish were not concerned with his recovery of the English crown and, worse still, did not intend that he should ever have any control over the Irish Parliament. He lost interest in Irish politics and the gap between him and his Irish subjects began to widen.

He went up to Londonderry to reason with the besieged inhabitants who, under that great champion of the Protestant Church Militant, the Reverend George Walker, Rector of Donoghmore, refused to listen to him. Musketeers on the town walls shot at him and he was forced to withdraw. On August 13 the town was relieved by General Piercy Kirke and an expeditionary force from England, and on the following day the veteran Marshal Schomberg landed with an army in Carrickfergus Bay. The Protestant Irish flocked to join Schomberg. James set up his headquarters at Drogheda, thirty miles north of Dublin, and round him Tyrconnel assembled the Irish army.

In September Schomberg moved south to Dundalk, where he was well supplied by English ships in the bay, but he had constant trouble with his ill-disciplined, untrained troops, inexperienced and inefficient officers, continual intrigues among his Huguenot troops and an appalling sickness rate. James had almost the same problems but he seemed to be invigorated by them, being, as one of his staff said, as active as a man of twenty, and spending long hours every day in the saddle. He kept up a continuous campaign of harassment, using small fighting patrols, which at least succeeded in thwarting Schomberg's intention of spending Christmas in Dublin.

In the following year William decided to settle the business in Ireland. He arrived at Carrickfergus on June 14 and on July 1 (1690) defeated James's army at the battle of the Boyne. William's army of English, Dutch, Danish, Irish and French (Huguenot) numbered some 8,000 Horse and 22,000 Foot. James had approximately the same number of cavalry and about 36,000 infantry.

The battle began at about six o'clock on a clear, bright morning. It was to be the last for James, and Marshal Schomberg, a good many officers and just over 2,000 men. William, despite a slight wound received while out on a reconnaissance on the previous evening, directed his side of the battle with competence—he was not an outstanding soldier. James, apparently, did not. His army was in a good position on the south bank of the river Boyne but it seems that no one was really clear whether there was to be a major battle or merely a rearguard action. It was known that Dublin was William's objective and James's army was in the process of falling back to defend the city.

On James's left, a couple of miles or more up the river, was the Slane bridge, guarded by 800 dragoons in case of an attempt by William to send a feint attack round that way. William launched a frontal assault across the river—which James assumed would be the main one—and sent a force of 5,000 cavalry and twice that number of infantry round by the bridge. Realizing almost too late that the main effort was being made against his left flank James moved troops to meet it, and in doing so was forced to weaken his front, already under great pressure. Both enemy attacks overran his forward infantry, which broke and fled, and there was nothing anyone could do to rally them. Earlier in the battle, Marshal Schomberg, commanding William's infantry, remained on the north bank of the river until he saw that a furious charge of one of James's cavalry units against the Dutch and French infantry regiments had driven them back into the river. The gallant old gentleman—he was over eighty—splashed his horse through the water, put himself at the head of the demoralized infantry and shouted: 'Allons, messieurs! Voilà vos persécuteurs!' A moment later he was shot in the neck and died instantly.

Walker, defender of Londonderry, was killed, fighting for William, and James's old friend the marquis d'Hocquincourt died fighting for James. The young Duke of Berwick's horse was shot under him in a charge, but though ridden over and badly bruised he was otherwise unhurt and lived to be a Marshal of France. James was not 'where the service was hottest', as he always had been in the past, though Berwick says he led the re-inforcements against the attack coming in on his left. His real fighting days were over, and so was his Irish venture.

Before he rode away southwards he gave orders that on no account was Dublin to be destroyed to prevent it being of any value to William—a plan suggested by his advisers. From Kinsale a French frigate took him back to France.

His hopes for Scottish support had been crushed in the previous year. There had been some show of resistance to the announcement that William and Mary were now King and Queen of Scotland, and the Duke of Gordon held Edinburgh Castle for James until compelled to surrender it on June 28. The Earl of Dundee took the field. It was he who at Rochester, before James's final departure, had implored him not to leave the country. 'Give me your commission,' he said. 'I will gather 10,000 of your troops. I will carry your standard at their head through England and drive before you the Dutch and their Prince!' James had said 'he believed it might be done but it would raise a civil war, and he would not do so much mischief to a nation who would soon come to their senses again'.

On July 17 Dundee was at the head of his Highlanders in that torrential, irresistible charge from the heights of Killiecrankie, but shot in the side, he died next day at Blair, and James's cause died with him. From the time of his departure from Ireland until 1694 the 'only foot of land, if it may be so called', that remained to him, was the little fort on the Bass Rock in Leith roads;* then that too was lost.

After the Boyne, Louis seemed to feel James was no longer able to play an effective part in winning back his throne. Two plans were made for 'invasions' of England, and twice James got as far as the French coast. The first, in 1692, was thwarted by the English admiral Russell's defeat of the French naval covering force off Cap de la Hague, near Cherbourg on May 19. The second, in 1696, came to nothing because of the failure of a Jacobite rising, and a design similar to the Rye House Plot, which was to have led to a landing by French troops. At Cap de la Hague James and

* The tiny garrison of about twenty men, women and children, formed an independent state, supplied by James through the medium of some French privateers. They had their own boat and one day managed to change it for a larger one but found they could not haul the new boat up to safety on its crane. One night it was stolen, and a sergeant and some soldiers were sent out to offer them indemnity if they surrendered. The garrison lured the soldiers close, on the pretence they could not hear what they said, and once within range of their firearms they disarmed the soldiers, seized their boat and forced the soldiers to help them get it up the rock so that it could not be stolen. The soldiers were subsequently sent off on a Danish ship which, by some means, had been made to supply the garrison with provisions. The garrison held out until the beginning of 1694 and was then 'reduced by famine'.

the invasion force stood on the cliffs and watched the French fleet, defeated in the sea battle, chased inshore and burnt. As the attacking sailors clambered up the sides of the French warships James could not hold back a cry of pride: 'Ah! None but my brave English could do so brave an action!'

He was disappointed by the defeat but he may have found some compensation in the birth of his daughter, Louise Mary—named after her godfather Louis—a week after he returned from Cap de la Hague. He had invited friends in England to be present at the delivery, but none came. His daughter Anne was full of remorse and wrote saying 'if wishes could recall what is past, I had long since redeemed my fault'. But the damage had been done.

The intrigues went on, even though, as time passed, James played less and less of a part in them. John Churchill, whom William, with good reason, never trusted, renewed his contact with James at Saint-Germain and was sent to the Tower on a warrant 'that he was charged with high treason and for abetting and adhering to their Majesties' enemies'. James's daughter Mary died on December 28, 1694. They had not met for fifteen years but Mary, completely dominated by her husband, would never tolerate the slightest whisper of disrespect of her father, and at the time of the battle of the Boyne she wrote a most pathetic letter to her husband begging him to spare James. It was a relief, in many ways, for William to be able to assure her that her father had again escaped.

By 1695, James, now convinced he had been born under a most unlucky star, was losing interest in politics. He began to live his own life with his family and withdraw more and more into their intimate world. He still hunted a great deal; until the age of sixty-six he still rode as fearlessly as he had as a young man, and he enjoyed sitting in the sun and talking, perhaps rather boringly, about his adventures and what might have been, but always dispassionately, as if discussing someone else.

In 1696 he was informed through French diplomatic channels that the Poles wished to offer him the throne of their country. His friends advised him to accept but he would not, on the grounds that acceptance would indicate he had abandoned all claim to the English throne and he owed it to his son to keep on trying—another reason he did not give might well have been that he was perfectly happy where he was. But in September of the following year, France, England, the States General and Spain signed the Treaty of Ryswick, which was in fact only an uneasy truce and a prelude to the War of the Spanish Succession. Yet from James's point of view, the treaty was the end of all his hopes, for among all the articles dealing with the details of ceasing hostilities and restoring property taken during the war there was one which guaranteed 'the peaceable possession of the throne of England' to William who, for the first time, was styled King of England in the French documents. In addition, Louis undertook 'not to disturb him in his possession'. James was saddened, disappointed but resigned, perhaps even, secretly, a little relieved. There seemed now to be no point in continuing the struggle.

He formed the habit of visiting the convent of La Trappe every year for a brief retreat, and apart from the religious aspects of his stay there, he was no doubt comforted by the way the monks entertained him as a king and, to a certain extent, as a martyr to his faith. He was accused of plotting against William's life but the evidence is slender indeed and charges of this sort would inevitably be important in the Whig campaign to denigrate him. When certain conspirators in England were caught and tried, men like Charnock, King, Rookwood and Sir William Perkins declared specifically that James knew nothing of any design to assassinate William.

Gradually he became a gentle, no doubt garrulous, elderly retired officer and king, content in the company of his wife and children, without ambition now, and, perhaps because he had at last realized his own shortcomings, reconciled and therefore free from the burdens of hope and fear. He was happy again. Not rich, not ostentatious, but comfortable in the magnificent palace Louis had given to him. He loved France for he had spent some of his happiest years as a soldier in her army, and he had no worries left. Above all he had his faith: his complete acceptance that all was in the hands of God and all, in the end, was ordered according to G d's will.

He enjoyed music and fine pictures and strolling with his wife down the broad gravel walk along the high terrace above the river, with its magnificent view across the valley. Life flowed on outside the gardens of the great château, leaving him behind.

On March 4, 1701, he fainted during a service in the chapel at Saint-Germain, but appeared to recover completely. Exactly a week later, while dressing himself in the morning, he had a stroke which left him partially paralysed on his right side, so that he had difficulty in walking and could not use his right hand. The doctors applied their usual 'remedies' of 'blistering' with hot poultices, bleeding, emetics and purges which he managed to survive, and in fact recovered the use of his hand and was able to walk reasonably well. His medical advisers told him that a course of 'the waters at Bourbon' would complete the cure, and three weeks later, as soon as he was strong enough after their ministrations, he went there.

When he returned he hardly limped at all but complained of pains in his chest, yet he began to regain his strength and 'took the air as usual, sometimes on horseback'.

Then, on Friday, September 2, he again fainted in the chapel, in Mary Beatrice's arms, and was carried to his room. He seemed to be better next day but on Sunday relapsed into a coma and it was apparent that he had an internal haemorrhage. Mary Beatrice, who was devoted to him, was extremely alarmed, particularly when he asked for the Sacrament. While waiting for the priest he sent for his son, now thirteen, and when the boy came in and saw his father on what was obviously his death-bed he, not surprisingly, burst into tears. James told him to adhere to the Catholic faith, respect and obey his mother the Queen and to be ever grateful to the King of France, to whom so much was owed, and he spoke with such strength and fervour that, fearing another relapse, those in the room suggested the Prince should withdraw.

'Do not take away my son,' said James, 'until at least I have given him my blessing.'

His nine-year-old daughter Louise was then brought in, in floods of tears, and he gave her the same advice and his blessing. Mary Beatrice, inconsolable, stayed with him all night and he tried to comfort her, saying that everything was in the hands of God. Next morning he was better and there were faint hopes of his recovery. On Tuesday Louis came to see him; he seemed stronger and slept well that night. Louis visited him again on the following Sunday, but on Monday any hopes that he might get better were abandoned. He drifted in and out of a coma and became feverish. Mary Beatrice, weeping, sat beside him and in one of his periods of consciousness he said: 'Do not afflict yourself: I am going, I hope, to be happy.'

'Sir, I doubt it not,' she said, 'and therefore it is not your condition I lament, but my own.' Overcome by grief she went out of the room.

On Tuesday, at three o'clock in the afternoon, Louis came again, for he had made up his mind to make a somewhat startling announcement. His Council had tried to dissuade him, pointing out that what he proposed to say would be contrary to the spirit and the letter of the Treaty of Ryswick and was likely to embroil France in another war with William—as indeed to a certain extent it did. But Louis went straight to Mary Beatrice, took her hand and told her that if God chose to take the father of her young Prince, he would be a father to him. Prince James Edward was properly grateful and said that His Most Christian Majesty would find him as dutiful and loyal as if he were his own child. Louis then went over to the bed where James lay, barely conscious.

'Sir,' said Louis, 'I am come to see how your Majesty finds yourself today.'

But James did not hear. A servant, leaning over him, told him that the King of France was there.

'Where is he?' said James, rousing himself.

And then, in the crowded room, Louis said what he had told his Council he would say.

'I am come, sir, to acquaint you that whenever it shall please God to call your Majesty out of this world, I will take your family into my protection, and will treat your son, the Prince of Wales, in the same manner as I have treated you, and acknowledge him, as he will then be, King of England.'

There was much weeping, a mixture of sorrow, joy and relief, and even Louis, who was not an emotional man, wept a little himself. The wretched James, trying to say something to Louis, was too weak to make himself heard in the confused noise, and Louis bade him goodbye and went away, leaving instructions with the Officer of the Guard to attend the Prince of Wales as soon as James was dead.

James rallied slightly the following day, but on the next grew much weaker and his hands shook. On Friday, September 16, at three o'clock in the afternoon, he died.

Poor Mary Beatrice, who had not been able to persuade herself to give up hope, was distraught, and she went off almost at once to the convent at Chaillot, where she had been many times before; and there, in an atmosphere of timeless peace, mourned the man she loved.

Later she wrote to Anne, James's faithless daughter: 'I think myself indispensably obliged to defer no longer the acquainting you with a message, which the best of men as well as the best of fathers left with me for you: some few days before his death he bid me find means to let you know that he forgave you all that is past from the bottom of his heart, and prayed to God to do so too, that he gave you his last blessing and prayed to God to convert your heart and confirm you in the resolution of repairing to his son the wrongs done to himself: to which I shall only add, that I join my prayers to his herein, with all my heart, and that I shall make it my business to inspire into the young man who is left to my care the sentiments of his Father: for better, no man can have.'

James's body remained for twenty-four hours in the room where he died; at night priests sang the office of the dead, and in the morning masses were said at two altars erected on either side of the huge room. In his Will he had said that his body was to be buried in the parish church of the place where he should happen to die, and that there was to be no more expense at his funeral than at that of any private gentleman. He wanted no other monument than a bare stone with the words 'Here Lies King James'. He had told his priest to insist on this, but Louis said it was the only thing he could not grant him.

When everything had been prepared for carrying away his body, the Duke of Berwick, the Earl of Middleton, James's chaplains and other servants set out at seven o'clock in the evening to take it to the church of the English Benedictine monks in Paris. The country people stood silent, and crossed themselves as the cortège passed. When it arrived in Paris, Dr. Ingleton, Almoner to the Queen, delivered the body with an elegant Latin oration to the Prior, to lie in a side chapel 'until it pleased God to dispose the people of England to repair in some measure the injuries they did him in his life by the honours they shall think fit to show him after death'.

In the parish church of Saint-Germain, across the square from the great bulk of the château, is a splendid memorial to him:

In This Church Lies

JAMES II

King of England

Born in London

in 1633

King in 1685

Dethroned in 1688

Welcomed

in France by Louis XIV

He held his Court in the

Castle of St. Germain en Laye

Where he died on the 16 of September

1701

His body is not there. Like so many other things it disappeared during the Revolution.

BIBLIOGRAPHY

ASHLEY, MAURICE. *Life in Stuart England*
AUBREY, JOHN. *Brief Lives*
BELLOC, HILAIRE. *James II*
BERWICK, FIRST DUKE OF. *Memoirs*
BRYANT, SIR ARTHUR. *Samuel Pepys, Saviour of the Navy*
    Samuel Pepys, The Years of Peril
BULSTRODE, SIR RICHARD. *Memoirs and Reflections upon the Reign and*
    Government of Charles I and Charles II
BURNET, BISHOP GILBERT. *History of My Own Times*
CANNON, RICHARD. *Historical Record of the Queen's Regiment of Foot*
CHURCHILL, SIR WINSTON. *Marlborough, His Life and Times*
    A History of the English Speaking Peoples
CLARENDON, EDWARD HYDE, LORD. *History of the Rebellion and Civil*
    Wars in England.
CLARENDON, HENRY, SECOND EARL. *Diary*
CLARKE, REV. J. S. *The Life of James II*
COWBURN, PHILIP. *The Warship in History*
DALRYMPLE, SIR DAVID. *Memoirs and Letters relating to the History of*
    Great Britain
DALRYMPLE, SIR JOHN. *Memoirs of Great Britain and Ireland*
DARTMOUTH. *MSS*
DAVIS, COLONEL JOHN. *History of the Second Queen's*
DICTIONARY OF NATIONAL BIOGRAPHY
EVELYN, JOHN. *Diary and Correspondence*
FEA, ALLAN. *King Monmouth*
FIELD OF MARS. Anon, 2 volumes
FORTESCUE, HON. J. W. *The History of the British Army*
FOX, CHARLES JAMES. *History of the Early Part of the Reign of James II*
FOXE, JOHN. *Book of Martyrs*
GREY, LORD. *The Secret History of the Rye House Plot and Monmouth*
    Rebellion

HAGGARD, LT.-COL. ANDREW. *Sidelights on the Court of France*
HALKETT, LADY ANNE. *Autobiography of*, ed. J. G. Nichols
HAMMOND, ANTHONY. *Memoirs of the Count of Grammont*
HMSO. *European Firearms*
HUME, DAVID. *The History of England*
HUME, SIR PATRICK. *Narrative of the Earl of Argyll's Expedition*
JAMES II. *Memoirs*, translated by A. Lytton Sells (1962)
KEMP, P. *History of the Royal Navy*
KENNET, EDWARD. *History of England*
LAUDER, SIR JOHN. *Historical Observer*
LISTER, T. H. *Life of Clarendon*
LONGUEVILLE, T. *Marshal Turenne*
MACPHERSON, J. *History of Great Britain*
   His Original Papers
MITFORD, NANCY. *The Sun King*
MORDAL, JACQUES. *25 Centuries of Sea Warfare*
OLDMIXON, J. *History of the Stuarts*
PARKER, CAPTAIN ROBERT. *Memoirs of the Most Remarkable Military
   Transactions, 1683–1718*
PENGUIN. *Book of Restoration Verse*
PEPYS, SAMUEL. *Diaries*
PETRIE, SIR CHARLES. *The Stuarts*
RAMSAY, ANDREW MICHAEL. *Histoire du Vicomte de Turenne*
RANKE, LEOPOLD VON. *History of England*
SAVAGE, JAMES. *History of Taunton*
THOMSON, REV. THOS. *The Comprehensive History of England*
THURLOE, JOHN. *State Papers*
TREVELYAN, G. M. *England under the Stuarts*
TURNER, F. C. *James II*
WOLSELEY, VISCOUNT. *The Life of John Churchill, Duke of Marlborough*
YOUNG, BRIGADIER PETER. *Edgehill 1642, The Campaign and the Battle*

INDEX

16; fights Battle of Edgehill, 16–20; march to London, 21; makes HQ at Oxford, 21; defeats Waller at Cropredy Bridge, 25; loses Battle of Naseby, 26; 26; escapes from Oxford, 27; joins Scots at Southwell, 31; finally taken to Hampton Court, 31; news of death reaches Paris, 44

Charles II, attends Strafford's trial, 1; leaves London, 4; accompanies father to York, 5; at Edgehill, 16–20; laziness, 23; escapes to Scilly Isles then Jersey, 25; takes over fleet at Hellevoetsluis, 40; takes fleet to sea, 41; attack of smallpox, 41; asserts himself, mother no longer guardian, 45; visited by Commissioners from Scotland, 45; decides to go to Jersey, 46; composition of court in Jersey, 46n; cancels plans for Ireland, 47; meeting with Scots at Breda planned, 47; leaves Jersey, 47; conditions imposed by Scots, 48; buys governorship of Jersey for James, 48; made to sign Covenant and declaration, he and Buckingham give offence, 49; crowned King at Scone, 50; Battles of Dunbar and Worcester, 50; arrives in France after Worcester, 56; involved in dealings with duc de Lorraine, 77–81; first lesson in international diplomacy, 80; leaves Paris, goes to Cologne, 98; writes to Henry about religion, 102; negotiates treaty with Spaniards, 106; establishes himself at Bruges, 106; sends for James, 107; meets James at Veurne, 108; trouble with James over Sir J. Berkeley, 109–110; hears of Cromwell's death, 121; goes to Fuenterrabia, 124; basic difference between him and James, 125; failure of mission to Fuenterrabia, 127; lands at Dover, 130; feelings about James's marriage, 134; no wish for blood-bath, 136; fear of civil war, 147; coronation, 148, marriage, 149; responsibilities as Protestant King, 151; exercise, night and morning, 166; goes to Oxford during plague, 167; row with James over Clarendon, 175; 'adheres to Church of Rome', 179; no belief in ability to turn country Catholic, 180; visits fleet after battle in Southwold Bay, 191; refuses to declare Monmouth legitimate, 198; first contact with Popish Plot, 204–5; tells James to leave the country, 207; declares Monmouth illegitimate, 208; becomes ill 209; sends James to Scotland, 211; recalls him, 214; sends him back, 216; action against Exclusion Bills and defeat of Whig Parliament at Oxford, 222–6; trouble with William of Orange, 226; peace at last, 233; death, 234; funeral, 240

Charles, Duke of Cambridge, 135

Charles Louis, Prince Palatine, 2, 7

Château d'Ablon, 87

Château Porcien, 89

Châtres, James joins French Army at, 67

Chauny, 68, 85

Chester, city of, 122, 263

Chiffinch, William, 252

Churchill, Arabella, 149; becomes James's mistress, 167–8; children by James, 168; marriage and death, 168n; house in St. James's Square, 252, 268

Churchill, John (later 1st Duke of Marlborough), joins James's household, 168; as a young soldier, 199; rides across Flanders with James, 210; returns from Brussels in James's household, 212; acts as courier between Edinburgh and London, 220; saved from the *Gloucester*, 229, 235; at Sedgemoor, 243, 266; attitude to Col. Beaumont's court martial, 268; responsible for treachery in Army, 272, 277; plot to kidnap James, 278; defects to William, 279; acid comment of Schomberg, 280; not trusted by William and sent to the Tower, 304

Churchill, Sarah, see Jennings

Clarendon Code, 152, 152n, 177

Clarendon, Edward Hyde, 1st Lord, sees standard raised at Nottingham, 9; at Edgehill, 17; reference to Battle of Newbury, 25; goes to Jersey, 25; description of Earl of Northumberland, 29; goes to Madrid with Lord Cottington, 48; in poverty in Paris, 56–7; pleads James's cause for joining French Army, 60; comments on James's reputation as a soldier, 76; misgivings about employment of his daughter at court, 105; prepares Declaration of Breda, 129; created Lord Chancellor, 136; urges marriage of Charles to Catherine of Braganza, 149; urges sale of Dunkirk, 149; not in favour of war with Dutch, 154; persuades Charles to lay up battle fleet, 171; fall of, 173–4; writes *History of the Revolution*, and death, 174

Clarendon, Henry Hyde, 2nd Lord, refuses to see sister on deathbed, 184, 210n, 240; sent to Ireland, 249; sees very little of Catherine Sedley, 252; finds life difficult in England, 263; sees James's baby son, 266, 274

Dupuy, 188
Durham, Bishop of, 198, 214
Dwarf, James's, 30

E

Ecclestiastical Commission, 256
Edgecote, 19
Edgehill, Battle of, 16–20
Edwards, at Faversham, 291, 292
Elizabeth, Princess, 4, 23; says farewell to Charles I, 44; death of, 44
Elizabeth, Queen of Bohemia, godmother to James, 2; offers James her house, 54; describes Anne Hyde, 105
Elvige, Lieutenant, 118
Ely, Bishop of, 241
Essex, Robert Devereux, 3rd Earl of, background, 15; commands Parliamentary forces, 15; at Edgehill, 16–20; withdraws to Warwick and marches to London, 21; gives safe conduct to Henrietta Maria, 23; penned up in Cornwall, 25; dismissed from the Army, 25
Essex, 4th Earl of, 211, 215, 222, 225, 232
Estrées, comte d', 186
Etampes, battle and siege of, 71–2; 74–6
Etaples, 126
Etréchy, 73, 76
Evelyn, John, diarist, at Spring Garden, 34; at Gravesend blockhouse, 36; description of Dort, 39; letters of, 56, 59; descriotion of Anne Hyde, 105; records Cromwell's death, 121; describes his funeral, 122; 'all anarchy and confusion', 122; describes state of the nation, 128; describes return of Charles to London, 130; comments on James's grasp of 'business', 133; writes of Henrietta Maria's reaction to James's marriage, 135; effect of Mary's death on Charles's court, 137; dines with Lord Sandwich in Prince, 156; reports news of Lowestoft victory, 163; James's dog in battle, 166n; hears guns in Four Days' Fight, 170; sees damage done to fleet, 171; says goodbye to Lord Sandwich, 186–7; admires James's skill on skates, 220; describes Prince George of Denmark, 233; writes of Charles's death, 237; hears proclamations, 239–40; describes Charles's funeral, 240; comment on James's coronation, 241; sees Titus Oates being punished, 247; fears of 'Romanists swarming at court', 270
Evertz, Cornelius, 159
Evertz, John, 159
Exclusion Bills, first, 208; second, 222–3; third, 225

Exeter, city of, William at, 275

F

Fairfax, 185n
Fairfax, Sir Thomas, replaces Essex as Commander-in-Chief, 25; besieges Oxford, 25–6; at Naseby, 26; receives surrender of Oxford, 28; told of James's escape, 37
Falconbridge, Lord, 213
Farmer, Anthony, 261, 261n, 262
Faubourg Saint-Antoine, Battle of, 81–2
Ferguson, rabid preacher, 230n, 232, 233, 243–4
Ferté, Henri, duc de la, 74; joins Turenne, 81; incident at Saint-Michel, 90; suggests ripping the belly of the messenger, 100
Feversham, Louis Duras, marquis de Blanquefort, 1st Earl of, 188, 188n; writes urgently to James in exile, 209; at Hounslow, 266; James's letter to, 286; goes to Faversham, 292; disbands Army, arrested by William, 293
Fifth Monarchy Men, 138, 141n
Fighting, not funny in 17th cent., 70
Finch, Captain, 187
Fire, The Great, of London, 171
Fireships, 158
First Bishops' War, 15
Fismes, 68
FitzJames, James, Duke of Berwick, see Berwick
Flammarans, marquis de, peculiar death of, 81n
Fleetwood, General, 121
Foragers, function of, 71
Fortescue, The Hon. J. W., comment on James as army administrator, 143
Fountain, 161
Four Days' Fight, 170
Fox, Stephen, 46n
Francis, Alban, 261
Frederick Henry, Prince of Orange, godfather to James, 2
Fronde, description of, 42; general situation in 1652, 61
Frondeurs, 42
Fuensaldaña, Luiz-Perez de Vivero, conde de, reinforces Condé, 90; note on, 90n; reluctance to fight out of hours, 95; flees from Arras, 100; removed from command, 107, 107n

G

Gadagne, Charles Félix de Galléan, comte de, at Etampes, 75; takes terms to the duc de Lorraine, 80; prepared to rescue James after Battle of the Dunes, 119–20

315

Liberty of Conscience, 152, 180, 251, 258, 270, 282
Ligny, 90, 91
Lindsay, Lady Sophia, 219
Lisle, Alice, 248, 248n
'Little Sincerity', 181
Littleton, Sir Thomas, 174
LLloyd, Captain, engineer, 103, 103n
Lloyd, Bishop, 265n, 300
Lockhart of Carnwarth, 217
Lockhart, Sir William, 108, 108n
London, 155, 172, 186–90
Londonderry, siege of, 301
Long Island, given to James, 150
Longueville, Marie de, 58
Lord High Admiral, 3, 9
Lorraine, Charles duc de, in Brussels, 51; description, 52; at Villeneuve Saint-Georges, 76–81, and 85–6; arrested by Spaniards, 97
Louis XIII, 24, 42
Louis XIV, rides into Paris, 89; coronation of, 99; ill, 121; greatest power in Europe, 148; buys Dunkirk, 150; intervenes in Dutch War, 170; linked with Medway raid, 172; invades Holland, 192; encourages marriage of Mary Beatrice and James, 196; anger at marriage of William and Mary, 201; makes possible Charles's defeat of Whigs, 225, 248; revokes Edict of Nantes, 251–2; arranges journey of Mary Beatrice, 286; makes promise about James III, 307
Louise Mary, Princess, birth, 304; blessed by James, 306
Louise de Querouaille (Madam Carwell), Duchess of Portsmouth, becomes Charles's mistress, 183; writes to James in exile, 209; presented as 'common nuisance', 214; responsible for James's return from exile in Scotland, 227–8; witnesses birth of Prince of Wales, 266
Louvois, marquis de, 251
Low, Surgeon, 34
Lowestoft, Battle of, 159–64
Lowd, servant to Lord Sandwich, 198
Lumley, Lord, 272
Lyon Quay, 35

M

Maassluis, 39, 212
Macartney, Irish officer, 281
Macaulay, 97, 146, 217
Macdonnel, Captain, 295
Macpherson, comment on Charles's principles 48; 'solemn promise' of James to Anne Hyde, 134; Charles's religion, 179

Mademoiselle, Anne-Marie-Louise d' Orléans, 44, 57, 71–2, 82
Magazines, 71
Magdalen College, 261
Mail service, 6
Main roads, 6
Majo, Lietenant, 189
Mardyck, 111, 118
Margaret Tudor, 2
Maria Theresa, Infanta of Spain, 123
Marie de Medici, 42
Marlborough, Earl of, 161
Marston Moor, Battle of, 25
Martinet, General, 192
Martinozzi, Laura, 194, 262
Mary, James's sister, 4, 5, 23; meets James in Holland, 39; death of husband, birth of son, 53, 98; takes Anne Hyde into her household, 105; at Breda, 113; feelings about Anne Hyde's marriage, 134; death of, 137
Mary, James's daughter (Queen), birth of, 135n, 166; friendship with Mary Beatrice, 197; marries William of Orange, 200–1; Princess Royal, 201, 208; sees James for last time, 212; becomes Queen, 299; gets no blessing from Archbishop, 300; death of, 304
Mary, 161, 174, 229
Mary Beatrice, d'Este (Mary of Modena), marriage, 194–5; character, 195; goes into exile with James, 208; seasickness, 212; in Scotland, 216–30; happy relationship with James's daughter Anne, 220; distressed about Catherine Sedley, 252; misgivings about Sunderland and Petre, 254; visits Bath and Holywell, 262–3; gives birth to son, 266; distressed by Anne's disloyalty, 271; flees to France, 285–6; travels to Saint-Germain, 297; peace during James's last years, 305; grief at James's illness and death, 306–7; goes to Chaillot, writes to the faithless Anne, 307
Maryland, 150
Massonett, 22, 22n
Mathews, Miles, 19
Maurice, Prince, 11, 28, 41, 46n
Maynard, Colonel, 36
Mazarin, Cardinal (Julius Mazarino), background and character, 42; problems, 56; unpopularity, 60; Spanish moves against, 63; rewards James for Corbeil, 67; orders siege of Étampes, 74; dealings with duc de Lorraine, 74; resolves to flee to Lyon, 84; goes into exile, 85; winter campaign, 91; soldiers' dislike of, 92, 103–7; ends war, 121; at Fuenterrabia, 123; 'Le diable de Mazarin!', 221

319

Pepys, Samuel, relationship with James, 133; great civil servant, 143–4, 170; great efforts to restore fleet, 171; saw the *Gloucester* sink, 228–30
Percy, Algernon, see Northumberland
Perkins, Sir William, 305
Perth, Earl of, 229
Peterborough, Earl of, 184; proxy marriage to Mary Beatrice, 194; description of Mary Beatrice, 195, 210
Petre, Father, 253, 254, 258, 268–9, 286
Petrie, Sir Charles, 245
Pheasants, Isle of, 123
Philip IV, of Spain, 48, 107
Philiphaugh, Battle of, 37
Philippe, duc d'Orléans (Monsieur), marriage, 182; death of wife, but not suspected of poisoning her, 183
Pikemen, 14
Pilkington, Sheriff, 231
Plague, The, 167, 167n, 172, 172n, 173
Plymouth, 161
Pontavert, 92
Pontoise, 84
Popish Plot, 176, 203, 203n; systematic persecution of Catholics, 209, 228
Portland Bill, 155
Portsmouth, Duchess of, see Louise de Querouaille
Powell, Justice, 266
Powis, Lady, 266, 280, 285
Powis, Lord, 207, 280, 285
Press Gang, 146
Price, Goditha, 153
Prince, 156, 186, 188
Proclamations, see Declarations
Protestant Champion, 181, 238
Providence, 9
Pulpit, use of, 177
Purcell, Henry, 22, 264
Pym, John, 3, 4, 5, 21, 24, 172n
Pyrenees, Treaty of, 124

Q
Queen's, The, 142, 243

R
Radcliffe, Sir George, James's govenor, 26, 28–30; in exile at Caen, 51; influence on James, 51, 54, 57; writes of James as a soldier, 65, 76
Raid, by Dutch up Medway, 172
Rathmines, Battle of, 45
Ravenal, Major General de, 95
Red Horse, Vale of the, 20
Resolution, 185
Rethel, 68, 89, 92, 94
Retz, Cardinal de, 57
Reynolds, Sir John, 111

Rheims, Louis XIV crowned at, 99
Richard III, 246, 298
Richelieu, Cardinal, 24, 42
Richmond, Duke of, 17
Riva, Italian servant, 285
Rochester, John Wilmot, Lord, 78, 210n
Rochester, Laurence Hyde, Lord, 210n, 211, 220, 221, 226; becomes Lord Treasurer, 240; victim of Sunderland's plots, 254, 258, 264, 269
Rockers, 2
Rocroi, 61, 95, 97
Ross, governor of Duke of Monmouth, 198
Roussillon, M. de, 90
Royal Army, training of, 9; composition of, 9; final defeat of at Naseby, 26; resentment against standing army, 249; state of in 1688, 272
Royal Catherine, 162
Royal Charles, 155, 158, 172, 186, 259
Royal James, 155, 187–9
Royal Oak, 160, 172
Royal Scots, The, 142, 142n
Rufford Abbey, 167
Rule of the Major Generals, 139
Rumble, The, 187
Rumbold, ex-Lieutenant, 230
Rumsey, Colonel, 230
Rupert, Prince, of the Rhine, joins Royal Army, 11; background and character, 11; captures Bristol, 23; loses at Marston Moor, 25; wounded at Oxford, 28; commands Royalist fleet, 41; goes to Ireland, 41; actions at sea, 45n; 2nd-in-command of James's fleet, 155, 158, 159; Four Days' Fight, 170, 191; takes command of fleet, 193, 193n
Russell, Admiral, at Cap de la Hague, 303
Russell, Captain, 276
Russell, Colonel John, 142
Russell, Lord, anti-Popery, 202; supports indictment of James, 214, 225; invites William to banquet, 226; arrested and executed, 232
Ruyter, de, 170, 172, 185–91
Rye House Plot, 168, 231, 233
Ryswick, Treaty of, 304

S
Saint-Cloud, 81
Saint-Denis, 81, 183
Saint-Germain-en-Laye, 40, 80, 285, 297
Saint-Ghislain, 103
Saint Ménéhould, siege of, 89
Saint-Quentin, 68
Saint-Philippe, 186
Saint-Venant, 111
Saint-Victor, 286
St. Andrew, 186

St. *Michael*, 185n, 188
St. Swithin's Day, 244
Salzbach, Battle of, 124n
Sancroft, Archbishop of Canterbury, 265, 274, 300
Sandwich, Lord, brings fleet to Scheveningen, 130; goes to sea, 155, 158–9; passed over for command, 170; premonitions and death at battle of Sole Bay, 186
Savoy Conference, 151
Savile, Sir George, see Halifax
Savile, Henry, 188, 188n
Sayes, 150, 150n
Scarborough, Sir Charles, 229
Scheveningen, 130
Schomberg, Armand Frédéric, comte de, wounded at Etampes, 75, 75n; comment on Churchill's defection, 280; arrives in Ireland, 301; killed at the Battle of the Boyne, 302
Schram, Admiral, 159
Scott, Sir Edward, 188
Scroggs, Chief Justice, 214
Seaton, Captain Sebastian, 162
Sedgemoor, Battle of, 243, 243n
Sedley, Catherine, Baroness Darlington, Countess of Dorset, replaces Arabella Churchill, 168; background, 212n; 'It cannot be my beauty . .', 212n; relationship with James as King, 252; children by James, 252n
Sieges, procedure at, 12
Select Knott, The, 122
Senart, forest of, 76, 77n
Shaftesbury, Anthony Ashley Cooper, Lord, use of London mob, 172; nicknamed 'Little Sincerity', 181, 191, 196; character, 196; attacks monarchy, 197, 198, 202; health, 204, 213; indicts James as Popish recusant, 214, 222, 223; defeated by Charles at Oxford, 225–6, 228; flees to Holland and dies, 231
Sharp, Dr., 257, 265
Sheldon, Ralph, 289–91
Shrewsbury, Lord, 272, 276, 295
Sidney, Algernon, 232
Sidney, Henry, Earl of Romney, 168, 272
Sidney, Robert, 225
Skating, 220
Sluys, 109
Smith, Sir Jeremy, 174
Soissons, 68
Soissons, Porte de, Laon, 68
Solemn League and Covenant, 24
Southampton, Lord Treasurer, 154, 171
Southerland, Lt. Col., 276
Southwell, 31

Southwold Bay, Sole Bay, 159, 187
Sovereign (of the Seas), 186
Spaniards, ambitions in France, 61; enforce loyalty to Philip IV, 109; conduct at Battle of the Dunes, 116–20; offer James post of Principe de la Mare, 127
Spencer, Robert, see Sunderland
Spragge, Sir Edward, 185
Spreul, put in The Boots, 218
Spring Garden, 34, 34n
Stafford, Lord, 207, 223
Stanley, Edward, 125
Stenay, 99
Stillingwert, Admiral, 159
Strafford, Thomas Wentworth, Earl of, 1, 3, 136
Straughan, Captain, 9
Strickland, Lady, 285
Strickland, Sir Roger, 268, 272n
Strode, M.P., 4
Stuart, Dr. Richard, 46n, 51
Sunderland, Robert Spencer, 2nd Earl of, 209n, 211, joins opposition to James, 215; supports Exclusion Bills, 222; 230; in pay of William and Louis XIV, 235; Principal Secretary of State, 241; controls access to James, 253; alliance with Petre, 254, 258; helps foment trouble at universities, 261–2; not trusted with Treasury, 264; witnesses birth of Prince of Wales, 266, 268; dismissed, 271; escapes to Holland, 286; claims honour of starting the Revolution, 286
Swiftsure, 155
Syon House, 31, 44, 295

T
Talbot, Dick, see Tyrconnel
Tangier, 149, 150, 223
Tarpaulins, 147
Test Act, 193, 255
Test case of Dispensing Power, 255–6
Test Oath, Scottish, 218
Thurloe, John, 48, 49, 98
Tilbury Hope, 35
Titus, at Sack of Jerusalem, 12
Tonge, Dr., 204
Tory, origin of term, 215n
Tot, Charles Henri, du, 91n
Toys, 3
Trelawney, Bishop, 265n
Trevannion, Captain, 295–6
Trevor, Sir John, 241
Tripp, Mr., Bampfield's associate, 34
Tudor, Henry, 298
Turenne, Henri de la Tour d'Auvergne, vicomte de, great soldier, 61; advance from Angers, 63; action at Bleneau,

Coninck Jacobus de II wart geboren.

De Koninck 15 Iaeren uit sijnde in Justirre

De Coninck slaet tegen den Admirael obdam.

I. Stuarts afscheyt der lords vlugt uyt Dublin na Waterfort.

Vertrekt uyt Yrlant met 500000 tt Sterlings